TEXTBOO

PRACTICAL C

TEXTBOOK ON
PRACTICAL CHEMISTRY

[For the students of BSc (General and Honours) courses of all Indian Universities]

Dr K S Mukherjee MSc, PhD

Formerly Professor and Head, Department of Chemistry
Formerly Principal, Siksha Bhavana (Dean, Faculty of Science)
Visva-Bharati, Santiniketan
West Bengal, India

New Central Book Agency
DELHI ● KOLKATA ● PUNE

TEXTBOOK ON
PRACTICAL CHEMISTRY

Publisher

NEW CENTRAL BOOK AGENCY (P) LTD

♦ 8/1 Chintamoni Das Lane, Kolkata 700 009

♦ 4262/3 1st Floor, Flat Nos. 105 & 106
   Ansari Road, Daryaganj, New Delhi 110 002

♦ Shop Nos. 3 & 4, Vinayak Towers
   681/B Budhwar Peth, Appa Balwant Chowk
   Pune 411 002, Maharashtra

Typesetter
New Central Book Agency (P) Ltd
8/1 Chintamoni Das Lane, Kolkata 700 009

Printer
New Central Book Agency (P) Ltd
Web-Offset Division, Dhulagarh, Sankrail, Howrah

Cover Designer
Soumen Paul

Cover Printer
Liba Graphics
40/4 Manteswartola Road, Kolkata 700 046

Project Supervisor
Sukumar Patra

Technical Editor
Dipan Roy

Project Team
Prabhat Jas, Mithu Karmakar, and Ananta Bhowmik

ISBN: 81-7381-592-5

First Published: August 2008

Price: COT pees One Hundred Ninety-five only]

20.00

Dedicated to my students

Contents

Part II
Quantitative Inorganic Analysis

[ix]

Part III
Inorganic Preparations

SECTION II
ORGANIC CHEMISTRY PRACTICAL

Part I
Qualitative Analysis of Single Organic Compound

Part II

Organic Preparations

Part III
Organic Quantitative Analysis

Part IV
Separation of Components of Organic Mixture and Isolation of Organic Compounds from Natural Source

SECTION III
PHYSICAL CHEMISTRY PRACTICAL

Preface

Undoubtedly, learning chemistry through practical training is an indispensable method for the students of all level. Unfortunately, most of the students suffer from unnecessary fear psychosis regarding the practical works in chemistry.

My long experience, however, reveals that there is no reason for such uncalled fear in performing experimental work in chemistry—provided the students are aware of the theoretical background behind each practical experiment. Also, the planning of the work to be done is to be properly chalked out before undertaking the practical works. With this objective the present manual, *A Textbook on Practical Chemistry* has been prepared to meet the needs of students of undergraduate level of all Indian universities.

In this manual, theory and techniques in detail and the subject matter have been presented in a clear and lucid language. At the end of each section of experiments sufficient number of questions and their answers have been provided to help the students in understanding the subject.

I am sure the book will be highly useful to students and teachers alike.

In preparing the manuscript of the book, I have consulted a large number of books by national and international authors. I am grateful to all of them. I sincerely appreciate the valuable assistance and helpful suggestions received from my son Sri Bodhisattwa Mukhopadhyay, MSc, Executive—Dabur Pharma Limited, Kalyani, West Bengal, and my daughter-in-law Mrs Sarada Mukhopadhyay, MA, Asst. Lecturer—Patha Bhavana, Visva-Bharati, Santiniketan, during the preparation of the manuscript. I also record my profound regard to my elder brothers Sri Sibsankar Mukhopadhyay, former Assistant Teacher—Ramkrishna Sikshapith, Tumbani, Birbhum, and Dr Durgasankar Mukhopadhyay, Former Head of the Department of Bengali, Calcutta University, for their constant encouragement. Appreciation and thanks are surely due to my wife, Gouri, for her constant inspiration during the preparation of the manuscript.

I am extremely grateful to the authorities and the production staff of New Central Book Agency (P) Ltd, for publishing this book promptly.

I would welcome suggestions from readers for further improvement of the text.

Rathayatra
4 July 2008
Phuler Madhu
Simanta Palli, Santiniketan

K S Mukherjee

Introduction

The most successful and proven method of learning scientific subjects particularly chemistry is through experiments. Again, experiments are to be performed in the laboratory. So it is desirable that students working in the laboratory must be familiar with some important equipments of chemistry laboratory and their functioning. They should also be aware of some special cares to be taken during working in the laboratory. They must have first hand information regarding the nature of experiments to be performed and the method of reporting the observations noted in proper format. A very short resume on the above aspects of chemistry laboratory is furnished below:

A. Equipments

1. **Exhaust Fan:** In chemistry laboratory there is always evolution of undesirable and irritating gases. As such every chemistry laboratory is provided with sufficient number of exhaust fans to remove irritating and poisonous gases and fumes that may evolve. Every student must ensure before the entrance in the laboratory that exhaust fans are operating.

2. **Working Table:** Students in a chemistry laboratory are provided with working tables. Each working table is fitted with sinks and water taps at one end and at the other end of the same

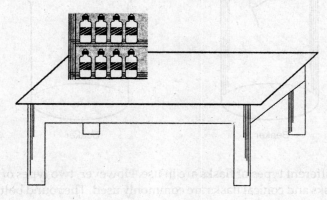

table gas taps are fitted for supplying gas required for heating purposes. The working table is fitted with a shelf for keeping bottles known as reagent bottoles containing commonly used reagents or chemicals. It must be remembered that the working table should be kept clean before and after working.

3. **Fume Cupboard**: To perform experiments evolving poisonous, obnoxious and undesirable fumes there is one or more fume cupboard fitted with exhaust fan in every chemistry laboratory.

4. **Balance Room**: For quantitative analysis weighing of the chemical samples is essential. For this purpose there must be a separate room where chemical balances are kept.

5. **Common Laboratory Apparatus**: In chemistry laboratory following apparatus are frequently used for carrying out the experiments and so the students should be familiar with the use and handling of these apparatus. These apparatus are made of glass or other substances.

(a) Glass Apparatus

    (i) **Test Tubes**: These are made of good quality glass materials and are employed for carrying out various tests.

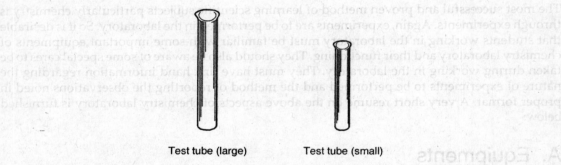

Test tube (large)   Test tube (small)

    (ii) **Beakers**: Beakers of different sizes (100ml, 200ml, 500ml and one litre) are used in the laboratory for making solutions required for different tests.

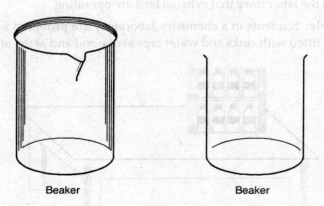

Beaker   Beaker

    (iii) **Flasks**: Different types of flasks are in use. However, two types of flasks, viz., round bottom flasks and conical flasks are commonly used. The round bottom flasks are used for the preparative purpose while conical flasks (Erlenmeyer flasks) are commonly used for the titration in quantitative analysis.

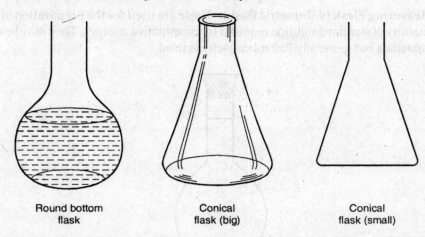

Round bottom
flask

Conical
flask (big)

Conical
flask (small)

(iv) **Funnels**: Funnels are used for separation of a compound from the solution of a mixture or reaction product.

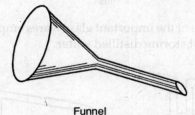

Funnel

(v) **Burette and Pipette**: These are made of good quality glass materials. The burette commonly used is of 50 ml capacity while pipette may be 20 or 25 ml capacity. These

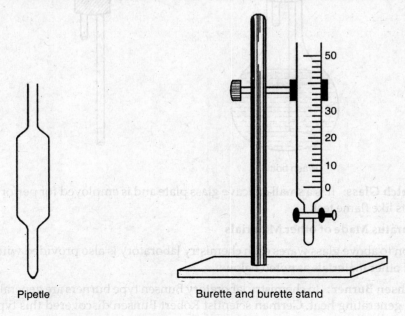

Pipetle

Burette and burette stand

are employed for volumetric titrations. During titration burettes are held in an iron stand fitted with burette clamp.

(vi) **Measuring Flask (volumetric flask):** These are used for the preparation of measured quantity of standard solution required for quantitative analysis. They may be of different capacities but generally 250 ml capacity is used.

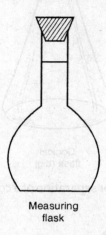

Measuring
flask

(vii) **Wash Bottle:** It is one of the important glass wares employed in chemistry laboratory. It is primarily used for storing distilled water.

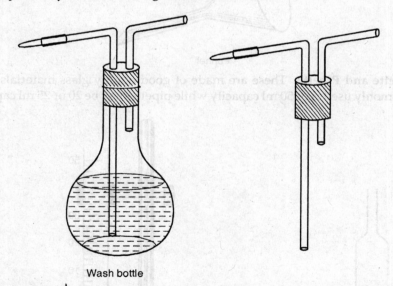

Wash bottle

(viii) **Watch Glass:** It is a small concave glass plate and is employed for performing certain tests like flame test.

(b) Apparatus Made of other Materials

In addition to above glass wares each chemistry laboratory is also provided with some other wares made of other materials as noted below:

(i) **Bunsen Burner:** In chemistry laboratory Bunsen type burners are generally employed for generating heat. German scientist Robert Bunsen discovered this type of burner.

The unique feature of this burner is that both luminous and non-luminous flames can be formed in this burner. When the burner is allowed to burn by closing the air-hole, luminous flame (reducing flame) is produced but when it burns with air-hole open non-luminous (oxidising) flame is obtained. Coal gas or any oil gas is used as fuel. It is generally made of either brass or any other metal.

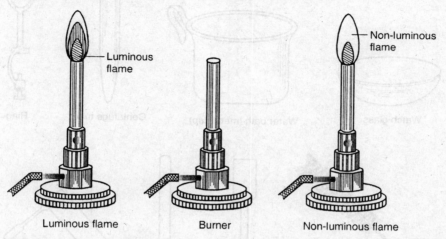

Luminous flame   Burner   Non-luminous flame

(ii) **Wire Gauze**: It is either square or round-shaped net made of iron wire with or without asbestos sintered at centre. The glass apparatus which is to be heated is placed on this net. It prevents glass or other container from possible cracking or excess heating.

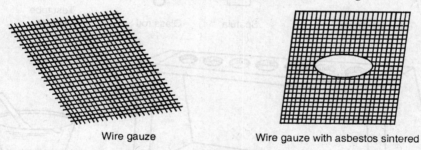

Wire gauze   Wire gauze with asbestos sintered

(iii) **Tripod Stand**: It is a three-legged iron stand and acts as a supporter for container which is usually used for heating.

Besides the appliances mentioned above a few others as pictured below are also frequently used for variety of purposes.

| Watch glass | Water bath (metal cup) | Centrifuge tube | Ring |

| Test tube brush | Spatula | Glass rod | Test tube holder |

Test tube support

Mortar and pestle

B. Special Cares to be taken for working in the Chemistry Laboratory

There are a variety of hazardous and poisonous chemicals in chemistry laboratory. So adequate precautions are to be taken by every student. Some of the important precautions to be taken are enlisted below:

(i) Every student must wear an apron during working in the laboratory.

(ii) Glass apparatus must sufficiently be cleaned before use. Depending upon the nature of dirty materials, water, concentrated sulphuric acid or sodium carbonate (washing soda) may be used for this purpose. These apparatus should be handled with care. Apparatus having cracks should not be used.

(iii) Corrosive chemicals should not be touched by hand—always spatula is to be used.

(iv) Reagent bottles should not be kept open.

(v) Many chemicals are poisonous and so no chemical should be tested by tung.

(vi) Inflammable liquids like alcohols, ether, etc. should not be brought near the flame.

(vii) Gas and water taps should be kept close when not in use.

(viii) Glass or porcelain apparatus should not be directly heated under flame—always wire gauze sintered with asbestos is to be employed.

(ix) Water should never be added to acid—acid is to be slowly added to water with stirring.

(x) Chemicals which can emit fumes on opening of the stopper of the container or on heating should only be handled in fume cupboard.

C. Nature of The Experiments to be Performed

According to the syllabi of most of the Indian Universities students of undergraduate courses, both General and Honours are required to perform the following different types of Experiments.

1. Qualitative analysis of inorganic mixtures containing three or four radicals (ions).

2. Quantitative inorganic analysis.

3. Inorganic preparations.

4. Qualitative analysis of single organic compounds.

5. Preparative organic chemistry involving typical organic reactions.

6. Quantitative organic analysis.

7. Separation of mixture of organic compounds and isolation of organic compounds from Natural source.

8. Some physical chemistry experiments.

 SECTION I

INORGANIC CHEMISTRY PRACTICAL

INORGANIC CHEMISTRY
PRACTICAL

Inorganic Qualitative Analysis

Part I

Planning for Systematic Inorganic Qualitative Analysis

As mentioned earlier (vide introduction p 7) qualitative inorganic analysis for students of undergraduate course generally involves the identification of three or four radicals (three for general and four for honours courses) present in a mixture. The radicals may be of two types, *viz.*, basic (cationic) and acid (anionic) radicals. It may be mentioned that basic radicals excepting ammonium ion are primarily metallic cations while acid radicals are non-metallic anions. It is, therefore, obvious that the compositions of these radicals in the mixture may be of the following three types:

(a) One basic radical and the rest are acid radicals, such as $ZnCl_2 + ZnSO_4$, $NaBr + NaCl$, $PbCl_2 + Pb(NO_3)_2$, $ZnCl_2 + ZnSO_4 + Zn_3(PO_4)_2$, etc.

(b) Two basic radicals and others are acid radicals. This type of mixture consists of either the same salt of two different cations like $ZnSO_4 + MgSO_4 + Mg_3(PO_4)_2$ or it may contain oxides of one or two basic radical(s) and salt(s) of other basic radical(s), i.e., $Al_2O_3 + KBr + AlCl_3$, where Al and K are two basic radicals, and chloride and bromide are the acid radicals.

(c) The third category of the sample may be the mixture of oxides of basic radicals; as for examples: $Al_2O_3 + PbO + ZnO + MgO$, $CuO + ZnO + Al_2O_3$ in which Pb, Zn, Mg, Cu, Al, etc. all represent basic radicals.

Now if the tests for different radicals are performed in a systematic manner, the identification of radicals in the above types of samples becomes a routine work. However, before undertaking the work of inorganic qualitative analysis it is felt that students should note some preliminary observations regarding the sample supplied.

This is because these observations not only provide valuable information regarding the radicals but also serve as useful guidlines in adapting appropriate procedure for systematic analysis. These observations are as discussed in sequel.

13

1.1 Physical Character of the Sample

Physical appearance and the colour of the sample can often provide significant clue for the identification of radicals. Thus, compounds of mercury and lead are heavy while those of aluminium and magnesium are relatively lighter. Again, from the colour of the sample valuable information may be obtained. However, it may be remembered that when two different coloured substances are present the colour of the mixture may be different from the colour of the individual compound and so enough confusion may arise. So it is advisable that from the colour final conclusion should not be drawn. For convenience a list of coloured compounds which are commonly supplied to the students is furnished below (Table 1.1).

Table 1.1: Colours of Some Common Inorganic Compounds	
Colour	Probable Compounds
Blue	Hydrated salts of Cupric ion
Green	Salts of Nickel, Ferrous Iron, trivalent Chromium
Pink	Hydrated salts of Cobalt and Manganese
Red	HgO, HgI_2, HgS, Pb_3O_4
Yellow	PbI_2, Chromates and $FeCl_3$
Black	PbS, MnO_2 COS, Ni_2O_3, CuO, CuS
Brown	Fe_2O_3, Fe_3O_4, $Fe(OH)_3$, CdO

Further, the colour of the solution prepared on dissolving the sample should also be noted, because it may sometimes give important clue regarding the nature of the substances present in the sample. It may be mentioned that the ions normally exhibit colours in dilute solution. Colours of dilute solutions of some ions are tabulated in table 1.2.

Table 1.2: Colours of Dilute Solution	
Colour	Probable Compounds
Green	Trivalent Chromium, Ferrous ion and Ni ion
Blue	Cupric ion
Pink	Manganese and Cobalt ions
Orange Yellow	Dichromate
Yellow	Ferric iron and Chromate

Once again, when more than one different coloured ions are present colour of the solution may differ to some extent. So colour of the solution may be considered only as a clue, not as the final conclusion.

1.2 Solubility of the Sample

Solubility test of the sample is an important and essential step for the identification of radicals present in the sample. It may so happen that some of the ions (radicals) present in the mixture may be soluble in water, some in hydrochloric acid solution and some other ions may be soluble in the solution of mixture of concentrated hydrochloric acid and concentrated nitric acid in the ratio 3:1 which is normally known as *aqua regia*. It may be mentioned that heat may be applied, if necessary.

It has further been observed that in some cases a portion of the given sample may not dissolve at all even in aqua regia. Such substances are generally called *insoluble radicals*. Thus, it is evident from the solubility test that a significant information may be obtained regarding the identity of the radicals of the given sample. Hence, it is advisable to perform the solubility test as discussed below before going into systematic analysis for identification of basic and acid radicals.

1.3 Solubility Test of the Sample

The solubility test of a given sample is performed as presented in Table 1.3.

Table 1.3: Solubility Test of a Given Sample

A portion of the solid sample supplied is taken in a beaker and sufficient amount of water is added to it. The beaker is boiled for a few minutes and following observations are noted.

Observation	Inference
1. No solid residue is left, i.e., the sample is completely soluble in water.	1. The given sample may contain Na, K, ammonium salts or other water soluble salts. The aqueous solution is to be analysed according to the procedure depicted in Tables 6.2 and 6.3.
2. Solid residue is present.	2. A portion of the sample is insoluble in water. It is filtered. Filtrate (I) and residue(1) are treated separately.
Filtrate (1)	**Residue (1)**
A portion of the filtrate (1) is taken in a test tube and evaporated to dryness and following observations are recorded.	Residue (1) is boiled first with dilute HCl and next concentrated HCl is added and following observations are recorded.
(i) No solid is present, i.e., the sample is insoluble in water and so filtrate (1) is rejected.	(i) No solid residue is present, i.e., the sample contains acid soluble portion. For further analysis Table 6.3 is to be followed.
(ii) Substantial amount of solid residue is left, i.e., a part of the sample is water soluble, hence filtrate (1) is analysed according to procedure presented in Table 6.3.	(ii) Solid residue is left. It is filtered and filtrate (2) and residue (2) are separately considered.
Filtrate (2)	**Residue (2)**
2-3 ml of the filtrate (2) is taken in a test tube and evaporated to dryness and following observations are noted.	The residue (2) is boiled with aqua regia in a beaker and following observations are noted.
(i) If no solid is present, acid soluble part is absent and filtrate (2) is rejected.	(i) No solid is left. The residue (2) is soluble in aqua regia. The Table 6.3 is followed for further analysis.
(ii) If there is solid residue, acid soluble part is present; wet analysis is to be done according to the methods suggested in Table 6.3.	(ii) Solid residue is left, it is filtered and filtrate (3) and residue (3) are separately analysed.

Contd.

Filtrate (3)	Residue (3)
Filtrate (3) is taken in a test tube and evaporated to dryness and observation are noted. (i) solid residue is present i.e. aqua regia soluble portion is present and Table 6.3 is followed for wet analysis. (ii) it no solid is left, the filtrate (3) is rejected as this indicates the absence of any aqua regia soluble portion.	It is insoluble part [vide (6.3.2)]

Thus, from the above discussion (Table 1.3) it is evident that the solubility test is not only an essential part for inorganic qualitative analysis but also plays an important role in suggesting the appropriate procedure for the wet analysis of basic radicals.

1.4 Systematic Planning for Qualitative Analysis

As mentioned earlier that the sample for qualitative inorganic analysis may contain either basic radicals or the mixture of both basic and acid radicals, the systematic qualitative analysis of inorganic substance involves the tests mentioned below:

It may be mentioned that the dry tests do not provide any conclusive evidence. They can suggest some valuable information regarding the identity of radicals. For this reason dry tests are also know n as *preliminary tests*. However, definite information are obtained from the analysis in the wet way.

1. Dry tests for basic radicals.
2. Dry tests for acid radicals.
3. Tests for interfering radicals.
4. Wet tests for acid radicals.
5. Tests for basic radicals in wet way.
6. Some special test.

Chapter 2

Dry Tests for Basic Radicals

Before undertaking the analysis of basic radicals in the wet way following dry tests are to be performed in the order mentioned below to have a preliminary idea regarding the nature of basic radicals present in the supplied sample. These dry tests are as under:

(a) Heating in a dry test tube.

(b) Bulb tube test.

(c) Oxidation on charcoal block.

(d) Cobalt nitrate test.

(e) Borax bead test.

(f) Reduction on charcoal block.

(g) Flame test.

(h) Fusion test for manganese and chromium.

2.1 Heating in a Dry Test Tube

Experiment: A little quantity of the powdered sample is taken in a dry test tube in such a way that no particle of the sample adheres to the side of the test tube, and holding the test tube in an almost horizontal position it is heated carefully at first gently and finally strongly. The changes, if any, is noted as shown in the tabular form.

Observation	Inference
A. *A gas is evolved* :	
(i) Substance decrepitates, and brown coloured gas is evolved.	(i) Nitrates and nitrites of heavy metals like Pb and Hg
(ii) A gas with smell of rotten eggs is evolved which turns lead acetate paper black.	(ii) Sulphide
(iii) Evolution of a gas with a smell of burnt sulphur.	(iii) Sulphite
(iv) A colourless gas having pungent odour of ammonia is evolved.	(iv) Ammonium salts
(v) A colourless odourless gas is evolved. It turns lime water milky.	(v) Carbonates
B. *Substance changes colour* :	
(i) Yellow when hot and white when cold	(i) Zn salts
(ii) Blackening	(ii) Salts of Cu, Ni, Mn and Co
(iii) Brown	(iii) Fe salts
(iv) Yellow	(iv) Pb
(v) Green	(v) Cr salts
C. *Original colour is white and on heating there is no change in colour*	C. Al, Ba, Ca, Sr, and Mg compounds
D. *Sample sublimes and a sublimate is formed at the cold part of the test tube.*	D. Ammonium, Hg, Pb salts
(i) Sublimate is white	(i) Pb, Hg and NH_4 salts
(ii) Sublimate turns black on warming with H_2S.	(ii) Hg
E. *Sample melts on heating at high temperature and solidifies on coolling.*	E. Na, K salts and chlorides of Pb, Mg, Ca and zn.

Chemistry behind this test: Inorganic compounds when heated in dry test tube several changes may occur. Some inorganic compounds may melt, some may volatilise while other may undergo decomposition, as a result of which change of colour or evolution of gases may occur. Some examples may be cited in this connection.

(a) $Pb(NO_3)_2 \xrightarrow{\text{heat}} PbO + 2N_2O_5 + O_2$

        (Brown vapour)

(b) $ZnCO_3 \xrightarrow{\text{heat}} ZnO + CO_2 + O_2$
        White   Yellow when hot

(c) $CuSO_4, 5H_2O \xrightarrow{\text{heat}} CuSO_4 + 5H_2O$
        Blue   White

2.2 Bulb Test Tube Test

Experiment: A portion of the sample is mixed with 4 times its bulk of Na_2CO_3 and this mixture is taken in a dry test tube and is heated holding it in horizontal position. *This test is performed only when sublimation occurs in dry test tube heating experiment.* The changes, if any, are recorded as before.

Observation	Inference
(i) Evolution of ammonia gas with its characteristic smell. It forms dense white fumes in contact with a glass rod moistened with conc. HCl.	(i) Ammonium salt
(ii) Shining grey mirror on the cooler part of the test tube which forms globules on rubbing with a glass rod.	(ii) Hg compounds
(iii) Shining black mirror but no glubule is formed on rubbing, but smell of garlic is obtained.	(iii) As compounds

Principles involved: Some inorganic compounds which can sublime on heating in a dry test tube are converted to their carbonates on heating with Na_2CO_3. When these carbonates are heated Hg and As compounds are converted to metallic form while ammonium compounds change to ammonia gas. Thus,

(a) $2NH_4Cl + Na_2CO_3 \longrightarrow (NH_4)_2CO_3 + 2NaCl$

$$\downarrow heat$$

$$2NH_3 + H_2O + CO_2$$

(b) $5As_2O_3 + 9Na_2CO_3 \longrightarrow 6Na_3AsO_4 + 9CO_2 + As_4$

$$\downarrow$$

Garlic odour
and forms black
mirror

(c) $HgCl_2 + Na_2CO_3 \xrightarrow{heat} HgCO_3 + NaCl$
White

$2HgCO_3 \xrightarrow{heat} 2HgO \longrightarrow 2Hg + O_2$
Metallic
globules

2.3 Oxidation on Charcoal Block

Experiment: A little portion of the original sample is taken in the cavity of charcoal block and is heated in the oxidising flame by means of a mouth blow pipe. Observations are recorded in the following table:

Observation	Inference
A. *An incrustation is formed.*	A. NH_4, Hg, As, Zn, Sn, Pb, Cd, Sb, Bi, compounds.
(i) Incrustation is white.	(i) NH_4, Hg, As, Sb compounds
(ii) Incrustation is yellow when hot and white on cooling.	(ii) Zn, Sn compounds.
(iii) Incrustation is yellow to orange.	(iii) Pb, Bi compounds.
(iv) Incrustation is brown in colour.	(iv) Cd
B. *Residue is left on charcoal which is incandescent when hot.*	B. Ca, Ba, Sr, Al, Mg, Zn, Sn compounds. (Cobalt Nitrate test is to be tried).
C. *Residue left on charcoal is coloured.*	C. Pb, Fe, Cu, Ni, Mn, Bi, Co, Cd, etc. compounds (Borax lead test is to be tried).
(i) Residue is green.	(i) Cr salts
(ii) Residue is brown to black.	(ii) Cu, Fe, Cd, Mn, Co, Ni.
(iii) Residue is yellow to red.	(iii) Pb, Bi, or Cr salts.
D. *The sample decrepitates on heating.*	D. *Chloride of Na and K.*
E. *Sample melts on heating and solidifies on cooling.*	E. Na and K salts.
F. *Substance volatilizes.*	F. NH_4, As, Hg, Sb-compounds, $SnCl_2$, $PbCl_2$
(i) White fumes with garlic odour.	(i) As compounds.
(ii) White fumes with smell of ammonia.	(ii) NH_4 compounds.
G. *Substance catches fire on heating.*	G. Nitrates and nitrities of Na and K.

Principle involved: Inorganic compounds when heated strongly in a charcoal cavity under the oxidising flame variety of changes may occur. Sometimes they volatilize, they may be converted to oxides or they may melt. In some cases the oxides so formed may be reduced to metal in presence of carbon of the block. The reactions that may occur may be illustrated as indicated below:

(a) $2AS_2O_3 + 9O_2 \longrightarrow 2AS_2O_3 + 6SO_2$

$\downarrow + 3C$

$As_4 + 3CO_2$

(Garlic odour)

(b) $ZnCO_3 \longrightarrow ZnO + CO_2$

$$Zn(metal) \longrightarrow ZnO \ (incrustation)$$
$$\text{Yellow} \qquad\qquad \text{White}$$

(c) $CaCO_3 \longrightarrow CaO + CO_2$

$$\downarrow$$
$$\text{Residue}$$

2.4 Cobalt Nitrate Test

Experiment: As mentioned earlier (2.3B) when white residue is left in the charcoal oxidation test, cobalt nitrate test is to be tried. The white residue left on charcoal block is moistened with a drop of cobalt nitrate solution and is strongly heated again in the oxidizing flame with the help of a mouth blow pipe. The changes are noted as below.

Observation	Inference
(i) Residue turns blue.	(i) Al, PO_4^{3-}, BO_3^{3-} and ASO_4^{3-}
(ii) Residue becomes bluish green.	(ii) Sn
(iii) Residue turns green.	(iii) Zn
(iv) Residue is pink.	(iv) Mg
(v) Grey coloured residue is formed.	(v) Ca, Ba, sr (Flame test to be attempted).

Reaction taking place: On heating, cobalt nitrate decomposes to cobalt oxide which reacts with the metallic oxides formed in the cavity of the charcoal block during heating under oxidizing flame and forms double oxides with characteristic colour. Thus,

$$2CO(NO_3)_2 \xrightarrow{\text{heat}} CoO + 4NO_2 + O_2$$

(a) $CoO + ZnO \longrightarrow CoZnO_2$
$$\text{Green}$$

(b) $CoO + Al_2O_3 \longrightarrow CoAl_2O_4$
$$\text{Blue}$$

In the case of phosphate, borate and arsenate corresponding double salts are obtained i.e.

$$Na_3PO_4 + CoO \longrightarrow NaCoPO_4$$

2.5 Borax Bead Test

Experiment: It has been mentioned earlier (vide 2.3C) that borax bead test is to be carried out when coloured residue is left on the cavity during charcoal oxidation test. A little amount of borax is taken on the tip of a clean platinum wire by dipping the heated platinum wire into borax and heating again in non-luminous flame till a transparent bead is formed. The hot transparent borax bead so formed is dipped lightly into the solid original sample and heated once again first in the oxidizing flame and next in the reducing flame. The colour of the bead is noted.

Observation in		Inference
Oxidizing flame	**Reducing flame**	
(i) Yellow to reddish yellow	(i) Bottle green	(i) Fe
(ii) Green	(ii) Green	(ii) Cr
(iii) Deep blue	(iii) Deep blue	(iii) Co
(iv) Green when hot and blue when cold.	(iv) Opaque red	(iv) Cu
(v) Yellowish brown	(v) Grey or black	(v) Ni
(vi) Amethyst	(vi) Colourless	(vi) Mn

Principle behind the test: On heating, borax decomposes into sodium metaborate and boric anhydride.

$$Na_2B_4O_7, 10H_2O \xrightarrow{\text{heat}} 2NaBO_2 + B_2O_3 + 10H_2O\uparrow$$

| (Borax) | Sodium metaborate | Boric anhydride | |

The mixture of metaborate and boric anhydride forms colourless transparent bead. The salts of cations like Co, Cr, Cu, Ni, Fe and Mn are converted to their oxides initially which then react with the bead forming metallic metaborate of higher valency in the oxidizing flame and this metaborate in contact with the carbon of reducing flame undergoes reduction forming either metaborate of lower valency or metal. The colour of the borax bead is due to the metaborate. Thus,

(a) Cu-salt $\xrightarrow{\text{heat}}$ CuO

Oxidizing flame: $CuO + B_2O_3 \longrightarrow Cu(BO_2)_2$
Cupric metaborate
Green when hot and blue when cold

Reducing flame: $2Cu(BO_2)_2 + C \longrightarrow [Cu_2(BO_2)_2] + B_2O_3 + CO$

$Cu_2(BO_2)_2 + C \longrightarrow 2Cu + B_2O_3 + CO$
Red

(b) Fe-salt

Fe-salt $\xrightarrow{\text{heat}}$ Fe_2O_3

Oxidizing flame: $Fe_2O_3 + 3B_2O_3 \longrightarrow Fe(BO_2)_3$
Ferric metaborate
(Yellow to reddish yellow)

Reducing flame: $Fe(BO_2)_3 + C \longrightarrow Fe(BO_2)_2$
Ferrous metaborate
(Bottle green)

(c) Co salt

Co salt $\xrightarrow{\text{heat}}$ CoO

Oxidizing flame: $CoO + B_2O_3 \longrightarrow Co(BO_2)_2$
(Blue)

Reducing flame: $Co(BO_2)_2 + C \longrightarrow$ No change and colour remains the same.

Similarly, in the case of Ni salt nickelous metaborate $[Ni(BO_2)_2]$ is formed in the oxidizing flame which is yellowish brown in colour and in the reducing flame this nickelous metaborate is converted to metallic Ni having grey or black colour.

Manganese salt forms manganic metaborate, $Mn(BO_2)_2$ having amethyst colour in the oxidizing flame, and in the reducing flame this metaborate changes to colourless manganus metaborate, $Mn(BO_2)_2$. Chromium salt yields $Cr(BO_2)_2$ in the oxidizing flame. This metasborate is green in colour. But this metaborate is not reduced in reducing flame and so same colour (green) is observed.

2.6 Reduction on Charcoal Block

Experiment: A small portion of original sample is mixed with 3 to 4 times its bulk of Na_2CO_3 on a watch glass. A portion of this mixture is taken into the cavity of the charcoal block and is heated in the reducing flame with the help of a mouth blow pipe. Changes are noted.

Observation	Inference
A. Metallic bead is formed.	A. Pb, Sn, Bi, Sb compounds.
(i) Bead is soft and malleable and it marks paper.	(i) Pb compounds.
(ii) Bead is white, does not mark the paper.	(ii) Sn compounds.
B. Red scales are formed.	B. Cu compounds.
C. Black magnetic mass is left on the charcoal.	C. Fe, CO, Ni and Mn compounds.
D. Pinkish white metallic bead with orange yellow incrustation.	D. Bi
E. White bead with white volatile incrustation.	E. Sb

Reactions taking place: Initially, metallic salts when heated with Na_2CO_3 is converted to corresponding metallic oxides. These oxides in presence of carbon of the reducing flame are converted to metallic bead. Thus,

(a) $PbCl_2 + Na_2CO_3 \longrightarrow PbCO_3 + NaCl$

$PbCO_3 \longrightarrow PbO + CO_2$

$2PbO + C \longrightarrow 2Pb + CO_2$
(Bead)

(b) $CuCl_2 + Na_2CO_3 \longrightarrow CuCO_3$

$CuCO_3 \longrightarrow CuO + CO_2$

$2CuO + C \longrightarrow 2Cu + CO_2$

(Red scales)

(c) $FeSO_4 + Na_2CO_3 \longrightarrow FeCO_3 + Na_2SO_4$

$FeCO_3 \longrightarrow FeO + CO_2$

$2FeO + C \longrightarrow 2Fe + CO_2$

(Black
magnetic mass)

(d) Bi salt $+ Na_2CO_3 \longrightarrow Bi_2(CO_3)_3$

$Bi_2(CO_3)_3 \longrightarrow Bi_2O_3 + 3CO_2$

$2Bi_2O_3 + 3C \longrightarrow 4Bi + 3CO_2$

(Pinkish
white bead)

2.7 Flame Test

Experiment: A platinum wire is cleaned and moistened with concentrated HCl taken in a watch glass. The platinum wire is heated for a few minutes in the non-luminous flame until the flame becomes colourless. The platinum wire is moistened again with concentrated HCl and is heated once again in the non-luminous flame. This process is repeated until no colour of the flame is observed. Finally, the platinum wire is moistened with concentrated HCl and this moistened wire is dipped into the powdered original sample and is held near the base of the non-luminous flame. The colour of the flame is observed first with the naked eye and next through double blue glass.

[**N.B.** Some salts like $BaSO_4$, $Ba_3(PO_4)_2$, $Ca_3(PO_4)_2$, etc. do not easily respond to the flame test. However, if they are heated in the reducing flame before the flame test, they are reduced to sulphides and phosphides and they can readily respond to this test. Further, when the presence of Pb, Sb, As, Cd and Bi are indicated in the previous tests, asbestos fibre may be used in place of platinum wire.]

Observation		Inference
in naked eye	**through double blue glass**	
(i) Violet	(i) Intense violet	(i) K
(ii) Golden yellow	(ii) Colourless	(ii) Na
(iii) Transient brick red	(iii) Light green	(iii) Ca
(iv) Crimson red	(iv) Purple	(iv) Sr
(v) Yellowish green	(v) Bluish green	(v) Ba
(vi) Bluish white	(vi) Colourless	(vi) Pb, As, Sb, Bi, Sn, Cd, etc.
(vii) Bluish green or green	(vii) Colourless	(vii) Cu, Borates

Principle: When the sample is heated with concentrated HCl, the chemical compounds of the sample are converted to their chlorides. The chlorides which are volatile can impart the characteristic colours. Thus,

(a) $Na_2SO_4 + 2HCl \longrightarrow 2NaCl + H_2SO_4$
(volatile)

(b) $BaSO_4 + 4C$ (from reducing flame) $\longrightarrow BaS + 4CO$

$BaS + 2HCl \longrightarrow BaCl_2 + H_2S$
(volatile)

(c) $SrSO_4 + 4C \longrightarrow SrS + 4CO$

$SrS + 2HCl \longrightarrow SrCl_2 + H_2S$
(volatile)

(d) $CaSO_4 + 4C \longrightarrow CaS + 4CO$

$CaS + 2HCl \longrightarrow CaCl_2 + H_2S$
(volatile)

(e) $K_2SO_4 + 2HCl \longrightarrow 2KCl + H_2SO_4$
(volatile)

2.8 Fusion Test for Manganese and Chromium

Experiment: This test is to be performed when Mn and Cr are detected in the earlier tests particularly in borax bead test, a portion of the original sample is mixed with two parts of Na_2CO_3 or NaOH and one part of KNO_3 or $KClO_3$ and the mixture is fused on a piece of broken porcelain with a mouth blow pipe. The mass is kept in the molten condition for a few minutes and then cooled. Following observations are noted.

Observation	Inference
(i) The mass turns yellow. It is dissolved in water and filtered. The filtrate is acidified with acetic acid and a few drops of lead acetate solution is added when yellow precipitate is formed. It is dissolved in water and acidified with dilute H_2SO_4 when orange colour is produced.	(i) Cr confirmed.
(ii) The mass turns green. It is dissolved in water and is acidified with dilute HNO_3 or CH_3COOH until acidic—pink colour develops.	(ii) Mn-Confirmed.

Principle: The oxidizing agent KNO_3 or $KClO_3$ oxidizes manganese and chromium and converts them to manganate and chromate. These salts are coloured—manganate is green and chromate is yellow in colour. When such masses are acidified they are converted to permanganate and dichromate respectively. Thus,

$$KNO_3 \xrightarrow{heat} KNO_2 + O$$

$$2KClO_3 \xrightarrow{heat} 2KCl + 3O_2$$

The oxygen liberated oxidizes Mn and Cr salts.

(a) $MnO + Na_2CO_3 + 2[O] \longrightarrow Na_2MnO_4 + CO_2$

                                                    Green
                                            (Manganate)

$4Na_2MnO_4 + O_2 + 2H_2O \longrightarrow 4NaMnO_4$

                                                    Permanganate
                                                  (Pink colour)

(b) $2Cr_2O_3 + 4Na_2CO_3 + 6O \longrightarrow 4Na_2CrO_4 + 4CO_2$

                                                          Chromate
                                                    (Yellow in colour)

$2Na_2CrO_4 + H_2SO_4 \longrightarrow Na_2Cr_2O_7 + Na_2SO_4 + H_2O$

                                               Orange
                                              colour
                                          (Dichromate)

2.6 Fusion Test for Manganese and Chromium

Experiment: This test is to be performed when Mn and Cr are detected in the yellow data particularly in borax bead Test. A portion of the original sample is mixed with two parts of Na$_2$CO$_3$ or Na$_2$CO$_3$ and one part of KNO$_3$ or KClO$_3$, and the mixture is fused on a piece of broken porcelain with mouth blow pipe. The mass is kept in the molten condition for a few minutes and then cooled. Following observations noted.

Observation	Inference
(i) The mass, lime yellow, it is dissolved in water and filtered. The filtrate is acidified with acetic acid and a few drops of lead acetate solution is added when yellow precipitate is formed. It is dissolved in water and acidified with dilute H$_2$SO$_4$, when orange colour is produced.	(i) Cr confirmed.
(ii) The mass, dark green, it is dissolved in water and is acidified with dilute HNO$_3$ or CH$_3$COOH until acidic—pink colour develops.	(ii) Mn-Confirmed

Principle: The oxidising agent KNO$_3$ or KClO$_3$ oxidizes manganese and chromium and converts them to permanganate and chromate. These salts are coloured—manganate is green and

Chapter 3

Dry Tests for Acid Radicals

After performing the dry tests for basic radicals, dry tests for acid radicals are to be undertaken. These tests provide some preliminary ideas regarding the inorganic sample under consideration. The dry tests for acid radicals consist of the following experiments:

(a) Treatment of the sample with dilute H_2SO_4 or dilute HCl.

(b) Treatment of the sample with concentrated H_2SO_4.

(c) Treatment of the sample with concentrated HCl.

(d) Heating of the sample with concentrated H_2SO_4 and MnO_2.

(e) Heating of the sample with concentrated H_2SO_4 and Cu-turnings.

(f) Chromyl chloride test.

(g) Heating of the sample with dilute H_2SO_4 and Zn-granules.

3.1 Treatment of the Sample with Dilute H_2SO_4 or HCl

Experiment: A portion of the sample is taken in a test tube, and a few drops of dilute H_2SO_4 or HCl are added to it and is warmed, if required. The effects if any, are observed as under:

Observation	Inference
(i) Effervescence in the cold occurs with evolution of a colourless and odourless gas which turns lime water milky.	(i) Carbonate (CO_3^{2-})
(ii) Evolution of a colourless gas with the smell of rotten egg and turns lead acetate paper black.	(ii) Sulphide (S^{2-})
(iii) Evolution of a colourless gas with the smell of burning sulphur and turns acidified potassium dichromate paper green or bluish green.	(iii) Sulphite (SO_3^{2-})

Contd.

Observation	Inference
(iv) Evolution of a colourless gas with the smell of burnt sulphur, turns acidified potassium dichromate paper green or bluish green and also deposition of white or yellow sulphur.	(iv) Thiosulphate $(S_2O_3^{2-})$
(v) Evolution of reddish brown coloured gas. It turns starch iodide paper blue.	(v) Nitrite (NO_2^-)

Reactions taking place: On treatment with dilute acid (H_2SO_4 or HCl) following changes occur:

(a) $M_2CO_3 + H_2SO_4 \longrightarrow M_2SO_4 + CO_2\uparrow + H_2O$
       (Carbonate)   Colourless
                                                      gas, turns lime
                                                      water milky

(b) $M_2S + H_2SO_4 \longrightarrow M_2SO_4 + H_2S\uparrow \xrightarrow{Pb(OAc)_2} PbS$ (Black)
       (Sulphide)   Colourless gas
                                           with smell
                                           of rotten egg

(c)
       $M_2SO_3 + H_2SO_4 \longrightarrow M_2SO_4 + H_2O + SO_2\uparrow$
       (Sulphite)   Colourless gas
                                                        with smell
                                                        of burnt sulphur

       $K_2Cr_2O_7 + H_2SO_4 + 3SO_2 \longrightarrow Cr_2(SO_4)_3 + K_2SO_4 + H_2O$
                                                      Green or
                                                      Bluish green

(d) $M_2S_2O_3 + H_2SO_4 \longrightarrow M_2SO_4 + S\downarrow + SO_2 + H_2O$
       Thiosulphate   ppt.
                                                        Colourless gas

(e) $2MNO_2 + H_2SO_4 \longrightarrow M_2SO_4 + 2HNO_2$

       $4HNO_2 \longrightarrow 2H_2O + 4NO + O_2$

       $4NO + 2O_2 \longrightarrow 4NO_2\uparrow$
                              Reddish brown gas

       [M is a monovalent metal ion.]

3.2 Treatment of the Sample with Concentrated H_2SO_4

Experiment: A portion of the original solid sample is taken in a dry test tube and is warmed with concentrated H_2SO_4. In addition to the effect observed in earlier experiment (vide Art. 3.1) following changes are noted:

Observation	Inference
(i) Evolution of a brown fumes which becomes more intense on adding cu-turnings.	(i) Nitrate (NO_3^-) Nitrite (NO_2^-)
(ii) Evolution of violet vapour.	(ii) Iodide (I^-)
(iii) Evolution of a brown gas which condenses to red droplets on the cooler part of the test tube.	(iii) Bromide
(iv) Evolution of a colourless gas with pungent smell which produces dense white fume in contact with a glass rod moistened with NH_4OH.	(iv) Chloride
(v) Evolution of a pungent gas which tuns a drop of water held on a glass rod, turbid oily drops are also formed on the wall of the test tube.	(v) Fluoride (F^-)
(vi) Produces yellow colour in cold, on warming vigorous reaction producing a gas which burns with blue flame and precipitation of sulphur occurs.	(vi) Thiocyanate (SCN^-)

Chemical reactions involved: When the sample is warmed with concentrated H_2SO_4 corresponding acids are formed. Thus,

(a) $2MX + H_2SO_4 \longrightarrow 2HX + M_2SO_4$ (X = halogen)

Halogen acid
(Decomposes forming
vapour of halogens)

(b) $2MNO_3 + H_2SO_4 \longrightarrow M_2SO_4 + 2HNO_3$

$4HNO_3 \longrightarrow 2H_2O + 4NO + 3O_2$

$4NO + 2O_2 \longrightarrow 4NO_2$

(c) $MSCN + 2H_2SO_4 + H_2O \longrightarrow COS\uparrow + NH_4HSO_4 + MHSO_4$

Blue flame
(Carbonyl
sulphide)

(d) HF is obtained from flourides. This HF reacts with the SiO_2 of the glass test tube to form volatile SiF_4. SiF_4 forms silicic acid.

$$4HF + SiO_2 = SiF_4 + 2H_2O$$

$$3SiF_4 + 4H_2O = H_4SiO_4 + 2H_2SiF_6$$

Silic acid
(white)

3.3 Treatment of the Sample with Concentrated HCl

Experiment: A small portion of the sample is taken in a dry test tube, and to it a few drops o concentrated HCl are added and heated. Following observations are recorded. The reaction occurring are similar to those of experiments in Art. 3.2.

Observation	Inference
(i) Evolution of a greenish yellow gas with irritating smell.	(i) Chromate (CrO_4^{2-}), manganate (MnO_2^{2-})
(ii) Violet vapour.	(ii) Iodide (I^-) and iodate (IO_4^-)
(iii) Brown vapour.	(iii) Bromide (Br^-) and Bromate (BrO_3^-)

3.4 Heating of the Sample with Concentrated H$_2$SO$_4$ and MnO$_2$

Experiment: A portion of the original sample is taken in a dry test tube and is heated witl concentrated H_2SO_4 and a little MnO_2. Following observations are recorded:

Observation	Inference
(i) Evolution of greenish yellow gas with the smell of chlorine.	(i) Chloride (Cl^-)
(ii) Evolution of reddish brown gas with irritating smell.	(ii) Bromide (Br^-)
(iii) Evolution of violet vapour with smell of iodine.	(iii) Iodide (I^-)

Principle: Reactions that occur in these experiments are follows:

(a) $NaCl + H_2SO_4 \longrightarrow NaHSO_4 + HCl$

$4HCl + MnO_2 \longrightarrow Cl_2\uparrow + MnCl_2 + 2H_2O$
(Greenish
yellow gas)

(b) $NaBr + H_2SO_4 \longrightarrow NaHSO_4 + HBr$

$4HBr + MnO_2 \longrightarrow Br_2\uparrow + MnBr_2 + 2H_2O$
(Reddish
brown gas)

(c) $NaI + H_2SO_4 \longrightarrow NaHSO_4 + HI$

$4HI + MnO_2 \longrightarrow I_2\uparrow + MnI_2 + 2H_2O$
(violet gas)

3.5 Heating of the Sample with Concentrated H_2SO_4 and Cu-turnings

Experiment: A portion of the sample is taken in a dry test tube and heated with a few drops concentrated H_2SO_4 and Cu-turnings.

Observation	Inference
Evolution of brown fumes	(Nitrate (NO_3^-), Nitrite (NO_2^-) and Bromide (Br^-))

Principle: Following reactions occur during this experiment:

(a) $2KBr + H_2SO_4 \longrightarrow KSO_4 + CuSO_4 + Br_2\uparrow$
(Brown fumes)

(b) $M(NO_3)_2 + 4H_2SO_4 + 3Cu \longrightarrow MSO_4 + 3CuSO_4 + 2NO + 4H_2O$

$2NO + O_2 \, (air) \longrightarrow 2NO_2$
(Brown fumes)

3.6 Chromyl Chloride Test

Experiment: A small portion of solid sample is taken in a clean, dry test tube and heated with concentrated H_2SO_4 and little $K_2Cr_2O_7$ (solid) by closing the mouth of the test tube with a cork fitted with a delivery tube. The end of the delivery tube is led into dilute NaOH solution kept in a test tube.

Observation	Inference
Deep brownish red vapour of chromyl chloride is evolved which forms yellow colouration in NaOH solution. On acidification with acetic acid Pb-acetate solution is added to the yellow solution, when yellow precipitate takes place.	Chloride (Cl^-)

Principle: Following reactions have been found to take place:

$MCl + H_2SO_4 \longrightarrow MHSO_4 + HCl$

$K_2Cr_2O_7 + 2H_2SO_4 \longrightarrow 2KHSO_4 + 2CrO_3 + H_2O$

$2CrO_3 + 4HCl \longrightarrow 2CrO_2Cl_2 + 2H_2O$

Chromyl chloride
(Brown fumes)

When the vapour of chromyl chloride is passed into NaOH, Na_2CrO_4 is formed. On treatment with lead acetate Pb-chromate is formed.

$$CrO_2Cl_2 + NaOH \longrightarrow Na_2CrO_4 + 2NaCl + 2H_2O$$

Na-chromate
(yellow solution)

$$Na_2CrO_4 + Pb(OAc)_2 \longrightarrow PbCrO_4\downarrow + 2NaOAc$$

Yellow ppt.

3.7 Heating of the Sample with Dilute H_2SO_4 and Zinc Granules

Experiment: A portion of the sample is taken in a test tube. To it a few pieces of zinc granules and a few ml of dilute H_2SO_4 (1:3) are added and warmed.

Observation	Inference
(i) A gas with the smell of rotten egg is evolved. It turns lead acetate paper black.	(i) Sulphide (S^{2-})
(ii) A gas with the smell of rotten egg is evolved which is passed into a NaOH solution taken in another test tube through a glass tube fixed at the mouth of the first test tube. A few drops of Na-nitroprusside solution when added to it violet colour develops.	(ii) Sulphide (S^{2-})

Principle: Under the condition H_2S is liberated from the sulphide if present in the sample which is responsible for the above observations.

$$M_2S + H_2SO_4 \longrightarrow M_2SO_4 + H_2S\uparrow$$

$$H_2S + Pb(OCOCH_3)_2 \longrightarrow PbS + 2CH_3COOH$$
Black

$$H_2S + NaOH \longrightarrow Na_2S + H_2O$$

$$Na_2S + Na_2[Fe(CN)_5NO] \longrightarrow Na_4[Fe(CN)_5NOS]$$
Na-nitroprusside   Violet

It may be mentioned that (i) if Hg and As are indicated in the dry test this test should be performed by very gentle heating for a short time, otherwise HgS and As_2S_3 may volatilize away. (ii) normally the sulphides which are decomposed by dilute or concentrated H_2SO_4 or HCl can be detected by this test. (iii) always a blank test without any sample should be carried out, as commercial zinc may be contaminated with sulphide.

Chapter 4

Tests for Interfering Acid Radicals

Some acid radicals (anions) such as phosphates, borates, arsenates, fluorides, silicates, chromates, dichromate and permanganate, etc. have been identified as interfering acid radicals. This is because such radicals, if present, interfere in the separation of metal ions (basic radicals) particularly of group IIIA onwards. The interference is due to the fact that these radicals, if present, there is possibility of formation of precipitates of group IIIB, IV and Mg along with group IIIA metal ions when the solution is made alkaline by NH_4OH solution for the separation of group IIIA metal ions. As a result, systematic separation procedure becomes complicated. It is, therefore, desirable that these radicals should be known before the start of wet tests of basic radicals so that necessary modification in the procedure for separation of metal ions may be intended for the removal of these acid ions and separation of basic radicals can smoothly occur. Important tests for interfering acid radicals are as described below:

4.1 Tests for Phosphate, Arsenate and Silicate

Experiment: A little of the substance is dissolved in dilute HCl taken in a test tube. To this solution 3-4 ml of ammonium molybdate solution is added. Next excess of concentrated HNO_3 solution is added. Following changes are observed:

Observation	Inference
(i) A canary yellow precipitate is formed.	(i) Phosphate (PO_4^{3-})
(ii) Yellow precipitate is formed after warming the solution.	(ii) Arsenate (ASO_4^{3-}) and Silicate (SiO_3^{3-})
(iii) 15% solution of tartaric acid is added to the above precipitate and heated when the precipitate (a) does not dissolve. (b) dissolves.	(iii) (a) Phosphate (b) Arsenate and silicate

Principle: Following reactions take place:

(a) $Na_2HPO_4 + 12(NH_4)_2MoO_4 + 23HNO_3$

Ammonium-
molybdate

$$(NH_4)_3[PMO_{12}O_{40}] + 21NH_4NO_3 + 2NaNO_3 + 12H_2O$$

Ammonium phospho
molybdate
(Canary yellow ppt. in cold)

(b) $Na_2HASO_4 + 12(NH_4)_2MoO_4 + 23HNO_3$

$$(NH_4)_3[AsMO_{12}O_{40}] + 21NH_4NO_3 + 2NaNO_3 + 12H_2O$$

Ammonium arseno-
molybdate
(Canary yellow ppt. after warming)

4.2 Test for Silicate

Experiment: A small portion of the sample is taken in an iron or lead crucible and is mixed with equal amount of CaF_2. 1 ml of conc. H_2SO_4 is added to the mixture and is heated gently on asbestos board. A drop of water taken on the tip of glass rod is held in the issuing gas.

Observation	Inference
The clear water drop turns turbid.	Silicate (SiO_3^{2-})

Principle: The turbidity is due to the formation of gelatinous precipitate of silicic acid.

$$CaF_2 + H_2SO_4 \longrightarrow CaSO_4 + 2HF$$

$$SiO_2 + 4HF \longrightarrow SiF_4 + 2H_2O$$
(Silica)

$$3SiF_4 + 4H_2O \text{ (water drop)} \longrightarrow H_2SiO_4 + H_2SiF_6$$
Silicic
acid (gelatinous)

4.3 Tests for Borate and Boric Acid

Experiment: A portion of the sample is taken in a test tube and to it 2 ml of alcohol and 2 ml of conc. H_2SO_4 are added. Test tube is gently heated and the issuing gas is ignited at the mouth of the test tube.

Observation	Inference
(i) The gas burns with greenish flame.	(i) Borate (BO_3^{3-}) and boric acid (H_3BO_3)
(ii) When sample and alcohol (without adding conc. H_2SO_4) are gently heated the issuing gas burns with green flame.	(ii) Boric acid (H_3BO_3)

Principle: Borate of metal ions is converted to boric acid by the action of conc. H_2SO_4. Boric acid on reaction with alcohol forms alkyl borate which is volatile and burns with the green flame.

$$Na_3BO_3 + H_2SO_4 \longrightarrow \underset{\text{Boric acid}}{H_3BO_3} + Na_2SO_4$$

$$H_3BO_3 + \underset{\text{Alcohol}}{3ROH} \longrightarrow \underset{\text{Alkyl borate}}{B(OR)_3} + 3H_2O$$

It may be mentioned that any alcohol may be used but methyl borate is more volatile than other alkyl borate. For this reason methyl alcohol is preferably used.

4.4 Tests for Chromate, Dichromate and Permanganate

Experiment: A small portion of the sample is treated with 2-3 ml of concentrated HCl and is warmed for a few minutes.

Observation	Inference
Evolution of greenish yellow gas with irritating smell of chlorine.	Chromate (CrO_4^{2-}), $Cr_2O_7^{2-}$ and permanganate (MnO_4^-)

Reactions taking place:

(a) $M_2CrO_4 + 2HCl \longrightarrow H_2CrO_4 + 2MCl$

(b) $M_2Cr_2O_7 + 14HCl \longrightarrow 2MCl + 2CrCl_3 + 3Cl_2 + 7H_2O$

(c) $2KMnO_4 + 16HCl \longrightarrow 2MnCl_4 + 2KCl + 3Cl_2 + 8H_2O$

N.B. Test for fluoride is similar to that of silicate (vide Art. 4.2).

Chapter 5

Wet Tests for Acid Radicals

For wet analysis of acid radicals, preparation of the solution of the supplied sample is essential. However, if the sample is completely soluble in water as is evidenced from the solubility test (vide Art. 1.3, p 15), the aqueous solution obtained by boiling the supplied sample with distilled water may be *directly used for wet tests* of acid radicals. But if the sample is partly soluble in water as it often happens, its aqueous soluble portion is taken away by filtration and the portion which remains insoluble in water is extracted with Na_2CO_3. Both water soluble portion and Na_2CO_3 extract are separately tested for acid radicals.

Further, the portion which remains insoluble in acid but is soluble in aqua regia (vide Art. 1.3 p. 15) is fused with NaOH and the mass is then extracted with water. The water extract so obtained is used for acid radicals.

5.1 Preparation of Sodium Carbonate Extract

When the mixture supplied is insoluble in water, sodium carbonate extract is prepared. The procedure for preparing this extract consists of mixing about 1 gm of the sample with atleast 2 gm of sodium carbonate in a conical flask of 250 ml capacity and 20-25 ml distilled water is added. The conical flask in covered with a funnel and the contents of the flask is boiled for 10-15 minutes, cooled and filtered. The filtrate thus, obtained is called sodium carbonate or soda extract. This extract is used for acid radicals as discussed below (vide Art. 5.2).

Chemistry involved in the process: When the mixture of the sample is boiled with sodium carbonate, double decomposition reaction occurs and there are formation of insoluble metal carbonate and water soluble sodium salt. Thus,

$$Na_2CO_3 \ + \ \underset{\text{Salt}}{MA} \ \longrightarrow \ \underset{\substack{\text{Metal} \\ \text{carbonate}}}{MCO_3} \ + \ \underset{\substack{\text{Sodium} \\ \text{salt (soluble)}}}{Na_2A}$$

$$Na_2CO_3 \ + \ CaCl_2 \ \longrightarrow \ CaCO_3 \ + \ \underset{\text{(soluble)}}{2NaCl}$$

Similar is the case with other salts.

5.2 Detail Tests for Acid Radicals

Experiment	Observation	Inference
1. A portion of Na_2CO_3 extract is taken in a test tube and a few drops of sodium nitro-prusside solution are added to it.	1. Violet colour develops	1. Sulphide (S^{2-})
2. A part of the extract is acidified with dilute HCl, boiled for a few minites to remove CO_2 and 1-2 ml of $BaCl_2$ solution is added.	2. (a) A heavy white precipitate insoluble in dilute HCl. (b) White precipitate is soluble in excess of dilute HCl.	2. (a) Sulphate (SO_4^{2-}) (b) Sulphite (SO_3^{2-}), Fluoride (F^-)
3. Another part of the extract is taken in a test tube and is acidified with dilute HCl, boiled to remove CO_2 and to it 1-2 ml of freshly prepared $FeSO_4$ solution is added with shaking. Next 2 ml of conc. H_2SO_4 is gently added down the side of inclined test tube so that a layer is formed at the bottom.	3. (a) A brown ring is formed at the junction of H_2SO_4 and the aqueous solution. (b) Whole solution turns brown.	3. (a) Nitrate (NO_3^-) [Bromide may also form similar ring so that test for bromide be performed.] (b) Nitrite (NO_2^-)
4. A part of the extract is acidified with dilute HCl, boiled to remove CO_2 and 1-2 ml of $CuSO_4$ solution is added. Next slight excess of NaOH solution is added and warmed.	4. A green or red precipitate is formed.	4. Arsenite (ASO_3^{3-})
5. Another part of the soda extract is acidified with dilute HCl and boiled to remove CO_2. To it solution of magnesia mixture is added till it becomes alkaline.	5. White precipitate	5. Phsophate (PO_4^{3-}) or Arsenite (ASO_3^{3-})
6. If the Na_2CO_3 extract is yellow it is (a) acidified with acetic acid and (b) treated with lead acetate solution.	6. (a) Original yellow colour of the solution turns orange on acidification. (b) Yellow precipitate is formed.	6. (a) Chromate (CrO_4^{2-}) (b) Chromate (CrO_4^{2-})

5.3 Detail Tests for Acid Radicals with Neutral Na_2CO_3 Extract Solution

Preparation of Neutral Na_2CO_3 extract solution: Na_2CO_3 extract is treated with dilute HNO_3 till the solution is acidic to litmus. To this solution, dilute NH_4OH is added drop by drop till it is just alkaline (faint smell of ammonia may be obtained). It is boiled to remove excess of ammonia. This solution now becomes exactly neutral. With this neutral solution following tests are performed:

[**N.B.** It may be mentioned in this connection that if there is formation of precipitate during neutralization, salts of As, Pb, Sn, Al, Zn and Sb may be present. The solution is to be filtered, and with the filtrate tests are to be performed rejecting the precipitate.]

Experiment	Observation	Inference
1. To a little portion of the neutral solution excess of $AgNO_3$ solution is added.	1. (a) A curdy white, yellow or yellowish precipitate is formed which is insoluble in HNO_3.	1. (a) Halides. [chart in Art. 5.4 to be followed for distinction]
	(b) White precipitate turns brown on warming.	(b) Borate
	(c) Brick red precipitate.	(c) Chromate
	(d) Yellow precipitate.	(d) Phosphate
	(e) White precipitate soluble in HNO_3 and in NH_4OH.	(e) Sulphite
	(f) White precipitate soluble in HNO_3 with separation of sulphur.	(f) Thiosulphate $(S_2O_3^{2-})$
	(g) Grey precipitate soluble in HNO_3 with separation of sulphur.	(g) Sulphide
2. To a part of neutral solution 1-2 ml $CaCl_2$ solution is added.	2. (a) White precipitate insoluble in acetic acid.	2. (a) Fluoride
	(b) White precipitate soluble in acetic acid.	(b) Phosphate Arsenate and silicate
3. To another part of the neutral solution $FeCl_3$ solution is added drop by drop.	3. (a) Reddish yellow precipitate is formed.	3. (a) Phsophate possibly
	(b) Blood red colouration.	(b) Thiocyanate

5.4 Distinction between Chloride, Bromide and Iodide

If the presence of halides are indicated in the earlier test (vide Art. 5.3 1a) following tests are performed to distinguish these halides:

Experiment	Observation	Inference
1. *When only one halide is present:* A portion of the neutral Na_2CO_3 extract is treated with excess of $AgNO_3$ solution.	1. (a) A curdy white precipitate in soluble in dilute HNO_3 but readily dissolves in NH_4OH.	1. (a) Chloride

Contd.

Experiment	Observation	Inference
	(b) Slightly yellowish precipitate insoluble in dilute HNO_3 but difficultly dissolves in NH_4OH.	(b) Bromide
	(c) Yellow precipitate insoluble in dilute HNO_3 and does not dissolve in NH_4OH.	(c) Iodide.
2. *When more than one halides are present*: A portion of Na_2CO_3 extract is taken in a beaker and is acidified with dilute HCl and a few drops of chlorine-water are added and the mixture is shaken with CCl_4.	2. (a) CCl_4-layer turns violet (b) More chlorine-water is added to the above layer and shaken. CCl_4-layer becomes reddish yellow. (c) Violet colour fades away and ultimately layer becomes colourless by the addition of more chlorine-water.	2. (a) Iodide (b) Bromide (c) Bromide *absent*.
3. A portion of Na_2CO_3 extract is acidified with conc. HNO_3 and solution of PbO_2 are added till the vapours of bromine and iodine are completely removed filtered and the filtrate is acidified with conc. HNO_3, and $AgNO_3$ solution is added.	3. A curdy white precipitate insoluble in HNO_3 but soluble in NH_4OH.	3. Chloride

5.5 Distinction between Nitrate and Nitrite

If in the dry test for acid radicals, on treatment of the solid sample with dilute H_2SO_4 brown vapours of NO_2 evolve [vide Art. 3.1(v)]; presence of both nitrate and nitrite is indicated. So it is desirable that distinction between these two acid radicals should be carried out. This is usually performed as discussed below:

Experiment	Observation	Inference
1. A few ml of Na_2CO_3 extract is taken in a test tube and is acidified with dilute H_2SO_4.	1. A reddish brown colour appears which turns starch-iodide paper moistened with dilute HCl blue.	Nitrite (NO_2^-) confirmed.
2. Now before performing test for nitrate (NO_3^-) nitrite must be removed. Na_2CO_3 extract taken in a test tube is treated with a strong solution of NH_4Cl or urea and dilute H_2SO_4. It is boiled until effervescence ceases (no blue colour of the starch iodide paper) with this ring test (vide 5.2.3) is performed.	2. Formation of a brown ring at the junction of H_2SO_4 and aqueous layer.	Nitrate (NO_3^-) confirmed.

Chemistry behind this test

(a) $NaNO_2 + H_2SO_4 + 2KI \longrightarrow H_2O + NO + K_2SO_4 + Na_2SO_4 + I_2$

Starch solution $+ I_2 \longrightarrow$ Starch iodide (blue)

(b) $NaNO_2 + H_2SO_4 \longrightarrow HNO_2 + NaHSO_4$

$2HNO_2 + CO(NH_2) \longrightarrow CO_2 + 3H_2O + 2N_2$
$\qquad\qquad$ urea

Thus, nitrite is decomposed and so test of nitrate may safely be done.

5.6 Distinction between Sulphide, Sulphite, Sulphate and Thiosulphate

When any one of the sulphur containing acid radicals is indicated in earlier tests following tests are to be carried out in order to confirm these acid radicals.

Experiment	Observation	Inference
1. A portion of Na_2CO_3 extract is taken in a test and is treated with a few drops of Na-nitroprusside solution and 2 or 3 drops of NaOH solution.	1. Violet colour develops.	1. Sulphide confirmed.
2. Before carrying out the test for other radicals sulphide is removed. For this purpose, Na_2CO_3 extract taken in a test tube is treated with $CdCO_3$(or $PbCO_3$) solution in excess, shaken well and filtered.	2. Residue is yellow(CdS) or black (PbS).	2. Sulphide is confirmed and is removed as residue. Filtrate is tested for other radicals.

Filtrate: To the filtrate, solution of $BaCl_2$ is added, shaken and is allowed to stand for a while and finally filtered.

Residue	Filtrate
(i) White in colour and is insoluble in dilute HCl. Sulphate confirmed.	Filtrate is acidified with dilute HCl and is boiled. SO_2 gas is evolved and sulphur is deposited. Thiosulphate $(S_2O_3^{2-})$ confirmed.
(ii) Residue is soluble in dilute HCl. To this acid solution chlorine-water is added—white precipitate Sulphite confirmed.	

Comments

(i) When the sample supplied is either completely or partly soluble in water the aqueous portion is treated with the concentrated solution of Na_2CO_3, warmed to precipitate out the heavy metal ions, if any. It is filtered and with the filtrate above tests as discussed in articles 5.2, 5.3 and 5.4 are performed as usual. The residue is fused with Na_2CO_3 and is extracted with water (vide Art. 5.1). Separate analysis of these two portions may be helpful in predicting the composition of the mixture of sample supplied.

(ii) **Aqua regia soluble substance**: When a portion of the original sample remains insoluble in HCl but soluble in aqua regia, the sample is fused with NaOH. For this purpose, solid NaOH is taken in an iron or nickel crucible and is heated over a flame until it melts. A portion of the sample is added to the molten mass, gently heated for a short time over a flame, cooled and is dissolved in distilled water. It is boiled and filtered. With the filtrate tests for sulphides (vide Art. 5.2.1) and halides (Art. 5.3.1 and 5.4) are performed.

(iii) **Chemistry involved in the above tests**

Following chemical reactions occur:

(a) *Test for sulphur containing radicals*:

$$Na_2S \ + \ Na_2[Fe(CN)_5]NO = Na_4[Fe(CN)_5NOS]$$

Sulphide   Violet colour

(b) $Na_2SO_4 + BaCl_2 \longrightarrow BaSO_4\downarrow + 2NaCl$

   Sulphate

(c) *Test for halides*:

$$NaCl + AgNO_3 \longrightarrow AgCl + NaNO_3$$

                                  White
                              precipitate

Similarly, bromide and iodide react. When NH_4OH is added, AgCl and AgBr form double salts, like

$$AgCl + 2NH_3 \longrightarrow [Ag(NH_3)_2]Cl$$

                                  soluble in ammonia

$$AgBr + 2NH_3 \longrightarrow [Ag(NH_3)_2]Br$$

                                  sparingly soluble in ammonia

(d) *Ring test for nitrate*:

$$NaNO_3 + H_2SO_4 \longrightarrow NaHSO_4 + HNO_3$$

$$6FeSO_4 + 2HNO_3 + 3H_2SO_4 \longrightarrow 3Fe_2(SO_4)_3 + 2H_2O + NO$$

$$FeSO_4 + NO \longrightarrow FeSO_4NO$$

(e) *Phosphate and Arsenate with magnesia mixture and* $AgNO_3$:

$$Na_2HPO_4 + MgCl_2 + NH_4OH \longrightarrow MgNH_4PO_4 + 2NaCl + H_2O$$
White

$$MgNH_4PO_4 + 3AgNO_3 \longrightarrow Ag_3PO_4 + Mg(NO_3)_2 + NH_4NO_3$$
Yellow

$$Na_2AsO_4 + MgCl_2 + NH_4OH \longrightarrow MgNH_4AsO_4 + 2NaCl + H_2O$$

$$MgNH_4AsO_4 + 3AgNO_3 \longrightarrow Ag_3AsO_4 + Mg(NO_3)_2 + NH_4NO_3$$
Red or brown

(f) $2Na_2HPO_4 + 3CaCl_2 \longrightarrow Ca_3(PO_4)_2 + 4NaCl + 2HCl$
White
precipitate

(g) $Na_2HPO_4 + FeCl_3 \longrightarrow FePO_4 + 2NaCl + HCl$
Reddish brown
precipitate

(h) *Test for chromate*:

$$Na_2CrO_4 + Pb(CH_3COO)_2 \longrightarrow PbCrO_4 + 2CH_3COONa$$
Yellow

$$Na_2CrO_4 + 2AgNO_3 \longrightarrow Ag_2CrO_4\downarrow + 2NaNO_3$$
Red

Chapter 6

Tests for Basic Radicals in Wet Way

6.1 General Principle

In the general scheme for separation of basic radicals (metal ions) in the wet way, metals have been classified into several groups marked as groups I, II, IIB, IIIA, IIIB, IV and V. It may be mentioned in this connection that this classification is completely different from periodic classification of elements. This classification has been proposed for inorganic analytical purpose only and that is why this classification is known as *analytical classification of metal ions*. This classification is primarily based on *solubility product principle*. It is known that solubility which is the product of molar concentration of the ions of an electrolyte (sparingly soluble ionic salt) is a constant quantity at a particular temperature and is different for different electrolyte. It is the limiting factor which indicates up to what concentration a particular electrolyte whould be soluble in a particular solvent under a particular condition. When the product of ionic concentrations of the electrolyte exceeds solubility product, precipitation occurs. This principle of solubility product has been applied under different condition specially under different pH to divide different metal ions into several small groups in such a way that the metals of the same group behave in the similar manner when the common reagent of the group is used and so similar precipitate is formed. It may be mentioned that each small group may contain one or more than one basic radicals (metal ions) and so precipitate of each analytical group must be analysed separately for the identification of individual radicals in the wet way. It is, therefore, felt pertinent that the division of groups with metal ions, group reagents and the nature of the precipitates of different groups should be known before undertaking the procedure for separation of metal ions into analytical groups. The information regarding these aspects may be furnished as depicted in Table 6.1.

Table 6.1: Different Groups, their Reagents and Nature of the Precipitates

Groups with metal ions	Group-reagents	Precipitates
Group-I Pb, Hg(ous) and Ag	Dilute HCl	White precipitates of chlorides: $PbCl_2$, Hg_2Cl_2, AgCl.
Group-IIA Hg(ic), Pb, Cu, Bi and Cd	Dilute HCl and H_2S	Sulphides: HgS, PbS, CuS, Bi_2S_3 (all black) CdS (yellow).
Group-IIB As, Sb and Sn	Dilute HCl and H_2S	Sulphides: AS_2S_3 (yellow), Sb_2S_3 (orange) SnS (yellowish brown).
Group-IIIA Fe, Al and Cr	NH_4Cl + NH_4OH	Hydroxides: $Fe(OH)_3$ (brown) $Al(OH)_3$ (white) $Cr(OH)_3$ (green).
Group-IIIB Zn, Mn, Ni and Co	NH_4Cl + NH_4OH + H_2S	Sulphides: ZnS (Greyish white) MnS (light brown), CoS and NiS (both black).
Group-IV Ca, Ba and Sr	NH_4Cl + NH_4OH + $(NH_4)_2CO_3$	Carbonates: all are white, $CaCo_3$, $BaCO_3$, $SrCO_3$.
Group-V Mg, Na, K and NH_4	NH_4Cl + NH_4OH + Na_2HPO_4	Only Mg is precipitated as $Mg(NH_4)PO_4$ Na, K and NH_4 are to be separately treated.

Comments

(i) When to the solution of the sample dilute HCl is added, Cl^- from HCl reacts with the metal ions and forms chlorides. But under this condition products of ionic concentrations of only $PbCl_2$, Hg_2Cl_2 and AgCl exceed their solubility products but not sufficient to exceed the solubility product of the chlorides of metals of subsequent groups. So only above three chlorides are precipitated in group I.

(ii) H_2S acts as an weak acid and so its degree of dissociation is very small. Again, in presence of dilute HCl its dissociation is further depressed due to the presence of common H^+ ion. So under this condition only a very small concentration of sulphide ion is available, with this very low value of concentration of sulphide ion (S^{--}), solubility product of sulphides of group II (both A and B) are only exceeded and hence they are precipitated.

$$H_2S \rightleftharpoons 2H^+ + S^{2-}, \quad HCl \rightleftharpoons H^+ + Cl^-, \quad 2H^+ + S^{2-} \rightleftharpoons H_2S$$

(iii) NH_4OH is an weak base and dissociates to a small extent into NH_4^+ and OH^-. Once again, in presence of NH_4Cl which dissociates into common ion NH_4^+ the degree of dissociation of NH_4OH is further decreased forming very low concentration of OH^- ion. This extremely low value of concentration of OH^- ion is sufficient enough to exceed only the solubility product of the hydroxides of group IIIA metal ions but not sufficient to exceed the solubility product of the hydroxides of subsequent metal ions. So only the hydroxides group IIIA are precipitated.

$$NH_4OH \rightleftharpoons NH_4^+ + OH^-, \quad NH_4Cl \rightleftharpoons NH_4^+ + Cl^-,$$

$$NH_4^+ + OH^- \rightleftharpoons NH_4OH \text{ (recombination)}$$

(iv) For the precipitation of group IIIB metal ions as sulphides higher concentration of sulphide is required. This is obtained by decreasing the concentration of common ion (H^+) in the solution. When NH_4OH solution is added, OH^- from NH_4OH reacts with H^+ liberated by the dissociation of H_2S as a result of which H^+ is removed from the system. So more H_2S will be dissociated increasing thereby the concentration of sulphide ion. Under this condition solubility product of sulphides of group IIIB is only exceeded and hence they are precipitated.

$$NH_4OH \rightleftharpoons NH_4^+ + OH^-$$

$$H_2S \rightleftharpoons H^+ + S^{2-}$$

$$H^+ + OH^- \rightleftharpoons H_2O$$

(v) To precipitate the carbonates of group IV metal ions very low concentration of carbonate ion (CO_3^{2-}) is needed. In presence of NH_4OH, $(NH_4)_2CO_3$ forms very low concentration of carbonate ion due to common ion (NH_4^+) effect. But this low concentration of carbonate ion is sufficient to exceed the solubility product of carbonates of Ca, Ba and Sr but not enough to cross the limit of the solubility product of magnesium carbonate. So only groupIV metal ions are precipitated as their carbonates ($CaCO_3$, $BaCO_3$ and $SrCO_3$) while Mg^{2+} ion remains in solution which may be precipitated as $Mg(NH_4)PO_4$ on addition of NH_2HPO_4 solution, i.e,

$$(NH_4)_2CO_3 \rightleftharpoons 2NH_4^+ + CO_3^{2-}$$

$$2NH_2OH \rightleftharpoons 2NH_4^+ + 2OH^-$$

$$2NH_4^+ + CO_3^{2-} \rightleftharpoons (NH_4)_2CO_3$$
(recombination)

6.2 Removal of Interfering Radicals

As mentioned before (vide Chapter 4), interfering radicals such as chromate, dichromate, permanganate, borate, fluoride, arsenate silicate and phosphate, if present, may interfere in the process of separation of basic radicals. Presence of chromate, dichromate and permanganate, hampers the separation of group I metal ions while arsenate, if present, interferes the separation procedure of group II basic radicals. But the interference by other radicals (borate, fluoride, silicate and phosphate has been observed in the separation of basic radicals of group III onwards. So it is desirable that such radicals, if present, must either be converted to non-interfering forms as in the case of chromate, dichromate, permanganate and arsenate or may be removed as in the case of other radicals, before undertaking the process of separation, of metal ions in the appropriate groups.

6.2.1 Processes for Removal or Reduction of Interfering Radicals

6.2.1.1 Reduction of Chromate, Dichromate and Permanganate

The original sample is boiled with concentrated HCl till the smell of chlorine ceases. The above acid radicals are reduced to chromic and manganese compounds and the solution thus obtained is used for the separation metal ions, Cr and Mn are separated in their respective groups. This reduction procedure is adapted before proceeding to group I metals. Reactions that may take place may be expressed as under:

(a) $CrO_4^{2-} + 16HCl \longrightarrow 2CrCl_3 + 8H_2O + 3Cl_2\uparrow + 4Cl^-$

(b) $Cr_2O_7^{2-} + 14HCl \longrightarrow 2CrCl_3 + 7H_2O + 3Cl_2\uparrow + 4Cl^-$

(c) $MnO_4^- + HCl \longrightarrow MnCl_2 + H_2O + Cl_2\uparrow + Cl^-$

6.2.1.2 Reduction of Arsenate

Arsenate, if present, the original sample is boiled with concentrated HCl in presence of $NaHSO_3$. The boiling is continued till the evolution of SO_2 is stopped. Now the solution can be safely used for the separation of group II metal ions. Arsenate present is reduced to arsenite. This process is usually performed on the filtrate of group I metals before passing H_2S to precipitate group II metal ions.

6.2.1.3 Removal of Borate, Fluoride and Silicate

These interfering radicals are removed by boiling the sample with concentrated HCl repeatedly for 4-5 times, cooled and filtered. The residue is SiO_2 and the filtrate is boiled with a few drops of conc. HNO_3 and is examined from group IIIA onwards. This removal procedure is taken with the filtrate of group II.

6.2.1.4 Removal of Phosphate

Phosphate, if present, must be removed before proceeding for group IIIA. To the filtrate of group II, NH_4OH solution is added drop by drop till the solution becomes turbid. To this solution equal volume of a buffer solution (prepared by mixing I M solution of acetic and I M solution of ammonium or sodium acetate in equal portion) is added and filtered. The precipitate, if any, contains group IIIA metals Al, Fe, Cr. The filtrate is taken in a beaker, boiled and freshly prepared dilute solution of $FeCl_3$ is added drop by drop till the solution becomes tea coloured. If there is any precipitate, it is filtered and the precipitate is rejected. With the filtrate tests for group IIIB, IV and V are performed as usual, but before proceeding to group IIIB onwards some precautions are to be taken.

    (a) Ca, Br and Sr may be separated out during phosphate removal. So before the addition of $FeCl_3$ solution tests for Ca, Ba and Sr are to be carried out in presence of buffer solution as shown below:

        (i) Appearence of white precipitate on addition of ammonium oxalate solution to the solution suggests Ca.

        (ii) To the solution a few drops of K_2CrO_4 is added—formation of yellow precipitate confirms Ba.

        (iii) Yellow precipitate of $BaCrO_4$ is filterd and to the filtrate $(NH_4)_2SO_4$ is added and boiled. If white precipitate appears, Sr is present.

$.3 Procedure for Group Separation

eparation of metal ions into different analytical groups involves two distinct steps, viz.,
) preparation of solution and (ii) examination of the solution for group separation.

.3.1 Preparation of the Solution of the Sample Supplied

he solution of the sample supplied is prepared according to the Table 1.3 (vide solubility test,
age 15). If *there is any water soluble portion*, presence of Na^+, K^+ and (NH_4^+) are to be ascertained (as
ost of the salts of these ions are soluble in water) according to the tests described in the Table 6.2
efore proceeding for general group separation. But if water soluble portion does not contain Na^+,
$^+$ or NH_4^+ ions, aqueous solution may be directly used for general group separation. It may be
entioned in this connection that solution of the sample prepared in different solvents such as
ater, HCl (dilute and concentrated HCl) and aqua regia are to be separately subjected to the
eneral group separation processes as presented in the tabular form (Table 6.3) provided the
imple is soluble in that particular solvent.

Table 6.2: Tests for Na^+, K^+ and NH_4^+

Experiment	Observation	Inference
1. (a) Aqueous solution + sodium cobaltinitrite solution.	1. (a) Yellow precipitate.	1. (a) Potassium confirmed.
(b) Concentrated aqueous solution + saturated solution of tartiaric acid.	(b) White precipitate appears.	(b) Potassium confirmed.
2. Aqueous solution + solution of magnesium uranyl acetate.	2. Yellow precipitate.	2. Sodium confirmed.
3. (a) Aqueous solution + NaOH solution and the mixture is heated.	3. (a) Smell of NH_3 and the vapour turns moist red litmus paper blue.	3. (a) Ammonium confirmed.
(b) Aqueous solution + Nessler's reagent	(b) Brown precipitate	(b) Ammonium present.

eactions involved

(a) $2KCl + Na_2[CO(NO_2)_6] \longrightarrow K_2Na[CO(NO_2)_6] + 2NaCl$

(b) $KCl + \begin{array}{c} CH(OH)-COOH \\ | \\ CH(OH)-COOH \end{array} \longrightarrow \begin{array}{c} CH(OH)-COOH \\ | \\ CH(OH)-COOK \end{array}$

(c) $NaCl + 3UO_2(C_2H_3O_2)_2 + Mg(C_2H_3O_2)_2 + HC_2H_3O_2 \longrightarrow NaMg(UO_2)_2(C_2H_3O_2)_5 + HCl$

(d) $NH_4Cl + NaOH \longrightarrow NH_3\uparrow + NaCl + H_2O$

(e) $HgCl_2 + 2KI \longrightarrow HgI_2 + 2KCl$

$HgI_2 + 2KI \longrightarrow K_2HgI_2$
(Nessler's reagent)

$NH_3 + 2K_2HgI_2 + 3KOH \longrightarrow IHg-O-HgNH_2 + 7KI + 2H_2O$

Table 6.3: General Group Separation

Aqueous solution of the sample is taken in a beaker, treated with dilute HCl, boiled, cooled and filtered.
[N.B. If chromate, dichromate and permanganate present should be removed (vide Art. 6.2).]

Residue: White precipitate Group-I present, may be PbCl$_2$, Hg$_2$Cl$_2$ or AgCl. For further analysis Table 6.4 is followed.	Filtrate: [N.B. If arsenate is present, the solution is boiled with NaHSO$_3$ till evolution of SO$_2$ ceases.] The boiled solution is taken in a test tube and H$_2$S is passed in warm condition till the precipitation is complete. It is filtered. The filtrate is diluted to make it faintly acidic (0.3M HCl) and H$_2$S is passed, (CdS is precipitated in this acidic condition), and filtered.		
	Residue:Total precipitate (coloured)	Filtrate: H$_2$S is boiled off. If borate, fluoride silicate and phosphate are present, they must be removed according to procedure presented in Art. 6.2. To the filtrate free from H$_2$S and interfering radicals 1-2 ml of dilute HNO$_3$ is added and boiled. Approximately 5 gms of NH$_4$Cl is added, boiled and NH$_4$OH is added slowly till smells of NH$_3$ comes out. It is filtered, if any precipitate.	
	Group-II A and B Black: HgS, PbS, CuS ⎤ Gr-II A and CdS (yellow) ⎦ AS$_2$S$_3$ (yellow) ⎤ Sb$_2$S$_3$ (orange) ⎥ Gr-II B SnS (brown) ⎦ Further analysis is to be performed according to Table 6.5.	Residue:Precipitate of Gr-IIIA Fe(OH)$_3$—brown Cr(OH)$_3$—green Al(OH)$_3$—white. Table 6.6 is to be followed for further analysis.	Filtrate: NH$_4$OH is added till smell of NH$_3$ persists. To this solution H$_2$S is passed till precipitation is complete, in warm condition.
		Residue:Precipitate of Gr-III B. ZnS—white NiS, CoS—black MnS—fleshy For further analysis Table 6.7 is to be followed.	Filtrate:H$_2$S is boiled off from the solution, it is concentrated and NH$_4$OH is added till the solution becomes strongly alkaline. To it excess of (NH$_4$)$_2$CO$_3$ is added, boiled and is allowed to stand for 5 minutes and filtered.
			Residue:Precipitate of Ca, Ba and Sr. White carbonates of Gr-IV. Table 6.8 is to be followed for further analysis.	Filtrate:To the filtrate Na$_2$HPO$_4$ solution is added and is shaken well. Appearance of white gelatinous precipitate indicates Gr-V, Mg. For Na, K and NH$_4$ aqueous solution is to be analysed (vide p. 48)

Table 6.4: Analysis of Group I precipitates [$PbCl_2$, Hg_2Cl_2 and AgCl]

The precipitate is washed with water on a filter paper and is transferred to a beaker and is boiled with distilled water and filtered hot.

Filtrate: Filtrate is divided into several parts:	Residue: The residue is washed with hot water to make it free from Pb, and NH_4OH solution is added and shaken well, it is filtered.	
(i) One part is allowed to cool when needle shaped crystalline precipitate is formed which disappears on heating. Pb confirmed.		
(ii) To another part of the hot solution KI solution is added—yellow precipitate of PbI_2 is formed which dissolves on boiling. Pb confirmed.	Filtrate: The filtrate is acidified with HNO_3 when curdy white precipitate appears. Ag confirmed.	Residue: It is black, dissolved in aqua regia and evaporated to dryness, residue left is dissolved in water, and $SnCl_2$ solution is added.
(iii) To another part of the hot solution K_2CrO_4 solution is added when yellow precipitate of $PbCrO_4$ appears. Pb confirmed.		White precipitate which turns grey. Hg(ions) confirmed.

Reactions occurring:

(a) $PbCl_2 + 2KI \longrightarrow PbI_2 + 2KCl$
                          (yellow)

(b) $PbCl_2 + K_2CrO_4 \longrightarrow PbCrO_4 + 2KCl$
                              (yellow)

(c) $AgCl + 2NH_3 \longrightarrow [Ag(NH_3)_2]Cl$

$[Ag(NH_3)_2]Cl \xrightarrow{\ HNO_3\ } AgCl\downarrow + 2NH_4NO_3$

(d) $Hg_2Cl_2 + 2NH_4OH \longrightarrow Hg + HgNH_2Cl + 2H_2O + NH_4Cl$
                                           Black

Aqua regia dissolves the black mixture and once again white precipitate of Hg_2Cl_2 is formed.

Table 6.5: Analysis of Group II Metal Ions

Among the precipitated sulphides of Group II (A and B), Hg(ic), Pb, Cu, Bi and Cd sulphides (Group IIA) are insoluble in yellow ammonium sulphide solution but the sulphides of other ions, As, Sb and Sn (Group IIB) are soluble in this solution. So the total precipitates of these groups (Group IIA and B) are taken in a conical flask and warmed at a temperature of 50-60 °C with yellow ammonium sulphide solution and filtered.

Residue	Filtrate
Group-II A sulphides of Hg(ic), Cu, Pb, Bi and Cd. For further analysis Table 6.5A is to be followed.	Sulphides of Group-II B, As, Sb and Sn ions. Further analysis is carried out according to Table 6.5B.

Table 6.5A: Analysis of Sulphides of Group IIA

The precipitate of Gr-II A is boiled with excess of HNO_3 in a beaker and filtered.

Residue: It is dissolved in aqua regia, evaporated to dryness, diluted with water, and $SnCl_2$ solution is added. White precipitate turns to grey. Hg(ic) confirmed.	Filtrate: The filtrate is boiled with dilute H_2SO_4 in presence of 10 ml of alcohol and filtered.		
	Residue: White precipitate Pb confirmed.	Filtrate: Alcohol is boiled off and NH_4OH solution is added and filtered.	
		Residue: White precipitate Bi confirmed.	Filtrate*: If the solution is colourless Cu is absent. To this solution H_2S is passed; yellow precipitate; Cd confirmed. If filtrate* is blue Cu is present. N.B. If Cu is present blue colour is discharged by adding KCN, and H_2S is passed when yellow precipitate of CdS appears.

Principle

(a) $HgS + 6HCl + 2HNO_3 \longrightarrow HgCl_2 + 2NO + 3S + 42O$
$\qquad$ (Aqua regia)

$HgCl_2 + SnCl_2 \longrightarrow Hg_2Cl_2 + SnCl_4$
$\qquad\qquad\qquad\qquad$ (White precipitate)

$Hg_2Cl_2 + SnCl_2 \longrightarrow 2Hg + SnCl_4$
$\qquad\qquad\qquad\qquad$ (Black)

(b) $Bi(NO_3)_3 + 3NH_4OH \longrightarrow Bi(OH)_3 + 3NH_4NO_3$

(c) $2Cu(NO_3)_2 + 4KCN \longrightarrow 2Cu(CN)_2 + 4KNO_3$

$2Cu(CN)_2 \longrightarrow 2Cu_2(CN)_2$

$2Cu(CN)_2 + 6KCN \longrightarrow 2K_3Cu(CN)_4$
$\qquad\qquad$ It is a colourless solution.

(d) $Cd(NO_3)_2 + 4KCN \longrightarrow Cd(CN)_2 + 4KNO_3$

$Cd(CN)_2 + 2KCN \longrightarrow K_2Cd(CN)_4$

$K_2Cd(CN)_4 + H_2S \longrightarrow CdS + 2HCN + 2KCN$
$\qquad\qquad\qquad\qquad\quad$ (Yellow precipitate)

Table 6.5B: Sulphides of Group IIB Metal Ions

The sulphides of Group IIB in the filtrate of Group II (Table 9) is acidified with dilute HCl and filtered. Filtrate is rejected. The residue is boiled with concentrated HCl and again filtered when residue and filtrate obtained are treated separately.

Residue	Filtrate
Yellow in colour. It is dissolved in conc. HNO_3 and warmed with ammonium molybdate solution. Canary yellow precipitate. As confirmed.	Filtrate is divided into two parts. (i) To one part NH_4OH is added till alkaline and 3-4 gm of solid oxalic acid is added to this alkaline solution and boiled. H_2S is passed through this boiled solution. Orange yellow precipitate appears. Sb confirmed.
	(ii) To the 2nd part of the filtrate a few pieces of iron wire is added, boiled for 5 minutes and filtered. $HgCl_2$ solution is added to the filtrate. A white precipitate appears which turns grey. Sn confirmed.

Principle: Sulphides of As, Sb and Sn dissolve in yellow ammonium sulphide solution with the formation of thiosalts, i.e.,

$$AS_2S_3 + 3(NH_4)_2S_2 \longrightarrow 2(NH_4)_3AsS_4 + S$$
$$\text{Thio salt}$$

$$2(NH_4)_3AsS_4 + 6HCl \longrightarrow 3H_2S + As_2S_5$$

Similarly, $\quad SnS + (NH_4)_2S_2 \longrightarrow (NH_4)_2SnS_3$

$$(NH_4)_2SnS_3 + 2HCl \longrightarrow SnS_2 + 2NH_4Cl + H_2S$$

$$Sb_2S_3 + 3(NH_4)_2S_2 \longrightarrow 2(NH_4)_2SbS_4 + S$$

$$2(NH_4)_2SbS_4 + 6HCl \longrightarrow Sb_2S_5 + 6NH_4Cl + 3H_2S$$

Filtrate contains chlorides of Sb and Sn.

(a) $2SbCl_3 + 3H_2S \longrightarrow \quad Sb_2S_3 \quad + 6HCl$
$$\text{(Orange yellow precipitate)}$$

(b) $SnCl_4 + Fe \longrightarrow SnCl_2 + FeCl_2$

$$SnCl_2 + HgCl_2 \longrightarrow Hg_2Cl_2 + SnCl_4$$
$$\text{(White)}$$

$$SnCl_2 + Hg_2Cl_2 \longrightarrow 2Hg + SnCl_4$$
$$\text{(Grey)}$$

Table 6.6: Analysis of Group IIIA Metal Ions

The precipitate of Group IIIA metal ions is taken in a beaker, 5ml of water and approximately 1 gm of solid sodium peroxide (Na_2O_2) are added and boiled until effervescence ceases. The reaction mixture is diluted with water and filtered.

Residue	Filtrate
It is dissolved is dilute HCl by warming and a few drops of potassium ferrocyanide $K_4Fe(CN)_6$ is added dropwise. Prussian blue precipitate. Fe confirmed.	Filtrate is divided into two parts. (i) To one part 1-2 gm of solid NH_4Cl is added and boiled white gelatinous precipitate appears. Al confirmed. (ii) Another part is acidified with acetic acid and 1-2 ml of Pb acetate solution is added. Yellow precipitate; Cr confirmed. [N.B. If Cr present filtrate becomes yellow.]

Chemistry involved

$$Fe(OH)_3 + 3HCl \longrightarrow FeCl_3 + 3H_2O$$

$$FeCl_3 + K_4[Fe(CN)_6] \longrightarrow KFe[Fe(CN)_6]$$
$$\text{Blue}$$
$$\text{precipitate}$$

It may be mentioned in this context that on treatment with Na_2O_2, $Fe(OH)_3$ remains unchanged but $Al(OH)_3$ is converted to sodium aluminate and $Cr(OH)_3$ to chromate. i.e.

(a) $2Na_2O_2 + 2H_2O \longrightarrow 4NaOH + O_2$

$Al(OH)_3 + NaOH \longrightarrow NaAlO_2 + 2H_2O$

$NaAlO_2 + NH_4Cl + H_2O \longrightarrow Al(OH)_3\downarrow + 2NaOH$

(b) $Cr(OH)_3 + 3Na_2O_2 \longrightarrow 2Na_2CrO_4 + 2NaOH$
    (Aq. solution)

$Na_2CrO_4 + Pb(OCOCH_3)_2 \longrightarrow PbCrO_4 + CH_3COOH$
$$\text{Yellow}$$
$$\text{precipitate}$$

Table 6.7: Analysis of Metal Ions of Group IIIB

The precipitate of Group III B contains CoS, NiS, ZnS and MnS. The precipitate is washed and is taken in a beaker. It is treated with 20 ml of dilute HCl, warmed and filtered.

Residue (Black)	Filtrate
(a) Borax bead test is performed. (i) Saphire blue bead; Co confirmed. (ii) Reddish brown bead; Ni confirmed.	H_2S is boiled off and excess of NaOH solution is added, warmed and filtered.

Contd.

	Residue (Black)	Filtrate	
		Residue	**Filtrate**
(b)	The residue is dissolved with aqua regia and evaporated to dryness. It is dissolved in water and is made alkaline with NH_4OH solution. To this alkaline solution a few drops of dimethyl glyoxime is added. Scarlet red precipitate appears. Ni confirmed.	Brown $Mn(OH)_2$ It is dissolved in (1:1) concentrated HNO_3, and solid PbO_2 or Pb_3O_4 is added, boiled, diluted and allowed to stand. Pink colour of permanganate confirms Mn.	Filtrate is acidified with acetic acid and H_2S is passed. White precipitate confirms Zn.

Chemistry involved: When the precipitate is treated with dilute HCl CoS and NiS remain unchanged but the sulphides of Mn and Zn go into solution. Thus,

(a) $NiS + 2HNO_3 + 6HCl \longrightarrow NiCl_2 + 2NO + S + 4H_2O$
　　　　　(Aqua regia)

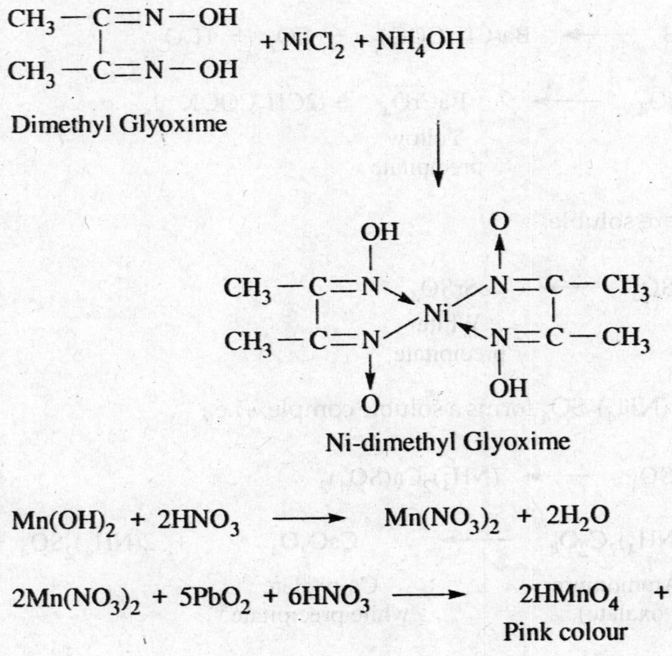

$$\begin{array}{l} CH_3-C=N-OH \\ \quad\quad | \\ CH_3-C=N-OH \end{array} + NiCl_2 + NH_4OH$$

Dimethyl Glyoxime

$$\begin{array}{ccc} & OH & O \\ & | & \uparrow \\ CH_3-C=N & \diagdown & N=C-CH_3 \\ & | & Ni & | \\ CH_3-C=N & \diagup & N=C-CH_3 \\ & \downarrow & | \\ & O & OH \end{array}$$

Ni-dimethyl Glyoxime

(b) $Mn(OH)_2 + 2HNO_3 \longrightarrow Mn(NO_3)_2 + 2H_2O$

$2Mn(NO_3)_2 + 5PbO_2 + 6HNO_3 \longrightarrow 2HMnO_4 + 5Pb(NO_3)_2$
　　　　　　　　　　　　　　　　　　　　　Pink colour

(c) $ZnCl_2 + 2NaOH \longrightarrow Zn(OH)_2 + 2NaCl$

$Zn(OH)_2 + 2NaOH \longrightarrow Na_2ZnO_2 + 2H_2O$
　　　　　　　　　　　　　　　　　White
　　　　　　　　　　　　　　　precipitate

Table 6.8: Examination of the Precipitates of Group IV Metals

The precipitate obtained is taken in a beaker and is washed with hot water. The washed precipitate is dissolved in minimum quantity of hot acetic acid and filtered. The residue is rejected and analysis is carried out with the filtrate taken in a beaker. The beaker with the solution is boiled. To it a few drops of K_2CrO_4 solution is added and filtered.

Residue: Yellow residue of $BaCrO_4$. For further confirmation flame test is to be done.	Filtrate: It is made alkaline by adding NH_4OH. Saturated solution of $(NH_4)_2SO_4$ is added to it, warmed and allowed to stand for five minutes. It is filtered.	
	Residue: White residue of $SrSO_4$. Flame test is carried out for further confirmation.	Filtrate: To filtrate NH_4OH solution is added. Next solution of ammonium oxalate is added. White, precipitate confirms Ca.

Reactions taking place: Group IV metal ions are precipitated as their carbonates. When these carbonates are treated with hot acetic acid, they dissolve forming their soluble acetates. Thus,

(a) $BaCO_3 + 2CH_3COOH \longrightarrow Ba(CH_3COO)_2 + CO_2 + H_2O$

$(CH_3COO)_2Ba + K_2CrO_4 \longrightarrow BaCrO_4 + 2CH_3COOK$
$$\text{Yellow precipitate}$$

Ca and Sn-chromates are soluble.

(b) $Sr\text{-chromate} + (NH_4)_2SO_4 \longrightarrow SrSO_4$
$$\text{White precipitate}$$

(c) But Ca-chromate with $(NH_4)_2SO_4$ forms a soluble complex, i.e.,

$Ca\text{-chromate} + (NH_4)_2SO_4 \longrightarrow (NH_4)_2Ca(SO_4)_2$

$(NH_4)_2Ca(SO_4)_2 + (NH_4)_2C_2O_4 \longrightarrow CaC_2O_4 + 2(NH_4)_2SO_4$
$$\text{(Ammonium oxalate)} \qquad \text{Ca-oxalate white precipitate}$$

Remark

(i) It may be mentioned that there is no separate confirmatory test for the precipitate of Group V. Appearence of precipitate in the Group V after the elimination of previous group metal ions confirms Group V ions.

(ii) If there is any soluble part in any solvent (H_2O, dilute HCl, concentrated HCl and aqua regia), solution in each solvent should be subjected to general group separation separately. But if there is no soluble portion in any solvent, general group separation for that solvent solution is not necessary.

6.3.2 Treatment of Insoluble Portion

If the sample or any portion of the sample remains insoluble in aqua regia the sample or the portion is considered as insoluble substance. A list of common insoluble substances is as below:

(a) Cr_2O_3 (ignited), green

(b) Al_2O_3 (ignited), white

(c) SnO_2 (ignited), white

(d) $PbCrO_4$, brown

(e) $PbSO_4$, $BaSO_4$, $SrSO_4$, white

(f) CaF_2, white

For the identification of these radicals following tests (Table 6.9) are carried out:

Table 6.9: Dry Tests for Insoluble Portion

Experiment	Observation	Inference
1. Borax bead test is performed.	1. Green bead in both the flames.	1. Cr_2O_3, $PbCrO_4$
2. Cobalt nitrate test.	2. (a) Blue colour (b) Bluish green	2. (a) Al_2O_3 (b) SnO_2
3. Flame test.	3. (a) Crimson red. (b) Transient brick-red (c) Yellowish green	3. (a) Sr (b) Ca (c) Ba

Table 6.10: Wet Tests for Insoluble Substance

The insoluble portion is treated with concentrated solution of ammonium acetate and a few drops of acetic acid is added. It is filtered

Filtrate: Contains $PbSO_4$ To the solution K_2CrO_4 solution is adde; yellow precipitate of $PbCrO_4$.	Residue: Contains $BaSO_4$, $SrSO_4$, Al_2O_3, Cr_2O_3 and SnO_2. The residue is mixed with fusion mixture (mixture of Na_2CO_3 and K_2CO_3) and 3-4 beads of $NaOH$ in an iron or nickel crucible and heated till the mixture melts, cooled, extracted with water and filtered.	
	Residue: Carbonates of Ba, Ca and Sr. It is dissolved in dilute HCl and analysis is carried out as in Group-IV.	Filtrate: Contains Na_2CrO_4, $NaAlO_2$, Na_2SnO_2, NaF, Na_2SiO_2. Filtrate is tested as follows: (i) To one part lead acetate and acetic acid are added. Yellow precipitate confirms Cr. (ii) 2nd part is acidified with HCl, and H_2S; is passed yellow precipitate; Sn confirmed. (iii) 3rd part is acidified with HCl, and NaOH solution in excess is added. NH_4Cl is also added. White precipitate confirms Al. (iv) Remaining part of the filtrate is acidified with HCl, and $BaCl_2$ solution is added. White precipitate confirms SO_4^{2-}.

Chapter 7

Semi-microanalysis of Ions

Fundamentally there is no difference between the macroanalysis as discussed (vide chapters 2-6) and the semi micro analysis of radicals. The semi microanalysis differs only in the quantity of sample used, time, space and labour from the macroanalysis. It is also termed as *spot test of radicals*.

In semi-microanalysis, the volumes of solutions used range from a few drops to 1-2 ml and the material required ranges from 0.01 to 0.1g. The apparatuses required for this analysis are also of reduced size. Semi-microanalysis has become very popular because of its consumption of less time, small quantity of chemicals, sensitivity of reactions and its ability to identify an ion in presence of other. This type of analysis not only helps in the identification of an ion in presence of other but also assists in testing the purity of a substance. Thus, semi-microanalysis may be defined as an accurate method of identifying radicals in reduced size apparatus with smaller quantity of substances and reagents in a short time in presence of one another.

7.1 Apparatus Required for Semi-microanalysis

Following apparatuses are generally used in semi-microanalysis:

1. **Test tubes:** Small test tubes made of good quality glass as shown in the figure are used in this analysis.

75 X 10 mm

4 ml

56

2. Centrifuge tube: This type of test tube is used for separating a precipitate from the small volume of liquid by centrifuging. It is also made of good quality glass.

3. Hand centrifuge machine: The hand driven centrifuge as shown in the figure is normally used. The process of centrifuging replaces the time consuming filtration procedure.

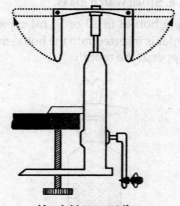

Hand driven centrifuge

4. Droppers: Generally two types of droppers are used in semi micro analysis—one for taking out reagents from the reagent bottle and other for removing supernatant liquid from the test tubes. The droppers are fitted with rubber bulbs.

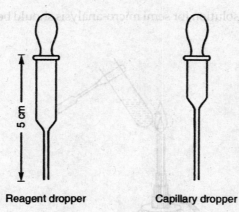

Reagent dropper   Capillary dropper

5. **Suitable stirrer:** The stirrer is used to mix solution in semi micro test tubes. These are made of glass of different lengths.

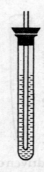

Suitable stirrer

6. **Filter paper,** 7. **Spot plate,** 8. **Silica watch glass.**

9. **Dropping bottle:** Dropping bottles of 30 or 50 ml capacity are used. These are of two types—in one type of bottle a dropper is inserted into the bottle through a stopper while the other type of bottle possesses a glass stopper at the month.

Dropping bottle

10. **Micro-burner:** The solution for semi micro-analysis should be heated on microflame of a micro-burner.

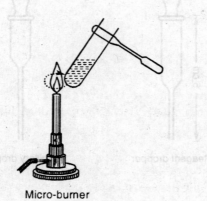

Micro-burner

7.2 Treatment of the Precipitate

(a) **Washing·of the precipitate**: In semi-microanalysis, washing of the precipitate is a must, otherwise it may be contaminated with the other ions present in the centrifuge. The precipitate is washed at least two to three times. The wash liquid is usually water but sometimes may be water mixed with an electrolyte like NH_4Cl.

To wash the precipitate in a centrifuge tube, 10-15 drops of water are added and the mixture is thoroughly stirred with a glass rod and the centrifuge tube is counter-balanced by another similar tube containing water to the same level and is centrifuged. The supernatant liquid is removed by a capillary dropper and combined with mother centrifugate (filtrate). The process is repeated and the wash liquid is discarded.

(b) **Dissolving of precipitate**: The reagent is added and the suspension is warmed, if necessary, on the water bath till the precipitate dissolves. If it partially dissolves the suspension may be centrifuged.

7.3 Systematic Analysis by Semi-micro Method

Systematic semi-microanalysis of different radicals (cations and anions) are as discussed below. It may be mentioned in this connection that since semi-micro tests may be performed in presence of other ions it is more fruitful and convenient to use test solution directly. However, semi-micro-analysis of ions may also be performed by adapting conventional general group separation scheme. Both the procedures are discussed in sequel.

7.3.1 Examination of Cations

Semi-microanalysis of cations belonging to different analytical groups may be carried out by adapting the following procedures:

7.3.1.1 Examination of Cations in Presence of Other Ions

In this procedure test solution of the sample is directly used without adapting general group separation process.

7.3.1.1(a) First Group Cations [Pb^{+2}, Ag^+, Hg^{2+}(ous)]

Pb^{2+}: To 1 ml of test solution 4 drops of 4(N) NaOH solution is added, boiled and centrifuged. The centrifugate (filtrate) is taken in a micro test tube and to it one drop of KCN and one drop of Na_2S solutions are added when black precipitate appears, Pb is confirmed.

Hg^{2+}(ous): 1 ml of test solution is acidified with a drop of dil HCl and to it one or two drops of potassium nitrite solutions are added. Black or grey spot for Hg^{2+} (ous) appears.

Ag^+: Approxmately 5 ml test solution is taken in a test tube and is treated with 1-2 ml of $(NH_4)_2CO_3$ and is allowed to stand for a few minutes. Lead and mercurous carbonates are precipitated out. 4-5 drops of clear solution (filtrate) is taken in a semi-micro test tube and to it 1-2 ml of 6(N)HNO_3 is added. A white precipitate appears which turns violet on exposure to sunrays. Ag is confirmed.

7.3.1.1(b) Second Group Cations (Hg^{2+}, Pb^{2+}, Bi^{3+}, Cu^{2+}, Cd^{2+}, As^{3+}, Sb^{3+}, Sn^{2+})

Hg^{2+}: 1-2 ml test solution is taken in a test tube and to it a small amount of solid NH_4CNS and little amount of solid cobalt acetate are added, and the inside of the test tube is scratched with a glass rod. Blue crystalline precipitate of $Co[Hg(CNS)_4]$ confirms Hg(ic).

Bi^{3+}: A filter paper is moistened with cinchonine-potassium iodide solution and to it 1 or 2 drops of slightly acidic test solution is added. Appearance of an orange-red ring of bismuth-cinchonine iodide confirms the presence of Bi.

Cu^{2+}: 5 ml test solution taken in a test tube is boiled, cooled and acidified with dilute HCl. A filter paper is moistened with this acidic solution and a drop of 10% Rochelle salt solution is added. Finally one or two drops of cupron solution (oxime of benzoin) is added and the filter paper is held over ammonia vapour. Green colour develops due to the formation of copper benzoin oxime.

Comment

(i) Rochelle salt is Na, K tartarate and is used to prevent the precipitation of other metal ions.

(ii) Cupron solution is prepared by dissolving 2 g of benzoin oxime in 50 ml alcohol.

(iii) Reaction taking place is

$$Cu^{2+} + Ph-\underset{\underset{OH}{|}}{CH}-\underset{\underset{N-OH}{||}}{C}-Ph \longrightarrow Ph-\underset{\underset{O}{|}}{CH}-\underset{\underset{N}{||}}{C}-Ph + 2H^{+}$$

Cd^{2+}: Test solution is made alkaline with NH_4OH and centrifuged. Supernatant liquid is taken in a test tube and to this one drop of KCN solution and one or two drops of Na_2S solution are added when yellow precipitate of CdS appears.

As^{3+}: The test solution is heated with dilute NaOH solution. 1-2 drops of this alkaline solution is taken in a semi-micro test tube and a few drops of H_2O_2 are added. This reaction mixture is heated on a water bath and 4 drops of $Mg(NO_3)_2$ solution are added with stirring. It is centrifuged. A few drops of $AgNO_3$ solution is added to the residue and acidified with dilute acetic acid. Brownish-red residue of Ag_3AsO_4 appears.

Sb^{3+}: To a few drops of test solution one or two drops of thiosulphate solution are added and warmed when orange red precipitate of Sb_2S_3 appears.

Sn^{2+}: 2 drops of methylene blue solution is taken in a test tube and to it 2 drops of test solution are added. Disappearance of blue colour of methylene blue confirms Sn^{2+}.

7.3.1.1(c) Third Group Cations (Fe^{3+}, Al^{3+}, Cr^{3+}, Mn^{2+}, Zn^{2+}, Ni^{2+}, Co^{2+})

Fe^{3+}: 5 ml of original test solution is taken in a test tube and to it a few crystals of ammonium thiocyanate are added. The mixture is acidified with concentrated HCl and is shaken with alcohol. The aqueous layer turns deep red due to the formation of $Fe(CNS)^{2+}$ ion.

Al^{3+}: 5 ml of original test solution is taken in a test tube and is treated with sufficient quantity of (N)NaOH solution when sodium aluminate is formed. Now a filter paper is moistened with this sodium aluminate solution and to the moist filter paper a drop of Alizarin-S solution is added. A violet colour develops. This violet colour is discharged by dropwise addition of acetic acid and finally red colour appears by the addition of excess of acetic acid. Al is confirmed.

Cr^{3+}: 5 ml of original solution is made alkaline with (N) NaOH solution and boiled with 3% H_2O_2. It is centrifuged. The supernatant liquid is acidified with dilute acetic acid and a few drops of lead acetate solution is added. Yellow precipitate of $PbCrO_4$ confirms Cr^{3+}.

Zn^{2+}: In a semi-micro spot plate 10-15 drops of diethyl aniline and 15-20 drops of potassium ferricyanide are intimately mixed and to this mixture one or two drops of test solution is added when orange to red precipitate for Zn^{2+} ion appears.

Mn^{2+}: 2 ml 10% $CuSO_4$ solution is taken in a test tube and to it 2-4 drops of bromine in NaOH solution are added. To this mixture a few drops of original test solution are added and heated. Supernatant liquid becomes pink. This is due to the formation of $HMnO_4$.

Ni^{2+}: 5 ml of original sample solution taken in a test tube is warmed with 2 ml of dilute HCl. Next it is made ammoniacal by adding ammonia solution. To this ammoniacal solution 3-4 drops of dimethyl glyoxime solution are added. A scarlet red precipitate indicates the presence of Ni.

Co^{2+}: Same test for Fe^{3+} is applicable for the detection of Co^{2+} but in this case the colour of the alcohol layer becomes blue due to the formation of $K_2[Co(CNS)_4]$.

7.3.1.1(d) Fourth Group Cations (Ba^{2+}, Sr^{2+}, and Ca^{2+})

Ca^{2+}: The solution of the unknown sample supposed to contain fourth group cations is taken in a centrifuge tube in semi-micro quantity, acidified with a few drops of (2N)HCl and a few drops of $(NH_4)_2SO_4$ solution are added and warmed on a water bath for a few minutes when Ba and Sr are separated as their sulphates but the Ca^{2+} practically remains in solution. It is centrifuged. The supernatant liquid is taken in another test tube and is treated with $(NH_4)_2C_2O_4$ (Ammonium oxalate). A white precipitate of Ca-oxalate appears. The precipitate is confirmed by flame test.

Ba^{2+} and Sr^{2+}: The residue obtained after centrifuging contains $BaSO_4$ and $SrSO_4$. The individual ions are identified by flame test.

7.3.1.1(e) Fifth Group Cations (Mg^{2+}, NH_4^+, Na^+, K^+)

Mg^{2+}: 1 ml of unknown solution is taken in a semi-micro test tube and to it 5-10 drops of EDTA solution are added, warmed on a water bath and centrifuged. To supernatant liquid 1 or 2 drops of Titan yellow solution are added. Development of red colouration confirms Mg^{2+} ion.

Na^+, NH_4^+ and K^+ are detected by their usual tests (vide 6.3.1, page 47).

7.3.1.2 Semi-micro Examination of Cations by Adapting Conventional Group Separation Scheme

For semi-microanalysis of cations through conventional group separation involves the following procedure:

7.3.1.2(a) First Group Cations (Ag^+, Hg^+ and Pb^{2+})

Approximately 5 ml solution of the test sample is taken in a centrifuge test tube and to it 4(N)HCL is added dropwise till the precipitation is complete. The reaction mixture is centrifuged. Residue and centrifugate are treated separately.

Residue: May be chlorides of Pb, Ag and Hg(ous) The residue is washed with water boiled and centrifuged in hot condition.			Centrifuge: It contains ions of other groups.
Residue: It is dissolved in 5 ml NH$_4$OH, warmed and centrifuged.		Centrifuge: May contain PbCl$_2$ which on cooling crystallises in needle shaped crystals. To it a few drops of 6(N) acetic acid and 1 ml of 0.5 (N) K$_2$CrO$_4$ solution are added. Yellow precipitate appears. Pb^{2+} confirmed.	
Residue: Black colour of the residue indicates Hg. It is dissolved in aqua regia, evaporated to dryness and to it 2 ml water and a few drops of SnCl$_2$ solution are added. Greyish white precipitate confirms Hg^{2+}.	Centrifuge: To it 1-2 ml 6(N)HNO$_3$ is added. A white precipitate appears which turns violet on exposure to sunrays Ag$^+$ confirmed.		

7.3.1.2(b) Second Group Cations (Hg^{2+}, Pb^{2+}, Bi^{3+}, Cu^{2+}, Cd^{2+}, As^{3+}, Sb^{3+}, Sn^{2+})

Centrifugate of first group may contain the above cations. So to this centrifugate, slowly H$_2$S is passed till the completion of precipitation and centrifuged again.

Residue: Residue is due to the sulphides of this group cations. The residue is boiled with yellow ammonium sulphide and once again centrifuged.		Centrifuge: May contain ions of Gr III onwards and is treated separately.
Residue: If there is any residue it is due to IIA group cations, i.e., PbS, HgS, CuS, Bi$_2$S$_3$ and CdS. This residue is boiled with 6(N)HNO$_3$, and centrifuged. If there is any residue, presence of Hg(ic) is indicated. It is further confirmed by SnCl$_2$ test as usual. The supernatant liquid is treated with strong NH$_4$OH and centrifuged. Appearance of precipitate suggests Bi^{3+}. The supernatant liquid contains Cu^{2+} and Cd^{2+}. Blue colouration of the liquid confirms Cu^{2+}. To blue colour solution a few drops of 2(M)H$_2$SO$_4$ and a few pieces of Fe turnings are added and centrifuged. To centrifugate H$_2$S is passed. Formation of yellow precipate confirms Cd^{2+}.	Centrifuge: It contains Gr IIIB cations as their sulphides. It is treated with strong HCl, boiled and centrifuged. (i) Presence of yellow residue confirms As$_2$S$_3$. The supernatant liquid is divided into two portions. (ii) One portion is neutralised with NH$_4$OH, acidified with oxalic acid and H$_2$S is passed. Red precipitate confirms Sb^{3+}. (iii) To other portion a few Fe turnings are added and warmed in water bath and centrifuged. To centrifugate 1-2 drops of HgCl$_2$ solution are added. Silky white precipitate appears. Sn^{2+} confirmed.	

7.3.1.2(c) Third Group Cations (Fe^{3+}, Al^{3+}, Cr^{3+}, Zn^{2+}, Mn^{2+}, Ni^{2+} and Co$^+$)

If the presence of phsophate has been indicated in preliminary test it is removed first. The centrifugate of Gr II is treated for removal of phosphate following procedure discussed in 6.2.1.4 after removing H$_2$S. Next a few drops of HNO$_3$ are added, boiled and cooled. To cold solution group reagents (NH$_4$Cl and NH$_4$OH) in semi-micro quantity are added and centrifuged. Residue and centrifugate are separately treated.

Residue: May contain Gr IIIA cations as their hydroxides. Residue is taken in test tube, boiled with dilute NaOH (2 ml) and H_2O_2 (2 ml) and once again *centrifuged*. If residue, presence of Fe^{3+}, is indicated, confirmed by usual test. If the centrifugate is yellow in colour, Cr^{3+} may be present—confirmed by lead-chromate test. The centrifugate is acidified with a few drops of dilute HCl and a slight excess of NH_4OH solution is added. Formation of white gelatinous precipitate confirms Al^{3+}.	**Centrifugate**: It contains Gr IIIB and other ions. To this solution H_2S is passed and centrifuged. Residue contains Gr IIIB cations and *centrifugate may contain Gr IV onward cations*. The residue is taken in a hard glass test tube and boiled with 1-2 ml dilute HCl and centrifuged. Residue is due to Co and Ni sulphides while supernatant liquid may contain Mn^{2+} and Zn^{2+}. For identification of Ni^{2+} and Co^{2+}, the residue is dissolved in aqua regia and usual tests for Co^{2+} and Ni are performed. Supernatant liquid is boiled to remove H_2S and treated with 1-2 ml dilute NaOH solution, warmed, cooled and centrifuged. Fleshy coloured residue, if any, indicates Mn^{2+}. To supernatant liquid H_2S in passed, white precipitate confirms Zn^{2+}.

7.3.1.2(d) Fourth Group Cations (Ca^{2+}, Sr^{2+} and Br^{2+})

Centrifugate of group IIIB is boiled to remove H_2S and is made alkaline with 1 ml NH_4OH. To this alkaline solution 1 ml of $(NH_4)_2CO_3$ solution is added, shaken and centrifuged. Appearance of white precipitate suggests the presence of group IV cations as their carbonates. This residue is tested for Ca^{2+}, Ba^{2+} and Sr^{2+} ions by semi-micro test discussed in 7.3.1.1.(d). The centrifugate is tested for Mg^{2+}, Na^+, K^+ and NH_4^+ by tests as depicted in 7.3.1.1(e).

7.3.2 Semi-microanalysis of Anions

The procedure for systematic analysis of anions by semi-micro method is practically identical to that for macroanalysis. The analysis is carried out with the Na_2CO_3 extract of the sample using small quantities of sample and other reagents in semi-micro apparatus. However, for the identification of a few anions some special spot tests are available as discussed below:

7.3.2.1 Test for Phosphate (PO_4^{3-})

Experiment	Observation	Inference
A drop of sample solution in conc. HNO_3 is placed on a filter paper, dried and a drop of molybdate reagent solution is added. To this a drop of benzidine reagent is added and the paper is held on ammonia vapour.	Blue colour develops.	PO_4^{3-} is confirmed.

7.3.2.2 Test for Sulphide (S^{2-})

Experiment	Observation	Inference
A drop of test solution is placed on the semi-micro plate and to it a drop of HCl, a few crystals of p-amino-dimethylaniline and a drop of 1% $FeCl_3$ solution are added.	Blue colour appears within a few minutes.	S^{2-} is confirmed.

Reactions

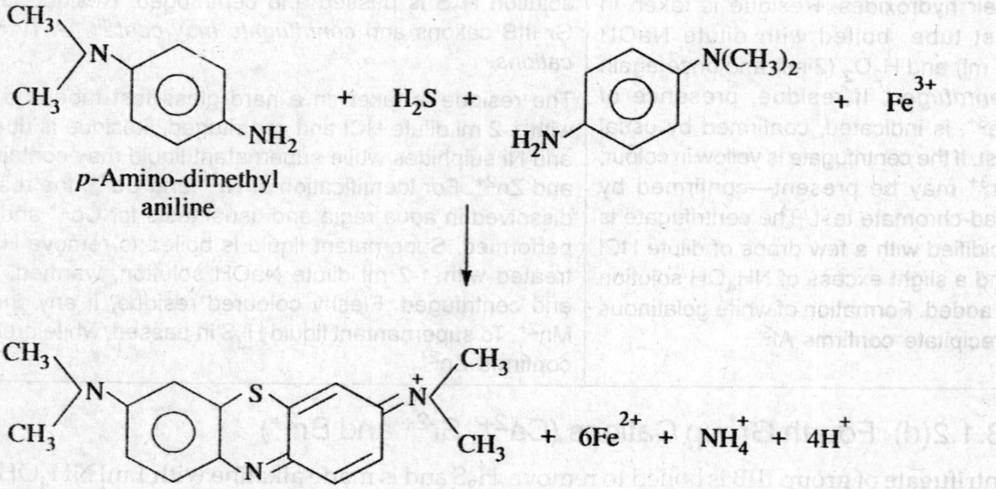

p-Amino-dimethyl aniline

$+ H_2S +$

$+ Fe^{3+}$

$+ 6Fe^{2+} + NH_4^+ + 4H^+$

7.3.2.3 Test for Nitrite (NO_2^-)

Experiment	Observation	Inference
A pinch of original salt is taken in the spot plate and is dissolved in water. It is acidified with acetic acid and is mixed with a drop of sulphanilic acid solution. Finally to it a drop of α-naphthyl amine solution is added.	A Red dye is formed.	NO_2^- is confirmed.

7.3.2.4 Test for Nitrate (NO_3^-)

Experiment	Observation	Inference
A small crystal of $FeSO_4$ is taken on a spot plate. To it a drop of solution of the sample is added. Next through the side of the spot plate very slowly a drop of conc. H_2SO_4 is added.	A brown ring is formed around the crystal of $FeSO_4$.	NO_3^- is confirmed.

7.3.2.5 Tests for Halides

Experiment	Observation	Inference
(a) **Test for chloride**: A pinch of sample is taken in a semi-micro test tube. To it a pinch of powdered potassium dichromate is added and is throughly mixed. This mixture is moistened with a drop of conc. H_2SO_4. The evolved gas (chromyl chloride)	A violet colour is developed.	Chloride is confirmed.

Contd.

Experiment	Observation	Inference
is passed to a glass tube containing 1% alcoholic solution of diphenyl carbazide. The glass tube with the reagent is fitted with the semi-micro test tube.		
(b) **Test for bromide**: A filter paper is moistened with a drop of 1% fuchsin bisulphite solution and this moist filter paper is held on the mouth of semi-micro test tube in which a pinch of sample, a pinch of powdered $K_2Cr_2O_7$ and a drop of conc. H_2SO_4 have been taken for chromyl chloride test as in (a).	The evolved gas turns moist filter paper into violet colour.	Bromide is confirmed.
(c) **Test for iodide**: A pinch of sample is taken in a semi-micro test tube and is mixed with a pinch of KNO_2. The mixture is acidified with HCl and a moist starch paper is held on the mouth of the test tube.	The paper turns blue.	Iodide is confirmed.

7.3.2.6 Test for Borate (BO_3^{3-})

Experiment	Observation	Inference
5 ml of Na_2CO_3 extract is taken in a semi-micro test tube, and to it a drop of bromothymol blue indicator is added and is neutralised by dropwise adding acid when blue colour changes to green. To this solution taken on a watch glass a drop of 50% glycerol solution is added.	Yellow colour develops.	Borate is confirmed.

Records of Experiments

The results of each experiment carried out for the identification of both acidic and basic radicals present in the supplied sample should be reported in the proper proforma as given below. This proforma contains three columns, viz., experiment, observation and inference. In column, experiment, a very short description is to be written, the result of the experiment is to be entered in the column, observation while the conclusion drawn from the result, is to be noted in inference column.

A model records of experimental results are given below for convenience.

Qualitative Analysis of Inorganic Mixture

Sample No: Date:

Physical character: A white powder.

Solubility: A portion of the sample is soluble in dilute HCl but other part remains insoluble even in aqua regia.

Dry Test for Basic Radicals

Experiment	Observation	Inference
1. A small portion of the sample is heated in a clean and dry test tube.	1. Substance decripitates and white residue remains.	1. Nitrates of heavy metals like Pb, Al, Ba, Mg, etc.
2. Sample is heated on charcoal cavity in oxidising flame.	2. Substance decripitates, a metallic bead is formed after strong heating, which marks on the paper.	2. May be nitrate of Pb.
3. The residue on the charcoal cavity is moistened with two drops of cobalt nitrate solution and heated again.	3. Blue residue.	3. May be Al.
4. Flame test.	4. Bluish white flame.	4. May be Pb.

Dry Test for Acid Radicals

Experiment	Observation	Inference
1. Sample is heated with dilute H_2SO_4.	1. No gas is evolved.	1. Carbonate, sulphite sulphide, thiosulphate, nitrite are absent.
2. Sample is heated with conc. H_2SO_4.	2. A light brown gas is evolved, becomes more intense on adding Cu-turnings.	2. May be halides, nitrate.
3. Sample is heated with conc. H_2SO_4 and MnO_2.	3. No characteristic smell of gas.	3. Halides absent.
4. Sample is heated with conc. HNO_3 and ammonium molybdate is added and heated again.	4. No canary yellow precipitate.	4. Phosphate and arsenate absent.
5. Sample is gently heated with conc. H_2SO_4 and a few drops of alcohol. The vapour is burnt on the mouth of the test tube.	5. No green flame.	5. Borate absent.
6. A small portion of the sample is heated with conc. H_2SO_4 and SiO_2. A drop of water on a glass rod is held before the issuing gas.	6. Water drop does not solidify.	6. Fluoride absent.

Wet Test for Basic Radicals

Preparation of solution: A portion of the sample is treated with sufficient quantity of water, boiled, cooled and filtered. The filtrate is evaporated to dryness when a white residue is obtained. This indicates that the sample contains a water soluble portion.

The residue remains insoluble in conc. HCl and aqua regia. So this portion may be considered as insoluble portion.

General Group Separation

A portion of the solid sample is boiled with conc. HCl, cooled and filtered.

White precipitate of Group I $PbCl_2$, Hg_2Cl_2, AgCl.	The filtrate is treated with NH_4OH to reduce the acidity. It is diluted, acidified with dilute HCl and H_2S is passed in warm condition and filtered.			
	Black precipitate of Gr II Metals.	**Filtrate**: Filtrate is boiled off H_2S, cooled and boiled again with a few drops of conc. HNO_3, solid NH_4Cl is added and NH_4OH is added drop by drop and filtered.		
		No residue, Gr III A absent.	**Filtrate**: A portion of the filtrate is taken in a test tube and H_2S is passed and filtered.	
			No residue Gr III B absent	Another portion is heated to reduce the volume and is made alkaline by adding NH_4OH. Then $(NH_4)_2CO_3$ is added, warmed and filtered.
				No presidue, Gr IV absent.
				The filtrate is treated with Na_2HPO_4 solution.
				No precipitate, Mg absent.

Analysis of The Precipitate of Group I

The precipitate obtained in Group I is washed with water and is transferred to a beaker, boiled with water and filtered.

No residue, Ag and Hg(ous) are absent.	**Filtrate** (i) One part of the filtrate is cooled under tap—white crystalline precipitate. Pb is confirmed. (ii) To another part of the filtrate 2 ml of KI solution is added; yellow precipitate, Pb confirmed.

Analysis of Insoluble Portion

Experiment	Observation	Inference
1. A portion of the sample is heated in charcoal cavity under oxidising flame.	1. White residue	1. Al_2O_3, $BaSO_4$, $SrSO_4$
2. The residue on the charcoal is moistened with cobalt nitrate solution and heated in oxidising flame.	2. Blue residue.	2. Al_2O_3
3. Flame test.	3. No characteristic flame.	3. Ba, Ca, Sr, absent.
4. The insoluble portion is mixed with MnO_2 and is treated with conc. H_2SO_4 and heated.	4. No gas is evolved.	4. Halides are absent.

Wet Test for Acid Radicals

Na_2CO_3 extract of the sample is prepared. With the extract following tests are performed.

Experiment	Observation	Inference
1. A portion of the Na_2CO_3 extract taken in a test tube is treated with sodium nitroprusside solution.	1. No colouration	1. Sulphide absent
2. Another part is acidified with dilute HCl and $BaCl_2$ solution is added.	2. No precipitate	2. Sulphate, Fluoride etc. absent.
3. A portion of the Na_2CO_3 extract is taken in a test tube. To it 1-2 ml of freshly prepared solution of $FeSO_4$ solution is added with shaking, 2 ml of conc. H_2SO_4 is gently added down the side of inclined test tube so that a layer is formed.	3. A brown ring is formed at the junction of H_2SO_4 and the aqueous solution.	3. Nitrate confirmed.
4. Na_2CO_3 extract is made neutral and to this portion $AgNO_3$ solution is added.	4. No precipitate.	4. Halides absent.

Semi-microanalysis

1. To 1 ml test solution 4 drops of 4(N) NaOH solution are added, boiled and centrifuged. To supernatant liquid one drop of KCN solution and one drop of Na_2S solution are added. Black precipitate PbS appears.

2. 5 ml original test solution is taken in a test tube and is treated with sufficient quantity of (N) NaOH solution. A filter paper is moistened with the solution of this reaction mixture, and to moist the filter paper a drop of Alizarin-S is added. A violet colour develops which turns red on addition of excess of acetic acid. Al is confirmed.

3. Ring test for NO_3^- is performed by using semi-micro quantity of Na_2CO_3 solution when positive result has been obtained.

Conclusion: Supplied sample, threfore, contains $Pb(NO_3)_2$ and Al_2O_3.

Questions and Answers for Viva Voce

1. Suggest the colour of the following substances: (a) Mercuric oxide (b) Cadmium sulphide (c) Ferric oxide (d) Lead sulphide (e) Chromic oxide (f) Antimony sulphide.

   Ans. (a) Red, (b) Yellow, (c) Brown, (d) Black, (e) Green, (f) Red.

2. What change occurs when the following substances are heated in a dry test tube? $CuSO_4$, $MnSO_4$, $Zn(NO_3)_2$, $Pb(NO_3)_2$, NH_4Cl, NiO.

   (i) Changes to black $\longrightarrow$ $CuSO_4$, $MnSO_4$ and NiO

   (ii) Yellow when hot, white when cold $\longrightarrow$ $Zn(NO_3)_2$.

   (iii) Yellow when hot and cold $\longrightarrow$ $Pb(NO_3)_2$.

   (iv) Smell of NH_3 $\longrightarrow$ NH_4Cl.

3. Name the burner that is used in the laboratory.

   Ans. Bunsen burner.

4. State the reason on heating in a test tube (a) blue copper sulphate becomes white (b) $Pb(NO_3)_2$ becomes yellow (c) red Cu_2O becomes balck (d) red Hgo forms a shining mirror.

   Ans. (a) $CuSO_4$, $5H_2O$ is blue, on heating water of crystallisation is lost. (b) $Pb(NO_3)_2$ decomposes into PbO which is yellow in colour. (c) Cu_2O becomes CuO. (d) HgO decomposes to metallic Hg.

5. What happens when ammonium compound is heated in a test tube?

   Ans. Smell of ammonia is obtained.

6. How would you differentiate metallic bead of lead from that of bismnth and antimony?

   Ans. Bead of lead marks the paper but others do not.

7. How and when cobalt nitrate test is performed?

   Ans. See the cobalt nitrate test.

8. Why $HgCl_2$ does not respond to chromyl chloride test?

   Ans. $HgCl_2$ is a covalent compound and it sublimes before the reaction starts.

9. **How carbonate and sulphite can be differentiated?**

   Ans. Although both the salts show effervescence due to liberation of CO_2 and SO_2 respectively, but SO_2 decolourises $KMnO_4$ solution while CO_2 does not.

10. **Why some radicals like borate, phosphate, etc. interfere in the qualitative analysis?**

    Ans. Such radicals if present may be precipitated in Group IIIA along with the expected radicals. For this reason they are removed before Group IIIA analysis.

11. **Why KI-starch paper is turned blue by Cl_2 gas?**

    Ans. Cl_2 oxidises KI to I_2 which forms blue complex with starch.

12. **Is chromyl chloride an oxidising agent?**

    Ans. Yes.

13. **What happens when a solution of chromate is acidified?**

    Ans. On acidification chromate is converted into dichromate and the yellow colour of the solution deepens. It is not a case of oxidation or reduction as there is no loss or gain of electron. It is an acid-base reaction.

14. **Why conc. HNO_3 is used in the test for phosphate and arsenate?**

    Ans. All phosphates and arsenates are soluble in conc. HNO_3.

15. **What is the function of tartaric acid in ammonium molybdate test?**

    Ans. Tartaric acid masks arsenate.

16. **Why in the test of fluoride, water drop becomes turbid?**

    Ans. Due to deposition of silicic acid and hydrofluorosilicic acid.

17. **Why ammonium molybdate is used in excess for testing phosphate?**

    Ans. Excess reagent favours the reaction.

18. **Why MnO_2 is used for testing chloride by heating with conc. H_2SO_4?**

    Ans. MnO_2 acts as catalyst in the oxidation of HCl formed from chloride by conc. H_2SO_4 to chlorine.

19. **How bromide is detected in presence of nitrate?**

    Ans. Mixture on treatment with conc. H_2SO_4 forms pale reddish brown gas due to HBr and Br_2.

20. **Why pure Na_2CO_3 is used as the conversion reagent for wet test of acid radicals?**

    Ans. Na_2CO_3 can convert all types of salts, both soluble and insoluble, into the soluble carbonates of the cations.

21. **Explain why sometimes sodium carbonate extract on acidification forms precipitate.**

    Ans. Some salts like that of aluminium and chromium during sodium carbonate extract are converted to their anionates. These anionates on acidification are precipitated as $Al(OH)_3$ and $Cr(OH)_3$.

22. **Name some sulphides extracted by sodium carbonate do not respond to sodium nitroprusside test.**

    Ans. CdS and PbS.

23. Free boric acid and borate can be differentiated by adding conc. H_2SO_4—Explain.

   Ans. Free boric acid can combine directly with the alcohol, but borate liberates boric acid on treatment with conc. H_2SO_4 which then combines with alcohol.

24. What is the formula of copper metaborate? Explain how it is formed in borax bead test.

   Ans. $Cu(BO_2)_2$.

   The reaction occurs as

$$CuSO_4 \rightleftharpoons CuO + SO_3$$

$$CuO + B_2O_3 = Cu(BO_2)_2$$

25. What should you expect to observe in borax bead test with each of the following substance:
   (i) Mn-compounds (ii) Co-compounds?

   Ans. (i) Colourless bead in reducing flame but amethyst violet in oxidising flame.

   (ii) Sapphire blue bead in both oxidising and reducing flame.

26. Why a little of the sample is taken in borax bead text?

   Ans. If excess of the sample is used the bead may be so dark in colour that it may be difficult to detect.

27. Which acid is used in flame test and why?

   Ans. Chlorides of metals are more volatile than other salts. So HCl is used.

28. How will you test ammonium compound without the help of a liquid reagent?

   Ans. A little of ammonium compound and sodalime are taken on a piece of paper, and it is pressed in between the folds of paper and is rubbed. Next the paper is opened when smell of ammonia is obtained.

29. A smaple is warmed with dilute HCl in a test tube and a lead acetate paper is held on the mouth of the test tube. The paper turns black. What is the acid radical of the sample?

   Ans. Sulphide.

30. Is there any gas which turns lime water milky?

   Ans. Yes, SO_2.

31. How can you distinguish bromide and iodide?

   Ans. The sample is mixed with MnO_2 and is heated with conc. H_2SO_4 in a test tube— Evolution of brown vapour indicates bromide. Evolution of violet vapour suggests iodide.

32. When a chloride is heated with dichromate and conc. H_2SO_4, a deep brownish vapour evolves. What is this vapour?

   Ans. Chromyl chloride, CrO_2Cl_2.

33. What reagents are used to test phosphate?

   Ans. Ammonium molybdate and nitric acid.

34. Is it necessary to use conc. H_2SO_4 in alcohol flame test for free boric acid?

   Ans. No.

35. Is it essential to use conc. H_2SO_4 in alcohol flame test for borate?

   Ans. Yes.

36. What causes the flame green in alcohol flame test in boric acid or borate?

    Ans. Alkyl borate.

37. What is the formula of sodium nitroprusside? What colour does it form on reaction with sulphide?

    Ans.   (i) $Na_2[Fe(CN)_5NO]$,

    (ii) Violet colour due to formation of $Na_4[Fe(CN)_5NOS]$.

38. Write down the reaction of sodium sulphide and sodium nitroprusside.

    Ans. $Na_2S + Na_2[Fe(CN)_5NO] = Na_4[Fe(CN)_5NOS]$

39. What is a reagent?

    Ans. The solution that is used for identification of radicals.

40. Is it necessary to perform cobalt nitrate test as a routine analysis?

    Ans. No.

41. What is the principle behind group separation?

    Ans. Solubility product and common ion effect.

42. What is meant by group reagent?

    Ans. Chemical used to precipitate metal ions of a particular group is called group reagent for that group.

43. Which one is soluble in water among the following: $PbCl_2$, $AgCl$, and Hg_2Cl_2?

    Ans. $PbCl_2$.

44. What are disadvantages of using yellow ammonium sulphide for separating Groups IIA and IIB precipitate?

    Ans. Yellow colour and separation of sulphur.

45. Why KCN is added to detect Cd^{++} in presence of Cu^{++} before passing H_2S?

    Ans. KCN forms complex with Cu^{++} as $K_2[Cu(CN)_3]$ which does not ionise and so is not precipitated by H_2S.

46. What is the group reagent for Group IIIA? Why NH_4Cl is added?

    Ans. See the reactions behind Group IIIA ions.

47. What is a salt?

    Ans. A salt is made up of cation and anion and they are formed by neutralisation reaction between an acid and a base. Thus,

    $$NaOH + HCl \rightleftharpoons NaCl + H_2O$$
    $$\text{Base} \quad \text{Acid} \qquad \text{Salt}$$

48. Why does milkiness disappear on passing CO_2 through lime water for a long time?

    Ans. Initially calcium carbonate, $CaCO_3$ is formed which causes milkiness but on passing CO_2 for a long time $CaCO_3$ is converted to soluble bicarbonate.

    $$CaCO_3 + CO_2 + H_2O \longrightarrow Ca(HCO_3)_2$$
    $$\text{Sparingly} \qquad\qquad\qquad \text{Soluble}$$
    $$\text{soluble}$$

49. Which radical is indicated by the evolution of reddish-brown gas on adding conc. H_2SO_4?

Ans. Nitrate and bromide.

50. How will you distinguish bromide and nitrate?

Ans. First to the salt conc. H_2SO_4 is added when reddish-brown gas evolves which may be due to either bromide or nitrate. To this copper turnings are added and is heated. If intense brown vapours appear, then it is nitrate.

51. What is organic layer test?

Ans. It is the test which is used to identify and distinguish bromide and iodide. Sodium extract is acidified with conc. HNO_3 and 1 ml of carbon tetrachloride is added. On vigorous shaking appearance of brown organic layer indicates the presence of bromide, and violet colour suggests iodide.

52. In organic layer test, what is the reason for the formation of coloured layers?

Ans. In presence of oxidising agent, HNO_3, bromide and iodide are oxidised to Br_2 and I_2 respectively, which are soluble in organic solvent like CCl_4, and so develops colour. Thus,

$$2Br^- + [O] + H_2O \xrightarrow[\text{agent}]{\text{Oxidising}} Br_2 + OH^-$$
$$\text{Brown}$$

$$2I^- + [O] + H_2O \longrightarrow I_2 + OH^-$$
$$\text{Violet}$$

53. Why do bromide and iodide not respond to chromyl chloride test?

Ans. Both chromyl bromide and chromyl iodide are non-volatile.

54. How sulphate and sulphite are distinguished?

Ans. Both of these are precipitated by $BaCl_2$ as $BaSO_4$ and $BaSO_3$ but $BaSO_3$ is soluble in conc. HCl whereas $BaSO_4$ is not.

55. Can $Ba(NO_3)_2$ be used in place of $BaCl_2$ in the detection of sulphate.?

Ans. Yes, $Ba(NO_3)_2$ is water soluble and can form insoluble $BaSO_4$ as white precipitate.

56. Can sodium bicarbonate be used in place of sodium carbonate?

Ans. No. This is because metal bicarbonates are soluble in water and hence interfering cations cannot be removed.

57. Ammonium molybdate test applied for phosphate on a solution becomes positive but, in fact, the solution does not contain phosphate—Explain.

Ans. The solution may contain Arsenate.

58. Which cations are absent if the supplied sample is coloured?

Ans. Cu^{2+}, Fe^{2+}, Fe^{3+}, Ni^{2+}, CO^{2+}, Mn^{2+}.

59. Why HCl is used in preparing the original solution of the basic radicals?

Ans. Most of the inorganic salts are soluble in HCl, and HCl does not interfere with the group analysis.

60. Why conc. H_2SO_4 or conc. HNO_3 is not used in preparing original solution?

Ans. This is because conc. H_2SO_4 and conc. HNO_3 are oxidising agents and can interfere in the analysis.

61. What should you do if original solution is prepared in aqua regia?

Ans. The solution is evaported to dryness and the mass is dissolved in water.

62. Can sodium carbonate extract be used for basic radicals?

Ans. No, because basic radicals, i.e., cations are removed as insoluble carbonate.

63. Why divalent lead is placed in both Gr I and Gr II?

Ans. Lead is not completely precipitated in Group I as $PbCl_2$. So the remaining Pb^{2+} is precipitated in Group II.

64. What is solubility product?

Ans. The product of ionic concentration in a saturated solution of a salt or electrolyte at a particular temperature is a constant quantity and is known as solubility product.

65. What is common ion effect?

Ans. The suppression of the dissociation of a weak electrolyte by the addition of a strong electrolyte having an ion common is known as common ion effect.

66. Why dilute HCl is added before passing H_2S in Group II solution?

Ans. When H_2S is passed through a solution along with Group II basic radicals, Group IV cations may be precipitated as sulphide. But the solubility products Group II metals are lower than those of Group IV metals. So to precipitate Group II metals only very small concentration of sulphide ion is required. For this reason a strong electrolyte HCl with common ion H^+, with H_2S is used. In presence of HCl, thus, concentration of sulphide ion becomes very small and so only Group II metals are precipitated.

67. Why the concentration of HCl should not be very high during passing H_2S for Group II metlas?

Ans. Very strong HCl will suppress the ionisation of H_2S and so there will be no precipitation of sulphides of Group II.

68. Why is cadmium solution should be sufficiently dilute before passing H_2S?

Ans. In dilute solution concentration of H^+ is decreased and concentration of sulphide ion is increased. As a result ionic product of Cd^{2+} and S^{2-} excedds the solubility product of CdS and so it is precipitated.

69. How Fe^{2+} and Fe^{3+} are differentiated?

Ans. This differentiation may be possible by the use of potassium ferricyanide solution. If blue colour is obtained, it is Fe^{2+}.

70. Can $(NH_4)_2SO_4$ in place of NH_4Cl be used?

Ans. No. Barium and strontium, if present, will be precipitated as sulphate.

71. Mention the test to which all the sulphur containing acid radicals respond.

Ans. Sample is mixed with Na_2CO_3 and is fused. To this fused mass dilute HCl is added. Evolution of H_2S gas occurs which turns lead acetate paper black.

72. What are the advantages of using $FeCl_3$ for the removal of phosphate?

    Ans. (i) It is easy to detect the presence of iron in the filtrate of Group II.

    (ii) $FePO_4$ is least soluble, that may be precipitated in acetic acid medium.

    (iii) The slight excess of ferric ions that have been added can be easily removed.

73. Why is H_2S passed in ammoniacal medium to precipitate Group IIIB metals as sulphides?

    Ans. To precipitate Group IIIB metals as sulphides high concentration of sulphide ion is required, which can be done by reducing the concentration of hydrogen ion of the solution.

    NH_4OH added in Group IIIB dissociates into $\overset{+}{NH_4}$ and $\overline{OH}$ ions. $\overline{OH}$ ion reacts with H^+ derived from H_2S and so concentration of sulphide is increased.

74. An insoluble salt is green in colour. What preliminary tests are to be preformed?

    Ans. Oxidising fusion test.

75. An insoluble sample is white in colour. What preliminary test is to be performed for its detection?

    Ans. Cobalt nitrate test and flame test.

76. Why magnesium does not respond to flame test?

    Ans. Mg atom is very small and its ionisation potential is very high. For this reason radiation emitted by this atom does not fall in the visible region.

77. Explain why magnesium and ammonium are not precepitated by any group reagent?

    Ans. Solubility products of the salts of these ions formed by the group reagents are very high and so they are not precipitated out.

78. How will you separate $PbSO_4$ from $BaSO_4$?

    Ans. The mixture of these two is treated with a concentrated solution of ammonium acetate when only lead acetate is precipitated out.

79. Explain why Hg_2Cl_2 turns black in coming contact with ammonia.

    Ans. Due to the formation of a complex salt as shown below:

    $$Hg_2Cl_2 + 2NH_4OH \Longrightarrow Hg(NH_2)Cl + Hg + NH_4Cl + 2H_2O$$
    Black

80. Explain why some acid radicals do not respond to dry tests.

    Ans. Some acid radicals like phosphate, silicate and arsenate do not form volatile acids on heating with mineral acids and so they do not respond to dry tests.

81. Explain why on addition of conc. H_2SO_4 alone, chlorine is not liberated from chloride?

    Ans. Conc. H_2SO_4 decomposes chloride into HCl but can not oxidise HCl to liberate Cl_2, that is why MnO_2 is added along with conc. H_2SO_4.

82. Bromide and iodide can be easily identified by the treatment with conc. H_2SO_4 alone—Explain.

    Ans. Conc. H_2SO_4 converts the salts (bromide and iodide) into HBr and HI which are oxidised by conc. H_2SO_4 respectively to Br_2 which is eliminated as brown vapour and I_2 eliminated as violet vapour. Hence bromide and iodide are easily identified.

83. How Hg_2^{2+} is identified?

Ans. The residue of Hg_2Cl_2 in Group I is dissolved in aqua regia, evaporated to dryness, cooled and to it 5 ml of water and 1 ml of $SnCl_2$ are added when white precipitate appears.

$$Hg^{2+} \ + \ Sn^{2+} \ \rightleftharpoons \ Sn^{4+} \ + \ Hg_2^{2+}$$

$$\text{White}$$

84. Why Group V, has no general reagent?

Ans. In Group V, Na_2HPO_4 is added in ammoniacal medium when $Mg(NH_4)PO_4$ is precipitated but other cations like Na^+, K^+ and NH_4^+ are not precipitated because the solubility products of these salts are very high.

Quantitative Inorganic Analysis

Part II

Chapter 1

Introduction

Quantitative analysis means the determination of amounts of different inorganic constituents in a given sample and is an essential part of analytical chemistry. The amounts of the constituents present are normally expressed either in gram/litre or in terms of normality. Generally following two methods are used for this analysis.

    1. Volumetric analysis, 2. Gravimetric Analysis

1.1 Volumetric Analysis

This type of analysis involves the determination of the constituent of the given sample in solution. This solution is allowed to react with the standard solution of an appropriate reagent. The standard solution is prepared by dissolving accurately weighed quantity of the reagent in an accurately measured volume of a solvent, primarily distilled water. It may be mentioned that the reagent should be such that can react with the constituent of the given sample completely and the end point of the reaction can be determined very accurately. The end point of the reaction sometimes is determined directly but in many cases an external chemical compound known as *Indicator* is added. During analysis a measured volume of the solution of the constituent of the sample is taken in an Erlenmeyer flask (conical falsk with a stopper) and from burrette the solution of the standard reagent is added slowly. This part of the process is known as *Titration*. The volume of the starndard reagent solution required at the end point is accurately noted and from this volume the amount of the constituent in the given sample is determined with the help of laws of chemical equivalence.

1.2 Gravimetric Analysis

In this process of quantitative analysis the measured volume of the solution of the constituent is allowed to react with the solution of an appropriate reagent so that it can react completely with the constituent and an insoluble compound of the constituent is precipitated out in a pure form under the reaction condition. It is filtered, washed to make it free from any adhering chemicals, dried, ignited, if required, cooled and weighed. From the weight of the precipitate, the amount of the constituent is determined from the knowledge of the molecular weight of the precipitate and the atomic weight of the constituent.

1.3 Apparatus Required for Quantitative Analysis

For quantitative analysis following special apparatuses are required in addition to ordinary apparatuses. The glass apparatuses used must be carefully cleaned before use.

(i) Burrette, (ii) Pipette, (iii) Weighing bottle, (iv) Measuring flask (volumetric flask)

(v) Chemical balance with its accessories.

1.4 Chemical Balance and Its Use

The most important and essential apparatus that is required for quantitative analysis is the chemical balance and it is frequently used. So it is desirable to present here a short description of a chemical balance and its mode of operation.

The most important part of a chemical balance is its beam. This beam has three knife edges made of very hard steel. The central knife edge rests on a smooth plate kept at the top of a balance column. The weighing pans are suspended from the terminal knife edges by means of stirrups. A pointer is fixed at the centre of the beam. When the weighing pans swing, the lower end of the pointer moves on the scale at the bottom column. Three knife edges are kept parallel to each other. The balance is covered by a glass case to protect the balance from dust and to prevent any movement of the pans by air. The case has two side doors. The general design of a typical balance is as shown in the following figure.

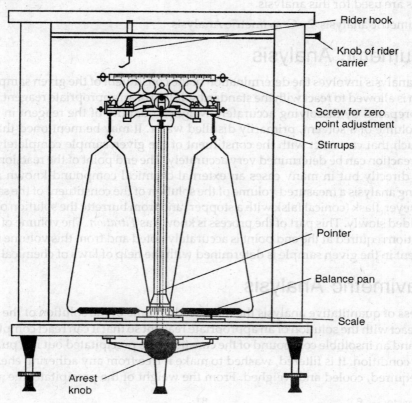

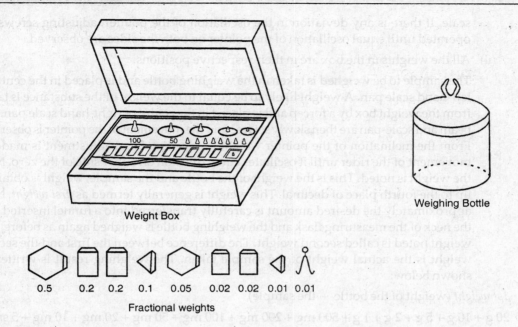

Weight Box

Weighing Bottle

0.5   0.2   0.2   0.1   0.05   0.02   0.02   0.01   0.01

Fractional weights

1.4.1 Mode of Operation of Chemical Balance

In any chemical balance there are two horizontal scales, one at the bottom (base) and the other at the top. The scale at the top is known as *Rider-scale* and the bottom scale is termed as *Pointer-scale*. The *pointer* of the balance oscillates equally on both the sides of the zero of the pointer-scale. It may be mentioned that in the general type of chemical balance known as *Sartorius balance*, the zero mark is at the centre of the scale and the rider which is a thin metal wire weighs 10 mg (0.01g). The thin wire of the rider is bent in such a way that it can be placed anywhere on the rider scale as a result weight adjustment up to 10 mg can be made. The second type of chemical balance is known as *Bunge balance*. In this balance the zero mark is at the left-hand end of the rider-scale and the rider weighing 5 mg (0.005g) is used.

The rider-scale of both the types of balances are divided into ten big divisions. Again each big division is divided into five small divisions in *Sartorius type* of balance while there are ten small divisions in each of the big division in *Bunge type* of balance. Thus, in *Sartorius* balance shifting of rider from zero to ten big divisions corresponds to passing over 50 small divisions (teeth). So shifting of rider by a single tooth is equivalent to $\frac{0.01}{50}$ g = 0.0002 g while in the Bunge balance value of shifting of rider by one tooth corresponds to $\frac{0.01}{100}$ g = 0.0001 g . Thus, from the position of the rider on the scale accurate weight can be determined.

1.4.1.1 Weighing

Before taking the weight of a substance, following care should be taken:

(i)   The beam of the balance must be in the horizontal position which is indicated by the oscillation of the pointer over equal division on either side of the zero of the pointer-scale. If there is any deviation in the oscillation of the pointer, adjusting screws are operated until equal oscillation of the pointer on both the sides are observed.

(ii) All the weights in the box are in their respective positions.

The sample to be weighed is taken in the weighing bottle and is placed in the centre of left-hand scale pan. A weight likely to be equal to the weight of the substance is taken from the weight box by a forcep and is placed in the centre of right-hand scale pan. The beam and scale-pan are then slowly set free and the movement of the pointer is observed. From the inclination of the pointer weight is adjusted. Final adjustment is made by movement of the rider until it oscillates equal division on either side of the zero. Now the weight is noted. This is the weight of the bottle and the sample, weight is obtained up to the fourth place of decimal. This weight is generally termed as *first weight*. Now approximately the desired amount is carefully transferred into a funnel inserted into the neck of the measuring flask and the weighing bottle is weighed again as before. The weight noted is called second weight. The difference between the first and the second weight is the actual weight of the sample taken. The weighing result is written as shown below:

1st weight (weight of the bottle + the sample)

20 g + 10 g + 5 g + 2 g + 1 g + 500 mg + 200 mg + 100 mg + 50 mg + 20 mg + 10 mg + 5 small division of the rider, i.e.,

= 20 + 10 + 5 + 2 + 1 + 0.5 + 0.2 + 0.1 + 0.05 + 0.02 + 0.01 + (16 × 0.002)

= 38.88 + 0.0032 = 38.8832 g.

Similarly, 2nd weight (weight of bottle + remaining amount of the sample)

20 g + 10 g + 5 g + 200 mg + 100 mg + 20 mg + 10 mg + 17 small division of the rider.

= 35.33 + (17 × 0.002) = 35.3334g.

Actual weight of the sample taken is (1st weight − 2nd weight), i.e., (38.8832 − 35.3334) g = 3.5498 g.

After the completion of weighing, different weights used are placed in their proper positions in the weight box and rider is brought back to zero position. The balance is also brought at rest. It must be remembered that during each weighing the glass windows of the balance must be kept close so that air current may not cause any erratic oscillation of the pan and the pointer.

1.5 Preparation of Solution

The solution of a solute required for quantitative inorganic analysis must have a certain concentration. The concentration of a solution is expressed by the following terms.

(i) *Standard solution*: When a known amount of solute is dissolved in a known volume of solvent standard solution is obtained. The actual strength of the standard solution is expressed in two terms; *viz.*, molality and normality.

(a) *Molality*: When one gram molecular weight of a solute is dissolved in one litre of a solvent *molar solution* of the solute is obtained. Thus, molality of a solution may be defined as the number of gram molecular weight of a solute present in one litre of its solution. It is abbreviated as M. Thus, 1M HCl solution contains 1 + 35.5 = 36.5 g of HCl per litre.

(b) *Normality*: Normal solution of a solute is that solution one litre of which contains one gram equivalent of the solute. So normality of a solution is stated as the multiplet or fraction of gram equivalent weight of a solute dissolved in one litre of the solution. It is expressed as

$$\text{Normality} = \frac{\text{amount of solute in grams per litre}}{\text{equivalent weight}}$$

(c) *Equivalent weight*: The equivalent weight of a substance is defined as the weight of the substance in gram which reacts with or displaces from the substance 1.008 g of H_2, 8 g of oxygen or 35.457 g of chlorine. The equivalent weights of acid, base and oxidising or reducing agent are expressed as indicated below:

(i) Equivalent weight of a base: $= \dfrac{\text{molecular weight of the base}}{\text{number of replaceable } \overline{OH} \text{ ions}}$.

Thus, equivalent weight of NaOH is $\dfrac{40}{1} = 40$.

(ii) Equivalent weight of an acid: $\dfrac{\text{molecular weight of an acid}}{\text{number of replaceable } H^+ \text{ ions}}$.

Oxalic acid, $\underset{\overset{|}{COOH}}{COOH}$, $2H_2O$ has molecular weight 126, but it has two replaceable H^+ ions. So its equivalent weight is $\dfrac{126}{2} = 63$.

(iii) Equivalent weight of an oxidising or a reducing agent is expressed as:

$$\frac{\text{molecular weight of the reagent}}{\text{change in oxidation number of the reagent}}.$$

Comments

(i) It may be mentioned in this connection that the equivalent weight of a substance is not a constant quantity. It depends upon the condition of the reaction as is evidenced from the following reactions.

In acidic medium

$$2K\overset{7+}{Mn}O_4 + 3H_2SO_4 \longrightarrow 2\overset{2+}{Mn}SO_4 + 3H_2O + K_2SO_4 + 5O$$

In this reaction manganese which has valency 7 in $KMnO_4$ is converted to divalent manganese. So the change in oxidation number is $7 - 2 = 5$. Thus, in acidic condition the equivalent weight of $KMnO_4$ is $\frac{1}{5}$th of its molecular weight, i.e., $\dfrac{158.026}{5} = 31.61$.

In basic medium: In basic condition reaction occurs as

$$2K\overset{7+}{Mn}O_4 + 2KOH \longrightarrow 2K_2\overset{6+}{Mn}O_4 + H_2O + O$$

The change in oxidation number is $7-6 = 1$. So its equivalent weight is

$$\frac{158.026}{1} = 158.026.$$

(ii) The equivalent weight when expressed in gram is known as gram equivalent weight.

1.5.1 Preparation of Standard Solution

After knowing the equivalent weight of the substance, desired standard solution is prepared. Standard solution is of two types, *viz.*, (i) primary standard and (ii) secondary standard solutions.

1.5.1.1 Primary Standard Solution

Primary standard solutions are those which can be prepared by accurately weighing the substance in chemical balance and dissolving the weighed substance in known volume of solvent in measuring flask (volumetric flask). Na_2CO_3, $H_2C_2O_4$, $2H_2O$ (oxalic acid), $K_2Cr_2O_7$, etc. are used for preparing primary standards because they can be directly weighed. It must be remembered that the primary standard substances should be sufficiently chemically pure.

1.5.1.2 Secondary Standard Solution

Secondary standard solutions are those which cannot be prepared by direct weighing. These are usually prepared by standardising their approximately standard solutions against suitable primary standard solution. Thus, standard solutions of HCl and H_2SO_4 are prepared by standard solution of Na_2CO_3. Generally, NaOH, $KMnO_4$, HCl, H_2SO_4 are used for preparing secondary standard solution.

1.6 Indicators

Indicators are a class of chemical compounds which indicate the end-point of a chemical reaction either by change of colour of the solution or by precipitation. Indicators are of three types.

(i) **Internal Indicator**: This type of indicators are directly added to the reacting solution such as phenolphthalein, methyl orange, methyl red, etc. Depending upon the nature of chemical reaction involved, internal indicators have been categorised as acid-base indicator, precipitation indicator, redox indicator, etc. The change of colour of the indicator is due to the structural change which originates from their existence in tautomeric forms.

(ii) **External Indicator**: This type of indicator cannot be directly added to the reacting solution. From time to time the reacting mixture is tested with the solution of these types of indicator. In the titration of $K_2Cr_2O_7$ solution against Mohr's salt (ferrous ammonium sulphate) solution, $K_3Fe(CN)_6$ solution is used as external indicator.

(iii) **Self Indicator**: There are certain chemicals which when dissolved form coloured solution. Such coloured solution during reaction with another substance may either discharge the colour or there may be change in colour. So during titration the end-point can be easily detected without using any indicator. Since in such reactions one of the reagents acts as the indicator, they are termed as self indicator. $KMnO_4$ constitutes an example of self indicator.

Chapter 2

Volumetric Analysis

As mentioned before volumetric analysis is always carried out in solution. The term *volumetric analysis* has been coined because it always involves definite volumes of solutions measured accurately. This analysis is based on the principle of the *Law of equivalents* which states that when a chemical reaction proceeds to completion, equivalent weight of one compound reacts exactly with the equivalent amount of another compound. So when a solution of known strength of one substance is allowed to react completely with the solution of unknown strength of another substance, the end-point is indicated by a sharp change such as the formation of precipitation or change of colour. However, in many cases in order to visualise clearly the end-point, *indicator* is added to the solution. Now knowing the volumes of two reacting solutions and from the knowledge of the strength of the one solutions, the strength of other is calculated using the formula,

$$S_1V_1 = S_2V_2,$$

where V_1 and V_2 are the volumes of two reacting solutions and S_1 and S_2 are the strengths of two solution out of which one is known.

2.1 Applications of Volumetric Analysis

Volumetric analysis is primarily applied for the following purposes:

    (i) To find out the stoichiometry of an equation.

    (ii) To determine the purity and composition of mixtures.

    (iii) To determine the molecular formula.

2.2 Types of Volumetric Analysis

Volumetric analysis may be of the following types:

    (i) Acidimetry and Alkalimetry

    (ii) Oxidation and Reduction Titration

(iii) Iodometry and Iodimetry

(iv) Precipitation Titration

(v) Complexometric Titration.

2.2.1 Acidimetry and Alkalimetry

In this type of volumetric analysis a certain volume of known strength of an acid or a base is titrated with required volume of a base or an acid as the case may be. Generally, phenolphthalein, methyl orange and methyl red indicators are used to detect the end-point.

2.2.1.1 Preparation of Standard Solutions

(i) **Standard($N/10$) Na_2CO_3 Solution:** Na_2CO_3 is a primary standard. Its equivalent weight is 53. For $N/10$ solution 5.3 g of Na_2CO_3 is required for one litre of the solution and for 250 ml solution 1.325 g is required. Accurately weighed quantity of Na_2CO_3 close to 1.325 g is transferred to 250 ml measuring flask through a funnel fitted at its mouth and the actual weight, say wg, is noted.

Now carefully distilled water is added to the flask through wash bottle and the entire quantity of Na_2CO_3 is washed down to the flask. The funnel is rinsed several times with distilled water to save any loss of Na_2CO_3. The flask is well shaken to dissolve the whole quantity of Na_2CO_3 and finally slowly and carefully distilled water is added up to the mark. If necessary at the final stage a dropper may be used. The flask is stoppered well and is shaken several times to make a uniform solution.

The strength of this solution is $\dfrac{w}{1.325}$ $N/10$.

(ii) **($N/10$) H_2SO_4 Solution:** H_2SO_4 is a secondary standard. So standard solution of H_2SO_4 cannot be prepared by direct weighing. However, at first, an approximately $N/10$ solution is prepared and in the next step its strength is accurately determined by titration against a standard solution of an alkali.

Concentrated H_2SO_4 is about 36(N). 2.8 ml of concentrated H_2SO_4 is measured by means of measuring cylinder and it is very slowly poured into a flask containing 500 ml of distilled water with constant stirring and cooling. This solution is transferred to a one litre measuring flask and more water is added to make up the volume up to the mark. The strength of this solution is approximately $N/10$. Finally its exact strength is determined by the titration against a standard solution of an alkali.

2.2.1.1.1 Standardisation of an Approximately ($N/10$) H_2SO_4 Solution with Standard ($N/10$) Na_2CO_3 Solution

Procedure: Burette and pipette are throughly washed and cleaned. Burette is rinsed several times with H_2SO_4 solution just prepared and it is completely filled up to zero mark with the acid. The burette with acid is fixed at a vertical position with a burette clamp. The pipette is rinsed several times with a few ml of ($N/10$) Na_2CO_3 solution and 25 ml of this solution is pipetted out from the measuring flask and is transferred to a 250 ml conical flask which was previously washed with distilled water. To this solution one or two drops of methyl red or methyl orange indicator solution be added. The conical flask is placed on a white paper kept below the burette nozzle. The initial burette reading is noted and H_2SO_4 solution is run out by opening the stopcock of the burette with the left-hand keeping the conical flask in the right-hand as shown in the figure.

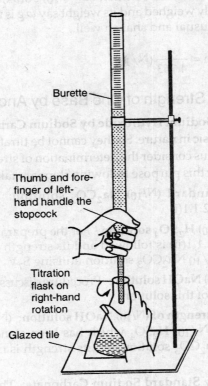

Burette

Thumb and fore-finger of left-hand handle the stopcock

Titration flask on right-hand rotation

Glazed tile

The running out of H_2SO_4 is continued with constant stirring until the solution becomes faintly yellow. Dropwise addition of acid is continued until the colour of the solution becomes pink. The end-point is noted. The solution in the conical flask is thrown away, washed with distilled water, the burette is filled up with acid solution up to the zero mark and the similar process is repeated three or more times until the concordant burette readings are obtained.

The exact strength of H_2SO_4 is $\dfrac{25 \times \text{strength of (N/10) } Na_2CO_3}{\text{volume of acid}}$.

(iii) Standard (N/10) Oxalic acid Solution: Oxalic acid is a primary standard and its equivalent weight is 63. For 250 ml (N/10) solution 1.575 g of oxalic acid is accurately weighed as before and taken in a 250 ml measuring flask and is dissolved in distilled water following the same procedure as in the case of Na_2CO_3 to make 250 ml solution of (N/10) oxalic acid.

(iv) Preparation of Standard (N/10) NaOH Solution: Sodium hydroxide cannot be obtained in pure form. So its standard solution cannot be prepared by direct weighing. Its equivalent weight is 40 and for the preparation of 250 ml (N/10) NaOH solution approximately 1 g of NaOH is weighed in a rough balance and is transferred in a 250 ml flask and dissolved in distilled water and finally the volume is made up to the mark to get an approximately (N/10) NaOH solution. This solution is standardised by the titration against a standard acid solution following the procedure adapted in the case of standisation of H_2SO_4.

(v) **Standard (N/10) Borax Solution**: Borax, $Na_2B_4O_7, 10H_2O$, is a solid chemical and can be obtained in pure crystalline form. So it may be used as a primary standard. Its equivalent weight is 190.72. So for the preparation of 250 ml solution of (N/10) borax, exactly 4.763 g is required. So about 4.7 g of borax is accurately weighed and its weight say w g is noted. It is dissolved in distilled water in a measuring flask as usual and shaken well.

$$\text{Strength of borax solution} = \frac{w}{4.763} \, (N/10).$$

2.2.1.2 Determination of Strength of One Base by Another Base

1. **Estimation of Strength of Sodium Hydroxide by Sodium Carbonate**: In this estimation both the involved substances are basic in nature. So they cannot be titrated against one another. So one common acid is to be used. Let us consider the determination of strength of N/10 order solution of each of the above reagents. For this purpose following steps are taken:

   (i) **Preparation of standard (N/10) Na_2CO_3 solution**: This solution is prepared as discussed in Art. 2.2.1.1(i).

   (ii) **Preparation of (N/10) H_2SO_4 solution**: For the preparation of this solution procedure depicted in Art. 2.2.1.1(ii) is followed and its strength is determined by the titration against standard $N/10$ Na_2CO_3 solution utilising $S_1V_1 = S_2V_2$ formula.

   (iii) **Preparation of (N/10) NaOH solution**: Procedure discussed in Art. 2.2.1.1(iv) is followed for the preparation of this solution.

   (iv) **Determination of strength of (N/10) NaOH solution**: (N/10) NaOH solution prepared is titrated against (N/10) H_2SO_4 which has been standardised by titrating against standard (N/10) Na_2CO_3 solution and its strength is calculated using $S_1V_1 = S_2V_2$ formula.

2. **Estimation of Borax by Standard Sodium Carbonate**: This estimation is similar to the estimation of sodium hydroxide by sodium carbonate.

In the first stage a standard solution of (N/10) Na_2CO_3 is prepared as usual. Next with this solution a (N/10) H_2SO_4 solution prepared as before is standardised. Finally the supplied borax solution is estimated by titrating it against the standard (N/10) H_2SO_4 solution using methyl orange as indicator and its strength is calculated with the help of $S_1V_1 = S_2V_2$ formula.

3. **Estimation of Sodium Bicarbonate and Carbonate in a Mixture**

Principle: In this estimation pH of the solution at the end-point plays the most vital role. It has been observed that methyl orange is a weak base and in aqueous solution it dissociates as

$$MOH \rightleftharpoons M^+ + OH^-$$

[M = rest of   Cation   Colourless
methyl orange   Reddish
molecule]   orange

When the solution is acidic, the hydrogen ion furnished by the acid combines with the OH^- liberated by the indicator to form unionised water. As a result, equilibrium is shifted to the right producing cation of the indicator which is reddish orange in colour. On the contrary in alkaline condition the dissociation of methyl orange is suppressed and the colour remains yellow. This characteristic of methyl orange suggests that it indicates end-point of titration at acidic range and, in fact, end-point with this indicator is indicated at the pH 4.5. So it is used as indicator in the titration of weak base by a strong acid.

Again, phenolphthalein is a weak acid and in aqueous solution it undergoes dissociation as under:

$$\underset{\text{Colourless}}{\text{Hph}} \underset{\text{Tautomerises}}{\rightleftharpoons} \underset{\text{Colourless}}{\text{Hph}} \rightleftharpoons \overset{+}{H} + \overset{-}{Ph}$$
$$\underset{\text{Pink colour}}{}$$

When the solution is acidic, the hydrogen ions furnished by the indicator suppress the dissociation of phenolphthalein shifting equilibrium to the left and it remains colourless. But in alkaline medium OH^- ion of the base combines with the H^+ liberated by the indicator and forms unionised water and so equilibrium shifts to the right giving more of the coloured anions and so the solution becomes pink in colour. So it can indicate end-point of a reaction in alkaline medium and in actual fact it indicates end-point at the pH 8.5 of the solution. So it is used in the titration of a strong base against an acid.

Na_2CO_3 and $NaHCO_3$ reacts with the acid in the following manner:

$$2Na_2CO_3 + H_2SO_4 \longrightarrow 2NaHCO_3 + Na_2SO_4$$
$$2NaHCO_3 + H_2SO_4 \longrightarrow Na_2SO_4 + 2H_2O + 2CO_2$$

The moment at which Na_2CO_3 is completely converted to $NaHCO_3$, the pH of the solution falls below 8.5. So phenolphthalein, if used as indicator, it cannot indicate any colour, i.e., its colour will disappear. Thus, when the solution of the mixture is titrated by an acid, the titre value corresponds to only half of Na_2CO_3 present in the mixture. But if the solution of the mixture is titrated by the same acid in presence of methyl orange, the pH of the solution at the end-point must be at 4.5, i.e., acidic range. This means more acid has to be added. But in excess of acid $NaHCO_3$ will be neutralised. Thus, in presence of methyl orange, neutralisation of $NaHCO_3$ originally present in the mixture as well as in Na_2CO_3, will be indicated. So titre value of this titration corresponds to total alkali (Na_2CO_3 and $NaHCO_3$).

Procedure: 25 ml of the solution of the mixture is taken in a conical flask and it is titrated with standard H_2SO_4 solution in presence of phenolphthalein as indicator. The experiment is repeated three times and titre values are recorded. Let the average of these titre values be V_1 which corresponds to half of Na_2CO_3. Another 25 ml of the solution is taken in a conical falsk and is titrated against the same acid in presence of methyl orange as indicator. Experiment is repeated as before and let the average titre value become V_2. This value corresponds to total alkali ($Na_2CO_3 + NaHCO_3$).

Calculation: Let us suppose the strength of H_2SO_4 used is S(N). Therefore, total amount of Na_2CO_3 present in 25 ml solution of the mixture is

$2V_1$ ml of S(N) acid.

$= (2V_1 \times S)$ ml (N) Na_2CO_3 solution

$= (2V_1 \times S \times 0.053$ g) of Na_2CO_3

or, $2V_1 \times S \times 0.053 \times 40$ g of Na_2CO_3 in one litre.

N.B. Equivalent weight of Na_2CO_3 is 53. So 1000 ml (N) solution of Na_2CO_3 contains 53 g. Hence, 1 ml of (N) Na_2CO_3 solution $= 0.053$ g of Na_2CO_3.

Now total bicarbonate present in 25 ml solution of the mixture is

$(V_2 - 2V_1)$ ml of S(N) acid

$= [(V_2-2V_1) \times S] \times 0.084$ g of $NaHCO_3$ solution

or, $[(V_2-2V_1) \times S] \times 0.084 \times 40$ g of $NaHCO_3$ in one litre.

N.B. 1 ml of (N) $NaHCO_3 = 0.04$ g of $NaHCO_3$ as the equivalent weight of $NaHCO_3$ is 84.

Comments: This mixture may be estimated by alternative method. In this alternative method, the titration of a requisite quantity of the solution is first carried out with phenolphthalein indicator. The end-point now corresponds to half of Na_2CO_3. Next to the same solution 1-2 drops of methyl orange indicator is added and titration is continued. The end-point indicates the total amount of Na_2CO_3 and $NaHCO_3$. For detailed procedure estimation of mixture of NaOH and Na_2CO_3 may be consulted.

Calculation: Let us assume that the first titre value is V_1 ml and thr second titre value is V_2 ml Therefore, total amount of Na_2CO_3 present is $2V_1$ ml of $S(N)$ acid and total of $NaHCO_3$ is (V_2-2V_1) ml of $S(N)$ acid. Next step of calculation is same as before.

4. Estimation of Caustic Soda and Sodium Carbonate: Principle is the same as in the case of sample 3, above. Both phenolphthalein and methyl orange indicators are utilised.

Procedure: 25 ml solution of the mixture is taken in a conical flask and is titrated with standard H_2SO_4 solution in presence of phenolphthalein as indicator till the pink colour disappears. The experiment is repeated three times and titre values are recorded. Let the average titre value be V_1 ml. At this stage half of Na_2CO_3 and whole of NaOH have been neutralised. Next 1-2 drops of methyl orange be added and the titration is continued till the end-point becomes just reddish orange. Similar experiment is repeated thrice and titre values are recorded. The average titre, V_2 ml corresponds to quantity of acid that is required for the neutralisation of remaining half of Na_2CO_3.

Calculation: Let us suppose the strength of H_2SO_4 is $S(N)$. Therefore, total amount of Na_2CO_3 is $2V_2$. So total amount of Na_2CO_3 present in 25 ml solution of the mixture is

$2V_2 \times S(N)$ acid $= 2V_2 \times S \times 0.053$ g

or, $2V_2 \times S \times 0.053 \times 40$ g per litre.

Now the total amount of NaOH corresponds to (V_1-V_2) ml of $S(N)$ acid.

Therefore, amount of NaOH present in 25 ml solution of the mixture is

$(V_1-V_2) \times S \times 0.04$ g

or, $(V_1-V_2) \times S \times 0.04 \times 40$ g per litre.

N.B. Equivalent weight of NaOH is 40.

5. Estimation of Ammonia in Ammonium Salt: Ammonia in ammonium salt can be estimated primarily by the following methods:

(a) By the use of Formaldehyde

Principle: When a solution of an ammonium salt is allowed to react with formaldehyde, hexamethylene tetramine is formed with the liberation of an acid.

$$NH_4X \quad + \quad 6HCHO \quad \longrightarrow \quad (CH_2)_6N_4 \quad + \quad HX$$

| | Formal-dehyde | | Hexamethylene tetramine | Acid |

From the above reaction it is evident that for each NH_4^+ ion present in the solution one equivalent of acid is liberated. The acid formed is titrated against a standard NaOH solution using phenolphthalein as indicator. It has been observed that 1 ml of (N) NaOH solution = 0.01703 g of ammonia.

Procedure: 25 ml solution of ammonium salt is taken in a conical flask. To it excess of neutral formaldehyde solution is added, till smell of formaldehyde is obtained. The flask with the solution is well shaken and is allowed to stand for at least five minutes. Finally it is titrated with a standard NaOH solution using phenolphthalein as an indicator till just pink colour is produced. The experiment is repeated three times and titre values are recorded. Let us assume that the mean value of titre values is V ml.

Calculation: Let us suppose that the strength of NaOH solution used is S(N).

So 25 ml solution of ammonium salt

$\equiv$ V ml $\times$ S(N) NaOH solution

$\equiv$ V $\times$ S ml(N) NaOH solution.

Hence 25 ml solution of ammonium salt contains $V \times S \times 0.01703$ g of ammonia,
or amount of ammonia present is $V \times S \times 0.01703 \times 40$ g per litre.

Comment: Commercial formaldehyde is usually found to be acidic. So before use it should be made neutral. For this purpose supplied formaldehyde is taken in a beaker and 1-2 drops of phenolphthalein solution be added. To this solution dilute NaOH solution is added drop by drop with stirring until a faint pink colour appears. This ascertains the neutral character of formaldehyde.

(b) Alternative Method of Estimation of Ammonia in Ammonium Salt

Principle: When a solution of an ammonium salt is boiled with an excess of measured volume of NaOH solution of known strength, ammonia is liberated and is quantitatively expelled because of the following reaction:

$$NH_4X \quad + \quad NaOH \quad \longrightarrow \quad NaX + H_2O + NH_3\uparrow$$
$$\text{Ammonium}$$
$$\text{salt}$$

The unconsumed NaOH is titrated against a standard solution of an acid. From this titre value volume of NaOH solution consumed for expulsion of ammonia is determined. It has been observed that 1 ml of (N)NaOH solution consumed $\equiv 0.0703$ g of NH_3.

Procedure: 25 ml of ammonium salt solution is taken in a conical flask. To it measured quantity of standard NaOH solution is added in excess. It is boiled carefully so that no spirting occurs till smell of NH_3 no longer persists. The solution is cooled and to it 1-2 drops of phenolphthalein indicator be added and is titrated with the standard H_2SO_4 solution until the pink colour of the solution just disappears. Same experiment is repeated three times and titre values of acid are recorded. Let the average value of the titre values be V_2 ml acid.

Calculation: Let us assume that the volume of standard NaOH solution added is V_1 ml. The strength of this standard NaOH solution is S_1 (N) and the strength of H_2SO_4 solution is S_2(N). Now V_2 ml of S_2(N) H_2SO_4 = $(V_2 \times S_2)$ ml of (N) H_2SO_4 solution $\equiv (V_2 \times S_2)$ ml of (N) NaOH solution.

Again, V_1 ml of S_1 (N) NaOH solution = $(V_1 \times S_1)$ ml of NaOH.

Therefore, the volume of standard NaOH solution consumed for the quantitative expulsion of NH_3 is $[(V_1 \times S_1) - (V_2 \times S_2)]$ ml. Amount of ammonia present in 25 ml salt solution is

$$[(V_1 \times S_1) - (V_2 \times S_2)] \times 0.01703 \text{ g}$$

or, ammonia present in one litre is

$$[(V_1 \times S_1) - (V_2 \times S_2)] \times 0.01703 \times 40 \text{ g}.$$

2.2.2 Oxidation-Reduction Titration

According to electronic theory removal of electron is oxidation and addition of electron is reduction. Thus, a substance which releases electrons is known as reductant (reducing agent) and the substance which accepts electrons is called oxidant (oxidising agent). In the oxidation-reduction reaction, oxidant is reduced while reductant is oxidised.

$$Fe^{+++} + e \longrightarrow Fe^{++}$$

$$\text{Oxidant} \qquad\qquad\qquad \text{Reductant}$$

It may be mentioned that oxidation-reduction reaction is not independent; oxidation-reduction reaction is an equilibrium reaction, i.e.,

$$2Fe^{+++} + 2e \rightleftharpoons 2Fe^{++}$$

This type of chemical reaction generates an electric cell known as *galvanic cell*. The reaction occurring at one electrode is oxidation, and in other electrode reduction reaction takes place. The potential of these two electrodes are known respectively as oxidation and reduction potentials. For a given electrode these two potentials are exactly equal in magnitude but opposite in sign. These potentials are expressed by the general equation as

$$E_M = E^0 M^{n+} \quad \frac{RT}{n} \quad \ln \quad \frac{a \; \text{Oxidant}}{a \; \text{Reductant}} \qquad \text{[Oxidation potential]}$$

where 'n' is the number of electrons involved in the reaction, 'a' indicates activities or usually concentrations of oxidant and reductant while M is the metal.

The above equation for a mixture of ferric and ferrous iron may be written as

$$E_{Fe} = E_{Fe}{}^{3+} - RT \ln \frac{a \; Fe^{3+}}{a \; Fe^{2+}}, \qquad \text{here } n = 1.$$

From this equation it is evident that the oxidation potential of iron can be changed by changing the concentration of Fe^{3+} and Fe^{2+}. It has been observed that for oxidation-reduction reaction to be complete, the difference of potential between these two electrodes (oxidation and reduction potentials) must be within the range of 0.20-0.40 volts according to the number of electrons involved. Such difference of electrode potentials has been observed in many oxidation-reduction reactions. Consequently, oxidation-reduction reactions are often applied for the quantitative analysis. Some of the important oxidants and reductants are enlisted below:

(a) Oxidant (oxidising agent): $KMnO_4$, $K_2Cr_2O_7$, iodine.

(b) Reductant (reducing agent)

$$Na_2S_2O_3 \text{ (Thiosulphate)}, \quad \begin{matrix} COOH \\ | \\ COOH \end{matrix} \quad \text{(Oxalic acid)}, \quad FeSO_4 \cdot (NH_4)_2SO_4, 6H_2O \text{ (Mohr's salt)}$$

2.2.2.1 Standardisation of Potassium Permanganate Solution

General consideration: Potassium permanganate acts as an oxidising agent because of the fact that in acidic medium it can afford oxygen as is evidenced from the following reaction.

$$2KMnO_4 + 3H_2SO_4 = K_2SO_4 + 2MnSO_4\ 3H_2O + 5[O]$$

Due to this characteristic property, $KMnO_4$ is frequently employed in oxidation-reduction titration. However, although it is a solid chemical, yet it cannot be obtained in perfectly pure form. As a result, it cannot be used as a primary standard. So its approximate standard solution is always standardised by titration with a standard solution of reducing agent. The most commonly used reducing (reductant) agent is oxalic acid. Oxalic acid is a fine crystalline substance and is obtained in perfectly pure form and hence is used as a primary standard [vide Art. 2.2.1.1 (iii)]. Thus, standardisation of potassium permanganate involves the following steps.

(i) Preparation of standard oxalic acid solution

Following the procedure as discussed in Art. 2.2.1.1 (iii), a standard $(N/10)$ oxalic acid solution is prepared by directly weighing 1.575 g of oxalic acid and dissolving it in 250 ml distilled water.

(ii) Preparation of an approximate standard solution of potassium permanganate

In acidic condition manganese in $KMnO_4$ changes its valency from 7 to 2. So change in the oxidation number is $7 - 2 = 5$. Hence in acid medium equivalent weight of $KMnO_4$ is $1/5$ th of its molecular weight [vide Art. 1.5 (c)]. Thus, the equivalent weight of $KMnO_4$ is $\dfrac{158.03}{5} = 31.61$.

Therefore, for the preparation of one litre of $(N/10)$ solution, 3.161 g of $KMnO_4$ is weighed in a rough balance and is transferred to a beaker. It is dissolved in 100 ml distilled water by throughly shaking and the supernatant liquid is transferred to a measuring flask containing 900 ml of distilled water, mouth of the flask is closed by a stopper and is thoroughly shaken to get an approximate $(N/10)$ standard solution of potassium permanganate.

(iii) Standardisation of Potassium permanganate solution by standard oxalic acid solution

Principle: At 70-80 °C temperature, potassium permanganate (oxidant) reacts with oxalic acid (reductant) as written below:

$$2KMnO_4 + 5C_2H_2O_4 + 3H_2SO_4 = 2MnSO_4 + K_2SO_4 + 8H_2O + 10CO_2$$

(Pink   (Oxalic
colour)   acid)

As soon as manganese starts changing its valency pink colour of permanganate gradually changes towards colourless region. The change of colour at the beginning is very slow but becomes fast as soon as there is formation of a small quantity of divalent manganese which acts as the catalyst. In this titration no external indicator is required, potassium permanganate solution acts as *self indicator.*

Procedure: The burette is washed and rinsed with $KMnO_4$ solution prepared and finally it is filled up with $KMnO_4$ solution in the usual way up to the zero mark. 25 ml of $(N/10)$ oxalic acid solution is pipetted out and is transferred to a conical flask of 500 ml capacity. It is diluted with approximately 200 ml of distilled water. To this solution one test tube (20 ml) of 1:2 H_2SO_4 solution is added and the reaction mixture is heated at about 60-70 °C. Potassium permanganate solution is run into this hot solution at first slowly, next rapidly but finally dropwise until a faint pink colour of the mixture persists at least for 30 seconds. Similar experiment is repeated thrice and titre values are recorded. The average of this titre values is taken, let us suppose, it is V_1.

Calculation: Let strength of oxalic acid is $S(N/10)$ and volume of $KMnO_4$ solution required for its oxidation is V_1 ml. So from equation of equivalence,

$$25 \times S(N/10) = V_1 \times S_1, \text{ where } S_1 \text{ is the strength of } KMnO_4 \text{ solution}$$

or, $S_1 = \dfrac{25 \times S}{V_1} (N/10)$.

2.2.2.1.1 Determination of Amount of Ferrous Iron in Mohr's Salt by Titration against Standard $KMnO_4$ Solution

Principle: Mohr's salt is ferrous ammonium sulphate, $FeSO_4, (NH_4)_2 SO_4, 6H_2O$. When it is titrated against a standard $KMnO_4$ solution following chemical reaction is involved.

$$FeSO_4, (NH_4)_2SO_4, 6H_2O \longrightarrow FeSO_4 + (NH_4)_2SO_4, 6H_2O$$

$$2KMnO_4 + 3H_2SO_4 \longrightarrow K_2SO_4 + 2MnSO_4 + 3H_2O + 5[O]$$

$$2FeSO_4 + H_2SO_4 + [O] \longrightarrow Fe_2(SO_4)_3 + H_2O$$

Thus, in this reaction ferrous iron acts as reductant while $KMnO_4$ functions as oxidant. In this titration $KMnO_4$ acts as *self indicator*.

Preparation of Mohr's Salt Solution: About 9.8 g of Mohr's salt is weighed and is taken in a 250 ml measuring flask. It is dissolved in 200 ml dilute H_2SO_4 (N) to prevent the hydrolysis of ferrous sulphate, shaken well and the volume is made up to 250 ml by adding distilled water and shaken again to the make solution homogeneous.

N.B. When the solution of Mohr's salt is supplied, this step is omitted.

Procedure: The burette is rinsed and filled with $KMnO_4$ solution previously standardised by oxalic acid, up to the zero mark. 25 ml of Mohr's salt solution is taken in a 500 ml conical flask and to it 150 ml of (N) H_2SO_4 and 5 ml of syrupy phosphoric acid are added. It is then titrated with $KMnO_4$ solution till the permanent pink colour is developed. The same experiment is repeated three times to get the concordant readings. The average titre value is taken.

Calculation: Let the exact strength of $KMnO_4$ solution be $S(N/10)$ and the average titre value be V_1. Thus, $V_1 \times S(N/10)$ ml of $KMnO_4$ solution is equivalent to 25 ml of Mohr's salt solution. It is known that 1 ml of $KMnO_4$ $(N/10)$ solution is equivalent to 0.005585 g of ferrous iron. Therefore, the amount of ferrous iron present in 25 ml solution of Mohr's salt is

$$V_1 \times S \times 0.005585 \text{ g}$$

or, $V_1 \times S \times 0.005585 \times 40$ g of ferrous iron is present in one litre solution of Mohr's salt.

Comments

(i) Mohr's salt is a solid crystalline substance and can be available in pure state. So it may be used as a primarily standard. In fact, standardisation of $KMnO_4$ has been carried out by titrating $KMnO_4$ solution against a standard Mohr's salt solution. Equivalent weight of Mohr's salt is 392. Hence 9.80 g of Mohr's salt is required for the preparation of 250 ml $(N/10)$ solution of Mohr's salt. So approximately 9.80 g of Mohr's salt is accurately weighed and 250 ml solution of $(N/10)$ order is prepared. With this solution standardisation of $KMnO_4$ solution is carried out following the same procedure as in Art. 2.2.2.1.1.

(ii) Syrupy phosphoric acid is added during the titration because it forms a complex $[Fe(HPO_4)]^+$ which helps in producing sharp colour change.

(iii) Just first appearance of permanent faint pink colour is to be taken as the end-point because pink colour may be deep if slight excess of $KMnO_4$ is present.

(iv) The above procedure is applicable for estimating the amount of ferrous iron in any given solution.

(v) Same procedure may be utilised in estimating the amount of Mohr's salt in a sample. In that case the calculation will be as below:

55.85 g of ferrous iron is present in 392 g of of Mohr's salt. This means 55.85 g of ferrous iron is equivalent to 392 g of Mohr's salt. Hence 0.00585 g of ferrous iron is equivalent to 0.0392 g of Mohr's salt. Therefore, Mohr's salt present in one litre solution is 0.0392 $\times 40 \times S \times V_1$, where S and V_1 are respectively the strength and volume of $KMnO_4$ solution.

2.2.2.1.2 Determination of Ferrous Iron, Ferric Iron and Total Iron (Ferrous and Ferric) in a Sample

Principle: Iron solution containing both ferrous and ferric iron may be estimated by the titration with $KMnO_4$ solution by carrying out experiment in two different steps. In the first following the procedure described in Art. 2.2.2.2 amount of ferrous present in the sample is determined. In the second step aliquot portion of iron solution is treated with the solution of stannous chloride to reduce the ferric iron into ferrous iron according to the equation,

$$2Fe^{3+} + Sn^{2+} \longrightarrow 2Fe^{3+} + Sn^{4+}$$

As a result of reduction, total iron (both ferric and ferrous) is present as ferrous iron. So from the second titre value, total iron may be obtained. The amount of ferric iron is obtained by subtracting the amount of ferrous iron determined in the first step.

Procedure

Step 1: 25 ml of the solution of the sample is pipetted out in a conical flask. If the solution contains HCl, 25 ml of Reinhardt solution is added and the mixture is diluted with distilled water. It is now titrated with standard $KMnO_4$ solution following the procedure described in Art. 2.2.2.2. By using the fact that 1 ml of $(N/10)$ $KMnO_4$ solution is equal to 0.005585 g of ferrous iron, amount of ferrous present in 25 ml and hence in the whole solution of the sample is determined.

Step 2: Once again 25 ml solution of the sample is pipetted out in a conical flask and to it one test tube of conc. HCl is added and the mixture is boiled when the solution turns yellow. To this hot solution, concentrated solution of stannous chloride is added dropwise with constant stirring until the solution becomes practically colourless and finally 2-3 more drops of stannous chloride solution are added to it. The solution is rapidly cooled and to this cold solution about 10 ml solution of mercuric chloride ($HgCl_2$) is added all at a time and is allowed to stand for 5 minutes, when a silky white precipitates appears. Solution is diluted with distilled water. In this way ferric iron is completely converted to ferrous iron. To it one test tube Reinhardt solution is added and is titrated with standard $KMnO_4$ solution. Similar experiment is repeated three times and average titre value is determined. From the titre value total iron (both ferric and ferrous iron) is obtained by using the fact that 1 ml of $(N/10)$ $KMnO_4$ solution is equivalent to 0.005585 g of ferrous iron. Finally total iron in the whole of supplied solution is determined. From this amount of total iron, the amount of ferrous iron determined in step 1 is subtracted to get the amount of ferric iron.

Comments

(i) Reinhardt solution is a mixed solution and contains $MnSO_4$, H_3PO_4 and H_2SO_4. If during titration with $KMnO_4$ chloride anion (Cl^-) is present in the solution, it may be oxidised by permanganate as is indicated by the following reaction:

$$2KMnO_4 + 16HCl = 2KCl + 2MnCl_2 + 5Cl_2 + 8H_2O$$

So it is natural that some more additional permanganate may be consumed than expected. This possibility is avoided by the addition of Reinhardt solution. $MnSO_4$ present in the solution provides excess Mn^{2+} ion and so ratio of $\dfrac{[MnO_4^-]}{[Mn^{2+}]}$ is reduced.

As a result, potential of this redox system

$$E = 1.50 + \frac{0.059}{5} \log \frac{[MnO_4^-]}{Mn^{2+}},$$

is reduced much below 1.36 volts. Hence the possibility of oxidation of Cl^- to Cl_2 becomes nil (E for $\dfrac{MnO_4^-}{Mn^{2+}}$ is 1.50 volts while that of $\dfrac{Cl^-}{Cl_2}$ is 1.40 volts). Again, H_2SO_4 present in this solution is not oxidised by $KMnO_4$. So it can be used as a necessary acid. But phosphoric acid present removes Fe^{3+} ion in the form of colourless complex $[Fe(HPO_4)]^+$ which decreases the redox potential of Fe^{3+}/Fe^{2+} system.

So reducing power of Fe^{2+} is increased. Further this complex helps in determining the sharp end-point.

(ii) Determination of ferric iron directly can be done by following the procedure described in the step 2.

2.2.2.1.3 Determination of Calcium in a Solution by Titration against Standard $KMnO_4$ Solution

Principle: The supplied solution is made acidic with hydrochloric acid, and calcium is precipitated as calcium oxalate by the treatment with oxalic acid or ammonium oxalate under hot condition followed by neutralisation with 1:1 ammonium hydroxide solution. Thus,

$$CaX_2 + \underset{\substack{\text{Oxalate}\\ \text{ion}}}{C_2O_4^{2-}} + H_2O \longrightarrow CaC_2O_4, H_2O + 2X^-$$

Calcium is quantitatively precipitated at the pH 4. Now this calcium oxalate just precipitated is treated with dilute sulphuric acid when oxalic acid is liberated quantitatively which is titrated against a standard $KMnO_4$ solution.

$$CaC_2O_4 + H_2SO_4 = CaSO_4 + \underset{\text{Oxalic acid}}{H_2C_2O_4} \tag{1}$$

$$2KMnO_4 + 3H_2SO_4 + 5H_2C_2O_4 = K_2SO_4 + 2MnSO_4 + 10CO_2 + 8H_2O \tag{2}$$

From equation (1), it is seen that from 1 mole of Ca-oxalate 1 mole of oxalic acid is liberated. Again, from equation (2), it is seen that $\frac{1}{5}$ th mole of $KMnO_4$ is equivalent to ½ mol of oxalic acid.

So from equations (1) and (2) it may be written that $\frac{1}{5}$ th mol of $KMnO_4$ = ½ Ca-oxalate.

Now we know that the equivalent weight of $KMnO_4$ is $\frac{1}{5}$ of its molecular weight. Thus, it may be concluded that 1000 ml (N) $KMnO_4$ solution can oxidise ½ molecular weight of oxalic acid which in turn is obtained from ½ molecular weight of Ca-oxalate. Hence, 1000 ml (N) $KMnO_4$ solution is equivalent to ½ of atomic wt. of calcium, i.e., 20 g.

$$\text{or, 1 ml of (N) } KMNO_4 \equiv \frac{20}{1000} = 0.02 \text{ g of calcium.}$$

Procedure: The supplied solution is transferred to a 500 ml beaker quantitatively. To it a drop of methyl orange is added and is made just alkaline with dropwise addition of NH_4OH solution. To this solution 5 ml conc. HCl is added dropwise until the colour of the solution appears faintly pink. The solution is boiled and a solution of ammonium oxalate in hot water is added slowly with constant stirring. Finally the solution is neutralised by adding (1:1) NH_4OH till smell of NH_3 is obtained. The solution is allowed to stand for half an hour when white precipitate of Ca-oxalate settles down.

The precipitate is filtered quantitatively by using quantitative filter paper taking usual precautions. The precipitate along with the filter paper is washed with water to make it free from oxalate and chloride ions. A beaker (500 ml) is placed below the funnel in which Ca-oxalate was filtered. The filter paper is pierced by a glass rod and the precipitate is washed down quantitatively to the beaker by spraying hot water. It is then acidified with dilute H_2SO_4 in such a way that Ca-oxalate is completely dissolved forming a clear solution. It is then titrated with standard $KMnO_4$ solution until the colour of the solution becomes just pink. Volume of $KMnO_4$ required is noted and amount of calcium present is calculated.

Calculation: Let the volume of $KMnO_4$ solution required be V and its strength is $S(N)$. Thus, amount of calcium present is $V \times S \times 0.02$ g.

2.2.2.1.4 Determination of Calcium in Limestone

Principle: The principle of determination of calcium in limestone is the same as discussed in Art. 2.2.2.4.

Procedure: About 1.2 g of limestone is accurately weighed and is taken in a 500 ml beaker. 10 ml of water is added to it and is covered with a watch glass. 10 ml of conc. HCl is slowly added to it in portion through the side of the beaker. When the effervescence is completely ceased, the solution is heated in a water bath for a few minutes. The solution is diluted to 50 ml and nearly 2 g of NH_4Cl is added and the reaction mixture is heated nearly to boiling. The solution is made just alkaline by adding (1:1) NH_4OH solution in presence of 2-3 drops of methyl orange. The solution is boiled again for 2-3 minutes and is filtered into a 250 ml measuring flask. The residue is first washed several times with hot water and next with hot 2% NH_4NO_3 solution. All the washings are collected into the measuring flask. The measuring flask and the solution are cooled and a few ml of conc. HCl is added and the volume is made up to the mark by distilled water. Thus, 250 ml solution of lime is obtained.

25 ml of this solution is now pipetted out into a 500 ml beaker and the procedure described in Art. 2.2.2.1.3 is followed.

Calculation: Let V ml is the volume of $KMnO_4$ solution required and its strength is $S(N)$. Thus, amount of calcium present in 25 ml of the solution prepared is $V \times S \times 0.02$ g.

Amount present in total solution (250 ml) is $V \times S \times 0.02 \times 10$ g.

Hence percentage of calcium in limestone is $\dfrac{V \times S \times 0.02 \times 10}{w} \times 100$,

where w is the weight of limestone taken.

2.2.2.1.5 Estimation of Manganese Dioxide and Available Oxygen in Pyrolusite

Principle: Pyrolusite is an ore of manganese. Manganese is present in this ore as manganese dioxide, MnO_2. MnO_2 is a strong oxidising agent and can oxidise oxalic acid quantitatively. The reaction taking place in this process is

$$2MnO_2 + 2H_2SO_4 = 2MnSO_4 + 2H_2O + O_2 \tag{1}$$

$$2H_2C_2O_4 + O_2 = 4CO_2 + 2H_2O \tag{2}$$

Oxalic acid

The oxygen liberated in the step (1) oxidises the reducing agent like oxalic acid. Thus, if an weighed quantity of pure pyrolusite is titrated against a standard solution of oxalic acid in presence of dilute sulphuric acid, amount of Mn present can be quantitatively determined. It has been observed that.

$$1 \text{ ml (N) oxalic acid} = 0.04346 \text{ g of } MnO_2 \tag{3}$$

$$\text{or } 1 \text{ ml of (N/10) oxalic acid} = 0.004346 \text{ g of } MnO_2 \tag{4}$$

Again, from equation (1) it is evident that two moles of MnO_2 produce one mole of oxygen (O_2), i.e. one mole of MnO_2 forms half mole of oxygen (O)

or, 86.93 g of MnO_2 generates 16 g of oxygen

From equation (3) it may be written as 0.04346 g of MnO_2 gives $\dfrac{16}{86.93} \times 0.04346$ g of O_2

or, 1 ml of (N/10) oxalic acid $\equiv \dfrac{16}{86.93} \times 0.04346$ g of available oxygen.

Procedure: About 0.1-0.2 g of pure, finely powdered and dry pyrolusite is accurately weighed into a 500 ml conical flask. To it accurately measured 50 ml of (N/10) oxalic acid and 50 ml of 4(N) H_2SO_4 are added and the mouth of the flask is covered with a short stemmed funnel. The reaction mixture is boiled gently by placing the conical flask on an asbestos sheet and the boiling is continued until not a single black particle is left. The flask is diluted with distilled water and the excess of oxalic acid is back titrated with a standard (N/10) $KMnO_4$ solution under hot condition in the usual way. The titre value is noted. From this titre value, amount of MnO_2 and quantity of available oxygen are calculated.

Calculation: Let the volume of $KMnO_4$ solution required for blank titration of 50 ml of (N/10) oxalic acid added initially be V_1 ml and its strength be $S(N/10)$. The volume of $S_1(N/10)$ $KMnO_4$ required for back titration be V_2 ml. Thus, volume of oxalic acid consumed in terms of $S_1(N/10)$ $KMnO_4$ is $(V_1 - V_2) \times S_1 (N/10)$ ml.

So the quantity of MnO_2 present in w g of pyrolusite (where w is the weight in gram of the pyrolusite taken) is $(V_1-V_2) \times S_1 \times 0.04346$ g of MnO_2

or, percent of $MnO_2 = \dfrac{\left(50 - V_1 \times \dfrac{S_2}{S_1}\right) \times S_2 \times 0.004346}{w} \times 100\%$.

Quantity of Available Oxygen

Quantity of available oxygen present in w g of pyrolusite is

$$\left(50 - V_1 \times \frac{S_2}{S_1}\right) \times S_2 \times \frac{16}{86.93} \times 0.004346$$

So the percent of available oxygen is $= \dfrac{\left(50 - V_1 \times \dfrac{S_2}{S_1}\right) \times S_2 \times 16 \times 0.004346}{86.93 \times w} \times 100\%$

2.2.2.1.6 Determination of Manganese in Steel

Principle: When a specimen of steel is dissolved in sulphuric acid, manganese present is converted to divalent salt. This divalent manganese salt solution on oxidation with sodium bismuthate is converted to pink permanganic acid. Now this permanganic acid is estimated by titration against a standard oxalic acid solution. Thus,

$$Mn + H_2SO_4 = MnSO_4 + H_2\uparrow$$

$$2Mn^{2+} + 5BiO_3^- + 14H^+ = 2MnO_4^- + 5Bi^{3+} + 7H_2O$$

$$2MnO_4^- + 5H_2C_2O_4 + 3H_2SO_4 = 2MnSO_4 + 8H_2O + 10CO_2 + SO_4^{2-}$$

1 ml of $(N/10)$ MnO_4^- solution formed is equivalent to 0.001099 g of Mn.

Procedure: Approximately 0.1 g of steel is accurately weighed in a 500 ml conical flask. To it 30 ml 1:1 H_2SO_4 is added and boiled for 5-10 minutes. Approximately 0.1 g of solid sodium bismuthate is added to the hot solution and boiled again for a few minutes until pink colour of permanganate along with a little precipitate of MnO_2 appears. To this solution 10% $NaHSO_3$ solution is added dropwise till the precipitate of MnO_2 completely dissolves and pink colour disappears. The solution boiled to remove excess of SO_2, cooled again, 2 g of sodium bismuthate $(NaBiO_3)$ is added and the reaction mixture is stirred for a few minutes. The solution is filtered through sintered crucible fitted with a Buchner flask, washed with dilute H_2SO_4 and collected in a 500 ml conical flask. Excess of standard oxalic acid is added when pink colour of the solution disappears. Excess of oxalic acid is back titrated against a standard $KMnO_4$ solution and titre value is noted.

Calculation: Let V_1 be the volume of $S_1(N/10)$ oxalic added initially and V_2 be the volume of $S_2(N/10)$ $KMnO_4$ solution required for back titration of excess oxalic acid. The amount of steel taken is w g.

Let us assume that volume of $S_2(N/10)$ $KMnO_4$ solution required for the blank titration of V_1 ml of of S_1 $(N/10)$ oxalic acid is V_3.

Thus, volume of permanganic acid formed from w g of steel is equivalent to (V_3-V_2) ml of $S_2(N/10)$ $KMnO_4 = (V_3-V_2) \times S_2$ ml of $(N/10)$ $KMnO_4$.

1 ml of $(N/10)$ $KMnO_4 = 0.001099$ g of Mn.

(**N.B.** Equivalent weight of Manganese is $\dfrac{55}{5} = 11$.)

Therefore, total amount of Mn present in w g of steel is $(V_3-V_2) \times S_2 \times 0.001099$ g.

Hence, percent of Mn in steel (supplied) is

$$\frac{(V_3-V_2) \times S_2 \times 0.001099}{w} \times 100\%.$$

2.2.2.2 Oxidation-Reduction Titration using Potassium Dichromate

Principle: Like potassium permanganate, potassium dichromate is an important oxidant and is frequently used in oxidation-reduction titration. However, it is a weaker oxidising agent than potassium permanganate as is indicated from its standard reduction potential, $E_0 = 1.34V$ (E_0 of $KMnO_4$ is 1.50V). But it has several advantages over potassium permanganate such as (i) It is obtained in sufficiently analytically pure form and is a stable molecule, so it can be used as a primary standard. (ii) In aqueous solution it reamins unaltered for a long time. (iii) Although it is readily reduced in acid solution in cold condition but remains unaffected by dilute hydrochloric

acid under the same condition. This is because its reduction potential is much below that of $\dfrac{Cl^-}{Cl_2}$

system. So during titration with dichromate, chlorine, if present, will not interfere. (iv) It is very much useful for the determination of iron present in any sample as it readily oxidises ferrous iron to ferric iron.

In acidic condition dichromate undergoes the following reactions:

$$K_2Cr_2O_7 + 4H_2SO_4 \longrightarrow K_2SO_4 + Cr_2(SO_4)_3 + 4H_2 + 3[O]$$

$$\text{i.e.,} \quad \overset{(+12)}{Cr_2}O_7^{2-} + 14H^+ + 6e \rightleftharpoons 2\overset{(+6)}{Cr}^{3+} + 7H_2O$$

Thus, the change of oxidation number is $(12 - 6) = 6$. Hence, its equivalent weight in acid medium is $\frac{1}{6}$th of its molecular weight, i.e., $\dfrac{294.2}{6} = 49.03$.

2.2.2.2.1 Preparation of Standard Solution of Potassium Dichromate

Approximately 1.2257 g of pure crystalline potassium dichromate is accurately weighed into a 250 ml measuring flask and is dissolved in 250 ml distilled water following the usual procedure.

If w g be the weight of dichromate actually taken, then the solution obtained is $\dfrac{w}{1.2257}$ $(N/10)$ potassium dichromate.

2.2.2.2.2 Determination of Total Amount of Ferrous Iron in a Given Solution

Procedure: The given solution is transferred quantitatively to a 250 ml measuring flask. The container is washed 2-4 times with dilute H_2SO_4 and the washings are taken in the measuring flask. The measuring flask is approximately filled up to the mark by the same dilute sulphuric acid. Finally the volume is made up to the mark by adding distilled water. The flask is thoroughly shaken to make it uniform. This becomes the stock solution of ferrous iron.

In a 500 ml conical flask 150 ml water is taken and to it very cautiously 10 ml concentrated H_2SO_4 and 5 ml of syrupy phosphoric are added, cooled and to it 25 ml of stock solution is added through a pipette. To this mixture, 4-5 drops of barium diphenylamine sulphonate solution are added which acts as the indicator. Now this solution is titrated with standard ($N/10$) potassium dichromate solution with constantly rotating the conical flask till the colour of the solution becomes green. Next the dichromate solution is added dropwise until the whole solution becomes bluish violet by the addition of just a drop of dichromate. This is the end-point. Burette reading is noted by deducting 0.05 ml (one drop) which is used up by the indicator. Similar experiment is repeated thrice and the average reading is noted for calculation of the amount of ferrous iron.

Calculation: Let 25 ml of ferrous iron solution require V ml of $S(N/10)$ dichromate solution for its oxidation.

$\therefore$ 25 ml of solution contains $V \times S \times 0.0056$ g of ferrous iron.

Hence the total amount of ferrous iron present in the whole of the supplied solution is

$V \times S \times 0.0056 \times 10$ g

[1 ml of ($N/10$) $K_2Cr_2O_7$ solution = 0.0056 g of Fe]

Comments

   (i) In this reaction ferrous iron is oxidised by dichromate to ferric iron as indicated by the following equation.

$$K_2Cr_2O_7 + 6FeSO_4 + 7H_2SO_4 = 3Fe_2(SO_4)_3 + Cr_2(SO_4)_3 + K_2SO_4 + 7H_2O$$

      In this oxidation-reduction reaction, the redox potential of Fe^{3+}/Fe^{2+} is 0.77 volt but that of indicator is slightly below this value. So in order to get the accurate result redox potential of Fe^{3+}/Fe^{2+} must be reduced below 0.77 volt so that potential at the end-point of Fe^{3+}/Fe^{2+} system coincides approximately with that of indicator. For this purpose phosphoric acid is added which removes Fe^{3+} ion by forming a colourless complex $[Fe(HPO_4)]^+$. As a result, redox potential is reduced and sharp end-point is obtained.

  (ii) Once the end-point is determined, indicator should be added at the middle of titration during repetition of the experiment. This helps in getting the accurate result.

2.2.2.2.3 Estimation of Ferrous, Ferric Iron and Total Iron (Fe^{3+} + Fe^{2+}) in a Sample

Principle: The analysis of this mixture consists of two steps. In step I, ferrous iron is estimated according to the process described in Art. 2.2.2.2.2 while in step 2 ferric iron is reduced to ferrous iron by using stannous chloride as reductant as shown below:

$$2Fe^{3+} + Sn^{2+} \rightleftharpoons 2Fe^{2+} + Sn^{4+}$$

Now the iron content of the solution is totally ferrous iron. This is estimated as usual. From step 2 total iron (Ferric + Ferrous) is obtained and from this value total ferrous iron obtained from the step 1 is deducted to get the total ferric iron present in the sample.

Procedure

Step 1 (Estimation of Ferrous Iron): The procedure described in Art.2.2.2.2.2 is followed. This gives total ferrous present in the sample.

Step 2 (Estimation of Total Ferric and Ferrous Iron): 25 ml of the supplied solution is pipetted out into a 500 ml conical flask. 20 ml of concentrated HCl is added to it and boiled. The hot solution is reduced by adding stannous chroride solution dropwise with constant stirring until the solution becomes practically colourless. Finally 2-3 more drops of stannous chloride solution are added and the solution is rapidly cooled. To this cold solution about 10 ml $HgCl_2$ solution is added all at a time and is allowed to stand for 5 minutes until a silky white precipitate appears. Solution is diluted and to it about 25 ml of mixture of conc. H_2SO_4 and syrupy phosphoric acid is added. This solution is now titrated with a strandard $(N/10)$ dichromate solution using diphenylamine sulphonate as indicator in the usual way. Similar experiment is repeated three times and each time burette reading is noted. Let the average titre value is V ml.

Calculation: Let the strength of dichromate solution be $S(N/10)$.

So the total amount of iron (ferric + ferrous) present in 25 ml solution is

$$V_1 \times S \times 0.0056 \text{ g} \tag{1}$$

Let the volume of dichromate required in step 1 is V, So total amount of ferrous present in 25 ml solution of the sample is

$$V \times S \times 0.0056 \text{ g} \tag{2}$$

Thus, amount of ferric iron present in 25 ml solution is

$$(V_1 \times S \times 0.0056 - V \times S \times 0056) \text{ g} \tag{3}$$

Thus,

(i) total iron (ferrous + ferric) present per litre is

$$V_1 \times S \times 0.0056 \times 40 \text{ g} \tag{4}$$

(ii) total ferric iron present per litre is

$$(V_1 \times S \times 0.0056 - V \times S \times 0.0056) \times 40 \text{ g}$$

(iii) total ferrous iron present per litre is

$$(V \times S \times 0.0056 \times 40) \text{ g}.$$

2.2.2.2.4 Standardisation of Mohr's Salt Solution by a Standard Dichromate Solution

Principle: Mohr's salt, $FeSO_4$, $(NH_4)_2SO_4$, $6H_2O$ contains ferrous iron. So a solution of Mohr's salt can be standardised by titration against a standard solution of dichromate in the usual way.

Procedure: 25 ml solution of Mohr's salt solution supplied is pipetted out in a 500 ml conical flask in which 150 ml of distilled water and a mixture of 10 ml concentrated H_2SO_4 and 5 ml syrupy phosphoric acid were previously taken (vide Art. 2.2.2.2.2). It is now titrated with standard $(N/10)$ potassium dichromate solution in presence of 4-5 drops of barium diphenyl amine sulphonate solution as indicator following the procedure described in Art. 2.2.2.2.2. The strength of Mohr's salt is determined with the help of the formula, $V_1 S_1 = V_2 S_2$. Thus, we may proceed as under:

Let S_1 be the strength of $(N/10)$ $K_2Cr_2O_7$ solution and V_1 be its volume required to oxidise ferrous iron in 25 ml of Mohr's salt solution. If S_2 is the strength of Mohr's salt solution, then

$$25 \times S_2 = S_1 V_1$$

$$\text{or, } S_2 = \frac{S_1 V_1}{25} \ (N/10).$$

2.2.2.2.5 Standardisation of Sodium Thiosulphate Solution by a Standard Dichromate Solution

Principle: In acid solution, potassium dichromate can be quantitatively reduced to trivalent chromium by potassium iodide according to the following reaction and an equivalent amount of iodine is liberated.

$$K_2Cr_2O_7 + 6KI + 14HCl = 2CrCl_3 + 8KCl + 3I_2 + 7H_2O$$

(Green)

The liberated iodine is titrated with a thiosulphate solution of unknown strength. Now knowing the strength of $K_2Cr_2O_7$ solution, strength of thiosulphate solution can be determined utilising the formula, $V_1 S_1 = V_2 S_2$.

Procedure: 25 ml of standard $(N/10)K_2Cr_2O_7$ solution is pipetted out into a 560 ml conical flask. To this 100 ml of distilled water is added and shaken well to make the solution uniform. To this solution 5 ml of pure and concentrated HCl is added and once again shaken well. To it 3 g of KI and 2 g of sodium bicarbonate dissolved in 15 ml of distilled water are added and the solution is swirled vigorously. The liquid mixture becomes dark red due to the liberation of iodine. The mouth of the conical flask is covered with a watch-glass and is kept in dark for at least 5 minutes. The watch-glass and the side of the flask are rinsed with distilled water. The solution is diluted to 250 ml and the liberated iodine is titrated with the thiosulphate solution prepared taken in the burette with constant shaking of the flask vigorously. When the liquid turns yellowish, 2 ml of freshly prepared starch solution is added. The inside of the concial flask is washed again with little water and thiosulphate solution is added drop by drop till the colour of the solution changes from greenish blue to light green. The end-point becomes prominent in white background. Burette reading is noted. Similar titration is repeated at least thrice, and mean value of the volume of thiosulphate required is determined.

Calculation: Let the strength of $(N/10)$ $K_2Cr_2O_7$ is S_1 and the volume of thiosulphate required is V ml. Thus,

$$25 \times S_1 = V \times S \text{ where (S) is the strength of thiosulphate solution.}$$

i.e., $S = \dfrac{25 \times S_1}{V}$ $(N/10)$ thiosulphate.

Comment

(i) Reduction of dichromate to trivalent chromium requires some time for its completion. During this period free hydroiodic acid that may be formed from excess of potassium iodide may be oxidised by the air particularly in presence of chromic salt. Hence to prevent the probabale oxidation of hydroiodic acid formed sodium bicarbonate is added and the solution is kept in the dark for a few minutes. Sodium bicarbonate creates a reducing atmosphere by generating CO_2 and in the dark probability of air oxidiation is greatly reduced.

(ii) Sodium thiosulphate pentahydrate, $Na_2S_2O_3, 5H_2O$ may be obtained in pure state but due to its efflorescent character, its exact water content is not known with certainty and so it cannot be used as a primary standard. It reacts with iodine according to the following equation:

$$2Na_2S_2O_3 + I_2 = Na_2S_4O_6 + 2NaI$$

So its molecular weight becomes its equivalent weight ($Na_2S_2O_3, 5H_2O$). So 6.2 g of it is dissolved in 250 ml water to get an approximately ($N/10$) solution and its exact strength is determined subsequently.

2.2.3 Iodometry and Iodimetry

In fact, both iodometric, and iodimetric titrations are oxidation-reduction titrations. They have been classified as a separate group for convenience only.

Iodometry deals with the estimation of iodine liberated in chemical reactions by a standard solution of a reducing agent whereas iodimetry involves the titration of a reducing agent with a standard solution of iodine which acts as an oxidising agent. In both these analyses, reaction of iodine with thiosulphate is the basis of titration.

$$I_2 \quad + \quad 2Na_2S_2O_3 = 2NaI \quad + \quad Na_2S_4O_6$$
$$\text{Thiosulphate} \qquad\qquad\qquad \text{Tetrathionate}$$

Powerful oxidising agents like permanganate, dichromate, hydrogen peroxide, etc. oxidise iodide quantitatively to iodine. Again, iodine being a more powerful oxidising agent than thiosulphate can oxidise the latter to tetrathionate. Both these titrations are carried out in acid medium. Thus when the strength of thiosulphate is determined by using the reaction between a strong oxidising agent and iodide in acid medium it is a case of iodometry. Because in such reaction iodine is liberated as is indicated by the following reaction which is titrated by thiosulphate solution.

$$K_2Cr_2O_7 + 6KI + 14HCl = 2CrCl_3 + 8KCl + 3I_2 + 7H_2O$$

But when a solution of iodine is directly used as one of the titrants the process involved is iodimetry.

2.2.3.1 Iodometric Titrations

Two most extremely common examples of iodometric titrations are (i) standardisation of a thiosulphate solution by a standard solution of dichromate and (ii) estimation of copper in a cupric salt solution.

2.2.3.1.1 Standardisation of Thiosulphate Solution by a Standard Dichromate Solution (vide Art. 2.2.2.2.5)

2.2.3.1.2 Estimation of Copper in a Given Solution

Principle: When a cupric salt solution is treated with an excess amount of potassium iodide, iodine is quantitatively liberated and cuprous iodide is precipitated according to the following reaction:

$$2Cu^{++} + 4\bar{I} = Cu_2I_2\downarrow + I_2$$

Cupric salt		Cuprous	Iodine
		iodide	

This liberated iodine is now titrated with a standard sodium thiosulphate solution. Equivalent weight of copper in this reaction is its atomic weight, i.e., 63.54. From the above reaction it is seen that one atom of copper liberates one atom of iodine.

Hence, 1 ml of $(N/10)$ $Na_2S_2O_3$ solution $\equiv 0.006354$ g of copper.

Procedure: 25 ml of copper solution supplied is pipetted out in a 500 ml conical flask. The solution is heated to boiling and to it 1 g of urea is added and boiled again for 5 minutes to remove completely nitrous acid and oxides of nitrogen, if present. The solution is cooled and is made alkaline by the addition of dilute ammonium hydroxide slowly till the permanent turbidity appears. Next 5 ml or a little more of glacial acetic acid is added when the turbidity completely disappears. The solution is cooled under tap and 2 g of potassium iodide in 20 ml water is added. The solution is rigorously shaken and the mouth of the conical flask is covered with a watch-glass. The reaction mixture is allowed to stand for a minute when a precipitate appears and the solution turns dark brown. The liberated iodine is titrated with a standard solution of thiosulphate in presence of 2 ml of freshly prepared starch solution and 1 or 2 drops of $(N/10)$ $AgNO_3$ till the blue colour begins to fade. Now one test tube of 2% ammonium thiocyanate is added and titration is continued till the colour changes to white.

Burette reading is noted and the experiment is repeated two to three times taking each time 25 ml of copper solution. Average value of burette readings is calculated.

Calculation: Let the strength of thiosulphate is $S(N/10)$ and the volume of thiosulphate required for final titration is V.

$\therefore$ 25 ml of copper solution = $S \times V$ ml of $(N/10)$ thiosulphate solution.

Thus, 25 ml of copper solution contains $S \times V \times 0.006354$ g of copper.

Hence the amount of copper per litre is $S \times V \times 0.006354 \times 40$ g.

Comments

(i) Presence of oxides of nitrogen interferes and for their removal, solution is boiled with urea.

(ii) Cu_2I_2 formed may absorb some iodine. Ammonium thiocyanate reacts with Cu_2I_2 forming $Cu_2(SCN)_2$ and so adsorbed iodine is removed.

(iii) In presence of $AgNO_3$ solution end-point becomes very sharp.

(iv) Glacial acetic acid is used to remove free mineral acid. In general copper salt solution contains traces of free mineral acid which may liberate iodine from KI giving an erroneous results.

2.2.3.1.3 Estimation of Copper in Brass

Brass is an alloy of copper and zinc which contains more than 64% of copper. Copper present in it is usually estimated by adapting following procedure.

About 1.50 g of brass is accurately weighed in a 500 ml beaker. 5 ml water and 10 ml of concentrated HNO_3 are added one after another down the sides of the flask. The mouth of the beaker is covered with a watch-glass and allowed to stand till the alloy is dissolved. The solution is diluted with 25 ml water and is boiled again for a few minutes with 1 g of urea to remove oxides of nitrogen present, if any. The solution is cooled and is transferred quantitatively to a 250 ml measuring flask and the volume is made up to the mark by the addition of water.

25 ml of this solution is pipetted into a 250 ml conical flask, diluted to 50 ml and neutralised by the addition of (1:1) NH_4OH solution drop by drop. Excess of ammonia is removed by boiling and cooled. To the cold solution 2 g of NH_4HF_2 is added and the conical flask is shaken well so that NH_4HF_2 dissolves completely. Next 2 g of KI dissolved in 20 ml of water is added to the solution. The liberated iodine is now titrated with a standard thiosulphate solution. Titre value is recorded. The experiment is repeated three times and average titre value is taken.

Calculations: Let the weight of brass taken be w g and 25 ml solution requires V ml of $S(N/10)$ thiosulphate solution.

Thus, 25 ml solution contains $V \times S \times 0.006354$ g of copper.

or, 250 ml solution contains $V \times S \times 0.006354 \times 10$ g.

Hence, percentage of copper in brass is $\dfrac{V \times S \times 0.006354}{w} \times 10 \times 100$.

Comments

   (i) NH_4OH is added to remove ferric ion as $Fe(OH)_3$, if present.

   (ii) NH_4HF_2 is added to prevent the interference of Fe^{3+} by forming a complex. It also helps as a buffer to maintain the pH at 3 so that the oxidation of iodide by interfering ions, As(V) and Sb(V) is prevented.

   (iii) Nitritre is decomposed by urea.

2.2.3.1.4 Estimation of Copper in Copper Wire

Approximately 1 g of copper wire is accurately weighed into a 500 ml beaker and following the procedure described above (vide Art. 2.2.3.1.3) solution is prepared. 25 ml of the stock solution is pipetted out in a 250 ml conical flask and once again following the procedure discussed in Art. 2.2.3.1.3 titration is carried out by adding glacial acetic acid instead of NH_4HF_2. Calculation is similar to previous method.

2.2.3.1.5 Determination of Chromium in Chromic Salt Solution

Principle: Chromium in chromic salt is present in trivalent state. It is estimated by oxidising Cr^{3+} quantitatively to Cr^{7+} by Na_2O_2 when Na_2CrO_4 is formed. This Na_2CrO_4, when acidified, is converted quantitatively to $Na_2Cr_2O_7$, which is estimated iodometrically following the usual procedure. Thus,

$$Na_2O_2 + H_2O = H_2O_2 + 2NaOH$$
$$2CrX_3 + 3H_2O_2 + 10NaOH = 2Na_2CrO_4 + 6NaX + 8H_2O$$
$$2Na_2CrO_4 + H_2SO_4 = Na_2Cr_2O_7 + Na_2SO_4 + H_2O$$
$$Na_2Cr_2O_7 + 7H_2SO_4 + 6KI = Cr_2(SO_4)_3 + 3I_2 + 7H_2O + Na_2SO_4 + 3K_2SO_4$$
$$I_2 + 2Na_2S_2O_3 = Na_2S_4O_6 + 2NaI$$

Procedure: 25 ml of supplied chromic salt solution is pipetted out into a 500 ml conical flask and is neutralised by adding solid $NaHCO_3$ in small portion at a time with shaking until effervescence is ceased. 1 g of Na_2O_2 is added to the solution in small portion at a time with stirring. The colour of the solution turns yellow. This yellow solution is diluted to 100 ml. The mouth of the flask is covered with a watch-glass and the solution is boiled with 25 ml of 25% $KHSO_4$ solution to decompose the excess of Na_2O_2 and is ultimately removed completely.

The solution is cooled and 10 ml of 1:1 H_2SO_4 is added to the solution and cooled again. To this cold solution 3 g of KI dissolved in 15 ml of distilled water is added and the solution is shaken vigorously. The solution becomes dark-red due to the liberation of iodine. The mouth of the conical flask is covered with a watch-glass and is kept in dark for 5 minutes. The watch-glass and the side of the flask are rinsed with distilled water and the solution is diluted to 250 ml and the liberated iodine is titrated with a standard thiosulphate solution with constant shaking of the flask. When the solution becomes yellowish, 2 ml of freshly prepared starch solution is added when the solution turns blue. Thiosulphate solution is now added drop by drop till the colour of the solution changes to light green. Titre value is noted. Experiment is repeated thrice and average titre value is determined.

Calculation: Let the strength of thiosulphate solution is $S(N/10)$ and its volume required to reduce iodine liberated be V. Thus,

25 ml of chromic salt solution $\equiv (V \times S)$ ml of $N/10$ thosulphate solution.

$$\equiv (V \times S) \text{ ml of } (N/10) \text{ chromium solution}$$

Thus, amount of chromium present 25 ml chromic salt solution is

$$V \times S \times 0.001734 \text{ g.}$$

or, $V \times S \times 0.001734 \times 40$ g of chromium is present per litre.

N.B. Equivalent weight of chromium is $\frac{1}{3}$rd of **its atomic weight, 52.01.**

2.2.3.1.6 Estimation of Barium in a Salt Solution

Principle: Barium salt solution when treated with a solution of chromate (sodium or potassium chromate) forms aqueous insoluble yellow precipitate of barium chromate. This reaction has been found to be quantitative and again on treatment of this barium chromate with acid quantitative amount of dichromate is formed. The amount of dichromate is estimated iodometrically by titration with a standard thiosulphate solution following usual procedure. Thus,

$$BaX_2 + K_2CrO_4 = BaCrO_4\downarrow + 2KX$$

Ba-Salt

$$2BaCrO_4 + 4HCl = H_2Cr_2O_7 + H_2O + 2BaCl_2$$

$$H_2Cr_2O_7 + 6KI + 14HCl = 2CrCl_3 + 3I_2 + 7H_2O + 6KCl + 2HCl$$

$$I_2 + 2Na_2S_2O_3 = Na_2S_4O_6 + 2NaI$$

Procedure: 25 ml of barium salt solution is pipetted out into a 500 ml beaker. It is made just alkaline by adding dilute NH_4OH solution until smells of ammonia is obtained. The solution is made just acidic by dropwise addition of dilute HCl using methyl orange indicator, and 2 g of ammonium acetate dissolved in little water is added to the solution. The mixture is heated nearly to boiling and a 10% solution of K_2CrO_4 is added dropwise with constant stirring until the solution becomes faint yellow in colour. It is allowed to stand for 5 minutes when the precipitate of $BaCrO_4$ settles down. The precipitate is filtered through *Whatman* NO 40 *filter paper*, washed with hot water several times until free from chromate as indicated by the test of filtrate with $AgNO_3$ solution (chocolate colour or precipitate indicates chromate).

Treatment of the Precipitate

The funnel containing the precipitate of $BaCrO_4$ on the filter paper is placed on the mouth of a 250 ml conical flask and is dissolved in 100 ml of dilute HCl (1:1). The filter paper is washed several times with distilled water till the filter paper becomes colourless.

3 g of KI dissolved in 15 ml water is added to the solution of barium chromate in the conical flask and the solution is shaken vigorously. The solution turns dark-red due to liberation of iodine. The mouth of the conical flask is covered by a watch-glass and is kept in the dark for 5 minutes. Watch-galss and the side of the conical flask are rinsed with distilled water and the solution is titrated with a standard thiosulphate solution until the solution becomes straw-yellow in colour. Now 2 ml of freshly prepared starch solution is added when the solution turns blue. The thiosulphate solution is now added dropwise until the blue colour disappears and a light green colour appears. Burette reading is noted. The whole experiment may be repeated.

Calculations

Let the strength and volume of thiosulphate required for final titration are $S(N/10)$ and V ml respectively.

$\therefore$ 25 ml of Ba-Salt solution $\equiv V \times S$ ml of $(N/10)$ thiosulphate solution.

1 ml of $(N/10)$ thiosulphate solution = 0.004548 g of Ba.

Hence amount of barium in 25 ml of barium salt solution is $V \times S \times 0.004548$ g

or, amount of barium present per litre is $V \times S \times 0.004548 \times 40$ g.

N.B. Equivalent weight of barium is $\frac{1}{3}$rd of its atomic weight, 137.36.

2.2.3.1.7 Estimation of Lead in a Lead-salt Solution

Principle: Lead is precipitated as aqueous insoluble yellow $PbCrO_4$ by the treatment with an aqueous solution of potassium chromate. It is filtered and treated with acid when $PbCrO_4$ is converted to dichromate which is titrated idometrically with a standard solution of thiosulphate by usual procedure. Thus,

$$PbX_2 + K_2CrO_4 = PbCrO_4 + 2KX$$

$$2PbCrO_4 + 4HCl = H_2CrO_7 + 2PbCl_2 + H_2O$$

$$H_2Cr_2O_7 + 6KI + 14HCl = 2CrCl_3 + 3I_2 + 6KCl + 2HCl + 7H_2O$$

$$I_2 + 2Na_2S_2O_3 = Na_2S_4O_6 + 2NaI$$

Procedure: Procedure is exactly similar to that followed in the estimation of barium. The equivalent weight of lead is $\frac{2}{3}$rd of its atomic weight, 207.21. Thus, 1 ml of $(N/10)$ thiosulphate solution = 0.006907 g of lead.

2.2.3.1.8 Estimation of Available Chlorine in Bleaching Powder

Principle: Commercial bleaching powder primarily contains calcium hypochlorite $Ca(OCl)Cl$ along with some amount of calcium hydroxide and calcium chloride. When bleaching powder is treated with dilute acid, chlorine present in it is quantitatively liberated. This is known as *available chlorine*. Thus,

$$Ca(OCl)Cl + H_2SO_4 = CaSO_4 + H_2O + Cl_2$$

Available chlorine

In practice, a solution or suspension of commercial bleaching powder is strongly acidified with acetic acid and is treated with potassium iodide when iodine is quantitatively liberated which is titrated against a standard solution of thiosulphate solution using starch as indicator.

$$Ca(OCl)Cl + 2CH_3COOH + 2KI = I_2 + 2CH_3COOK + CaCl_2 + H_2O$$

Procedure: 5 g of bleaching powder is accurately weighed into a clean glass or porcelain pot and is triturated with a small quantity of distilled water by a pestle when a thin cream is formed. It is allowed to stand for a few minutes and the milky supernatant liquid is poured off into a 500 ml measuring flask. The residual mass in the mortar is further triturated with a little water and the supernatant liquid is poured off into the measuring flask. This process is repreated till the whole of the sample of bleaching powder taken, has been transferred to the flask. The mortar and pestle is washed with little water and washing is transferred to the measuring flask. The measuring flask is filled up by distilled water up to the mark and is thoroughly shaken.

50 ml of the solution thus, prepared, is pipetted out into a 250 ml conical flask and is diluted with 25 ml of distilled water. To it 2 g of potassium iodide in 20 ml of distilled water and 10 ml of glacial acetic acid are added and shaken well. The liberated iodine is rapidly titrated with a standard solution of sodium thiosulphate solution in presence of starch as indicator. Burette reading is noted and the experiment is repeated thrice. Average burette reading is taken for calculation.

Claculations: Let the volume of thiosulphate required be V and its strength is $S(N/10)$.

Thus, available chlorine present in 50 ml of the solution is $V \times S \times 0.003545$ g.

Hence available chlorine present in 500 ml of the solution prepared, i.e., w g of bleaching powder actually taken is

$$V \times S \times 0.003545 \times 10 \text{ g}.$$

So the percent of available chlorine in the sample of bleaching powder is

$$\frac{V \times S \times 0.003454 \times 10}{w} \times 100\%.$$

Comment: Since standardisation of thiosulphate solution is carried out with the help of standard dichromate solution, this iodimetric estimation of available chlorine may be looked upon as a method of dichrometry.

2.2.3.2 Iodimetric Titrations

As mentioned before iodimetric titrations involve titration of iodine solution with a solution of reducing agent. Consequently, this type of titrations requires the preparation of standard solutions of iodine and reducing agents separately. Two most commonly used iodimetric titrations are discussed in sequel.

2.2.3.2.1 Titration of Iodine Solution by Thiosulphate Solution

Principle: This titration is based on the following reaction:

$$I_2 \quad + \quad Na_2S_2O_3 = Na_2S_4O_6 \quad + \quad 2NaI$$

$$\text{(Oxidant)} \quad \text{(Reductant)}$$

Since solid iodine is sparingly soluble in water it is dissolved in KI solution. In this solution iodine is present as a complex.

$$KI + I_2 = KI_3$$

Iodine molecules are released when iodine reacts with a reducing agent. So this solution behaves as a solution of iodine only.

— **Preparation of Standard Solution of Iodine**

About 3.173 g of solid iodine is accurately weighed in a dry glass stoppered weighing bottle and is transferred in a 250 ml measuring flask containing 4 g of KI dissolved in 100 ml of distilled water. It is shaken well and the volume is made up to the mark by adding distilled water to get an approximately $(N/10)$ iodine solution (**N.B.**: Equivalent weight of iodine is 126.93).

Titration of Iodine Solution

25 ml of iodine solution thus prepared, is taken in a 250 ml conical flask. It is now titrated with a standard sodium thiosulphate solution with continuous shaking until the colour of the solution turns pale yellow. Now 2 ml of freshly prepared starch solution is added when the solution becomes blue. Thiosulphate solution is now added dropwise till the blue colour just disappears. The burette reading is noted. Similar titration is repeated three times and average titre value is determined.

Calculations: Calculation is carried out utilising the equation $S_1V_1 = S_2V_2$.

Let the strength of thiosulphate solution is $S_2(N/10)$ and its volume required to reduce 25 ml iodine solution be V_2.

So, $25 \times S_1 = S_2V_2$

where S_1 is the strength iodine solution. Thus, strength of iodine solution prepared is

$$S_1 = \frac{S_2V_2}{25} \ (N/10).$$

2.2.3.2.2 Estimation of Arsenious Oxide

Principle: Arsenious oxide is an weaker oxidising agent than iodine. So it acts as reductant when reacts with iodine. Thus,

$$As_2O_3 \ + \ 2I_2 \ + \ 2H_2O = As_2O_5 \ + \ 4HI$$
$$\text{(Reductant)} \ \text{(Oxidant)}$$

In this titration As_2O_3 is actually dissolved in NaOH solution when Na_3AsO_3 is formed. Na_3AsO_3 thus formed undergoes oxidation by iodine.

$$As_2O_3 + 6NaOH = 2Na_3AsO_3 + 3H_2O$$
$$Na_3AsO_3 + I_2 + H_2O = Na_3AsO_4 + 2HI$$

Procedure

Preparation of $(N/10)$ Iodine Solution: $(N/10)$ iodine solution is prepared and its strength is determined according to process described in Art. 2.2.3.2.

Preparation of $(N/10)$ Arsenious Oxide Solution: About 1.236 g of arsenious oxide is accurately weighed in a 250 ml measuring flask. It is dissolved in least amount of NaOH solution.

A drop of phenolphthalein indicator is added to this solution and to it dilute H_2SO_4 is added drop by drop till the pink colour of the solution disappears. To this solution solid sodium carbonate is added in portion till the effervescence ceases and the solution becomes alkaline. The solution is made up to the mark to get 250 ml of (N/10) As_2O_3 solution.

Tritration of As_2O_3 Solution by Standard Iodine Solution: 25 ml of standard iodine solution prepared previously pipetted out into a 250 ml conical flask and it is titrated with the standard arsenious solution prepared taken in a burette. The addition of arsenious oxide solution is continued till the iodine solution becomes straw yellow. Now 2 ml of freshly prepared starch solution is added to the solution when the solution becomes blue. Arsenious oxide solution is now added drop by drop till the blue colour just disappears. Burette reading is noted and titration is repeated thrice. Average burette reading is determined for calculation.

Calculations: Let the strength of iodine solution be S_1(N/10) and that of arsenious solution is S_2. The volume of arsenious oxide required to reduce 25 ml solution of iodine solution is V_2. Thus, the strength of arsenious oxide solution is

$$S_2 \times V_2 = 25 \times S_1$$

$$\text{or, } S_2 = \frac{25 \times S_1}{V_2} \text{ (N/10)}.$$

2.2.3.2.3 Estimation of Zinc in a Zinc-Salt Solution

Principle: When a zinc salt solution is allowed to react with H_2S at pH 7-8, zinc is precipitated quantitatively as ZnS. ZnS, thus, formed on treatment with HCl liberates equivalent amount of H_2S which is estimated by reacting with the stronger oxidising agent than H_2S. Iodine solution is normally used as an oxidising agent for this purpose. Iodine oxidises H_2S to elemental S. Reaction takes place in the following way:

$$ZnX_2 + H_2S \xrightarrow{\text{at pH 7-8}} ZnS\downarrow + 2HX$$

$$ZnS + 2HCl = H_2S + ZnCl_2$$

$$H_2S + I_2 = S\downarrow + 2HI$$

Procedure: 25 ml of zinc salt solution is pipetted out into a 250 ml conical flask. To it 2-3 drops of phenolphthalein indicator solution is added. To it dilute solution of NH_4OH is added dropwise until faint pink colour appears. To this solution 15 ml of an acetate buffer made of equal volume of 2(N) chloro acetic acid and 1(N) sodium acetate is added for maintaining the desired pH. The mouth of the conical flask is closed by a velvet cork fitted with two glass tubes—one serving as inlet while the other acts as outlet. The conical falsk fitted with glass tubes is warmed at a temperature with of 60 °C and H_2S is passed through the inlet tube. After 2-3 minutes the outlet tube is closed and passing of H_2S is continued for at least 15 minutes to complete the precipitation of Zn as ZnS. The reaction mixture is allowed to stand for half an hour and is filtered through Whatman filter No. 42. The precipitate is washed with H_2S solution in 1% NH_4Cl solution several times.

Treatment of the Precipitate: The filter paper containing the precipitate of ZnS is transferred to a conical flask and 50 ml of distilled water is added. It is boiled for a few minutes to remove any H_2S, if present, cooled and to this cold solution, measured volume of excess standard solution and 20 ml of 4(N) HCl are added. The reaction mixture is shaken vigorously and the excess of iodine is back titrated with a standard solution of thiosulphate solution in presence of starch solution as indicator.

Calculation: Let the volume of (N/10) iodine solution added be V_1 and its strength is S_1. V_1 ml of S_1(N/10) iodine solution requires V_2 ml of S_2(N/10) thiosulphate solution for its complete reduction.

Again, volume of S_2(N/10) thiosulphate required for back titration is V_3 ml.

Thus, volume of iodine solution consumed by H_2S liberated from ZnS in terms of S_2(N/10) thiosulphate solution is

$(V_1 - V_2) \times S_2$(N/10) thiosulphate solution.

Thus, 25 ml of Zn-salt solution $\equiv (V_1 - V_2) \times S_2$(N/10) thiosulphate solution.

Therefore, the amount of Zn present is

$$(V_1 - V_2 \times S_2 \times 0.003269 \text{ g in 25 ml}$$
$$\text{or } (V_1 - V_2 \times S_2 \times 0.003269 \times 40 \text{ g per litre.}$$

N.B. Equivalent weight of Zn is ½ of its atomic weight, i.e., $\dfrac{65.38}{2} = 32.69$.

Comment: Standard iodine solution is prepared according to process described in Art. 2.2.3.2.

Chapter 3

Quantitative Analysis of Metal Ions in Binary Mixture

It has been observed that the quantitative analysis of a particular metal ion is seriously affected by the presence of other metal ions. So it is essential that the individual component of the mixture must either be separated or metal ions excepting one must be completely inhibited. Inhibition may be done either by complex formation or by controlling the reaction conditions in such a way that during the estimation of one component interference by other is totally prevented.

Some typical examples of quantitative analysis of binary mixture are described below.

3.1 Estimation of Iron and Chromium in a Mixture

Principle: The estimation of this binary mixture is based on the fact that when the mixture is treated with a solution of Na_2O_2, iron is precipitated as $Fe(OH)_3$ while chromium is oxidised to yellow solution of Na_2CrO_4. The precipitate of $Fe(OH)_3$ is quantitatively filtered out and is estimated after dissolving in HCl by a standard dichromate solution. The filtrate contains chromate solution which is converted to dichromate on acidification. The dichromate solution is now treated with excess of standard Mohr's salt solution and the excess Mohr's salt solution is back titrated with standard dichromate solution. Chemical reactions involved in this analysis are as under:

$$Na_2O_2 + H_2O = H_2O_2 + 2NaOH$$

$$Fe^{2+} + H-O-OH = Fe^{3+} + 2OH^-$$

$$Fe^{3+} + 3OH^- = Fe(OH)_3 \downarrow$$

$$2Fe^{3+} + Sn^{2+} = 2Fe^{2+} + Sn^{4+}$$

$$2Cr^{3+} + 3HO-OH + 10\,OH^- = 2CrO_4^{2-} + 8H_2O$$

$$CrO_4^{2-} + 2H^+ = Cr_2O_7^- + H_2O$$

$$Cr_2O_7^- + 6Fe^{2+} + 14H^+ = 2Cr^{3+} + 6Fe^{3+} + 7H_2O$$

Procedure: The supplied solution is quantitatively transferred to a 250 ml measuring flask and the volume is made up to the mark with distilled water and the flask is shaken well to make it a uniform solution.

25 ml of this stock solution is pipetted out into a 500 ml beaker. To it NaOH solution is added dropwise till turbidity appears. 1 g of Na_2O_2 taken in a corked test tube is added in portion with stirring. The solution is diluted to 100 ml and boiled for at least 10 minutes to decompose Na_2O_2 covering the mouth of the beaker by a watch-glass. The reaction mixture is cooled and is allowed to settle the precipitate formed. The precipitate is filtered through Whatman filter No. 41 keeping the precipitate in the beaker as much as possible and collecting the filtrate in another beaker. The precipitate in the beaker is washed 2-3 times with hot water. The filtrate and the washings are collected quantitatively for the estimation of chromium. The precipitate is worked out for the determination of iron.

Treatment of the precipitate for iron: The precipitate, $Fe(OH)_3$, remains in the beaker and in the filter paper. The precipitate in the filter paper is dissolved in hot dilute HCl (1:1), washed with hot water. Both the solution and washings are collected in the beaker which contains the major portion of the precipitate. The precipitate is now dissolved in minimum quantity of 1:1 HCl and heated. To this hot solution $SnCl_2$ solution is added dropwise until the solution becomes practically colourless. Finally 2-3 drops of $SnCl_2$ solution are added in excess and the solution is rapidly cooled. To this cold solution 10 ml of $HgCl_2$ solution is added all at a time and is allowed to stand for 5 minutes until a silky white precipitate appears. Solution is diluted and to it 25 ml of mixture of conc. H_2SO_4 and syrupy phosphoric acid is added. This solution is now titrated with a standard dichromate solution using diphenyl amine sulphonate as indicator in the usual way.

The amount of iron present in 25 ml solution is $V \times S \times 0.0056$ g

where V is the volume of dichromate required and S is its stremgth
or, the amount of iron present in 250 ml stock solution is $V \times S \times 0.0056 \times 10$ g
or, iron present in one litre of the solution = $V \times S \times 0.0056 \times 10 \times 4$ g.

Estimation of chromium: The filtrate and washings collected in the second beaker contain chromium as chromate. It is yellow in colour. The volume of this filtrate is reduced to 50 ml and is acidified with (1:4) H_2SO_4 when the colour changes from yellow to orange. To it about 50 ml of a standard Mohr's salt solution is added. To this solution 25 ml of mixture of (1:4) H_2SO_4 and syrupy phosphoric acid is added. It is now back titrated with a standard solution of dichromate in presence of diphenyl amine sulphonate indicator in the usual way. Let the final burette reading be V_2 ml.

Calculation: Let 50 ml of Mohr's salt solution $\equiv V_1 \times S_1$ ml of $(N/10)$ $K_2Cr_2O_7$.

So volume of Mohr's salt consumed in terms of dichromate solution is $(50 - V_2)$ ml of $S_1(N/10)$ dichromate

or, Amount of chromium present in 25 ml solution is $(50 - V_2) \times S_1 \times 0.001734$ g.
or, $(50 - V_2) \times S_1 \times 0.001734 \times 10$ g in 250 ml.
or, $(50 - V_2) \times S_1 \times 0.001734 \times 10 \times 4$ g in one litre.

Comments: Same procedure may be utilised for the estimation of binary mixture of dichromate and ferric iron.

3.2 Estimation of Iron (III) and Copper in a Mixture

Principle: Ferric iron readily forms a complex with NH_4HF_2. As a result it will not interfere in the estimation of copper. Thus in a mixture of ferric iron and copper, copper may be estimated by iodometric titration in presence of NH_4HF_2. Iron is estimated by precipitating it as $Fe(OH)_3$ and following the method described in Art. 3.1. Reactions involved are as under:

$$2Fe^{3+} + NH_4HF_2 = (NH_4)_3FeF_6$$
$$\text{complex}$$

As a result of such complex formation standard potential of Fe^{3+}/Fe^{2+} system comes down below that of $I_2/2I^-$ and so Fe^{3+} can not oxidise iodine to iodide. But copper cannot form such complex and can oxidise iodide to iodine, i.e.,

$$2Cu^{2+} + 4I^- = Cu_2I_2 + I_2$$

$$2S_2O_3^- + I_2 = S_4O_6^{2-} + 2I^-$$

$$2Fe^{3+} + Sn^{2+} = 2Fe^{2+} + Sn^{4+}$$

$$Cr_2O_7^- + 14H^+ + 6Fe^{2+} = 2Cr^{3+} + 6Fe^{3+} + 7H_2O$$

Procedure: The supplied solution is diluted to 250 ml into a measuring flask by quantitatively transferring the solution to in 250 ml measuring flask.

Estimation of Copper: 25 ml of the stock solution is pipetted out into a 250 ml conical falsk. It is neutralised by dropwise addition of dilute NH_4OH till turbidity persists. About 3 g of NH_4HF_2 is added and shaken well. 2 g of potassium iodide dissolved in 20 ml water is added and the solution is vigorously shaken. The mouth of the conical fask is covered with watch glass and kept in dark for a few minutes when a precipitate appears and the solution becomes dark brown due to the liberation of iodine. Liberated iodine is titrated with a standard solution of thiosulphate in presence of starch as indicator in the usual way. Amount of copper present is

$$S \times V \times 0.006354 \times 40 \text{ g per litre}$$

where V and S are the volume and strength of thiosulphate solution.

Estimation of Iron: 25 ml of the stock solution is pipetted out into a 250 ml conical flask and iron is precipitated as $Fe(OH)_3$ in hot condition by adding NH_4OH till the smell of NH_3 is felt. The solution is boiled and allowed to stand for settling down the precipitate. The precipitate is filtered, washed several times with hot water and is dissolved in hot dilute HCl as done in Art. 3.1. Finally this solution is titrated with a standard solution of dichromate following the same procedure as in Art. 3.1. Amount of iron present is

$$S \times V \times 0.0056 \times 40 \text{ g per litre,}$$

where V is the volume of dichromate required and S is its strength

3.3 Determination of Quantity of Iron and Manganese in a Mixture

Principle: Both iron and manganese when present in a mixture can be directly estimated without any interference to each other. Iron is directly estimated by titration with a standard solution of $K_2Cr_2O_7$ in presence of barium diphenyl sulphonate indicator after necessary reduction of ferric iron into ferrous iron by $SnCl_2$ solution as described in Art. 3.1.

Again Mn^{2+} present can be directly estimated by oxidising it to permanganic acid with an oxidising agent like sodium bismuthate and the permanganic thus formed is estimated by titration against a standard solution of oxalic acid. Reactions involved are as under:

$$2Fe^{3+} + Sn^{2+} = 2Fe^{2+} + Sn^{4+}$$

$$6Fe^{2+} + Cr_2O_7^- + 14H^+ = 2Cr^{3+} + 6Fe^{3+} + 7H_2O$$

$$Mn^{2+} + 5BiO_3^- + 14H^+ = 2MnO_4^- + 5Bi^{3+} + 7H_2O$$

$$2MnO_4^- + 5H_2C_2O_4 + 3H_2SO_4 = 2MnSO_4 + 8H_2O + 10CO_2 + SO_4^{2-}$$

Procedure: The supplied solution is diluted to 250 ml into a measuring flask by distilled water.

Estimation of iron: 25 ml of stock solution is pipetted out in a 500 ml conical flask and boiled with 20 ml conc. HCl. To this hot solution, $SnCl_2$ solution is added dropwise until the solution becomes practically colourless. Finally 2-3 drops of $SnCl_2$ solution are added in excess and the solution is rapidly cooled and 10 ml of $HgCl_2$ solution is added at a time. It is allowed to stand for a few minutes until a silky white precipitate appears. Solution is diluted and to it 25 ml of mixture of conc. H_2SO_4 and syrupy phosphoric acid is added. This solution is now titrated with a standard solution of dichromate in presence of diphenyl amine sulphonate as indicator in the usual way.

The amount of iron present is

$$V \times S \times 0.0056 \times 40 \text{ g per litre,}$$

where V and S are the volume and strength of dichromate solution respectively.

Estimation of Manganese: 25 ml of stock solution is pipetted out into a 250 ml beaker. To it 30 ml of (1:1) H_2SO_4 is added and boiled for 5-10 minutes. About 0.1 g of sodium bismuthate is added to this hot solution and boiled again until pink colour of permanganic acid appears.

The solution is allowed to stand for a few minites and filtered through sintered crucible fitted with a Buchner flask, washed with dilute H_2SO_4 and collected in a 500 ml conical flask. Excess measured quantity of standard oxalic acid is added. Excess oxalic acid is back titrated against a standard $KMnO_4$ solution and the titre value is noted.

Calculation: The volume of S_1(N/10) $KMnO_4$ solution required for blank titration with oxalic acid is V_1 ml and that required for back titration is V_2.

Thus, volume of permanganic acid formed from 25 ml solution is $(V_1 - V_2) \times S_1$(N/10) ml. The amount of manganese is $(V_1 - V_2) \times S_1 \times 0.001099 \times 40$ g per litre.

3.4 Determination of Copper (II) and Chromium (VI) in a Mixture

Principle: The quantitative analysis of the components of this binary mixture may be carried out by separating copper from the mixture as black precipitate of cupric oxide by the treatment with NaOH. The cupric oxide thus formed is quantitatively filtered and is estimated iodometrically in the usual procedure. The filtrate after the separation of cupric oxide contains chromium as dichromate which may be estimated by iodometric method. The chemical reactions taking place in this analysis are as indicated below.

$$CuX_2 + 2NaOH = Cu(OH)_2 + 2NaX$$

$$Cu(OH)_2 \xrightarrow{heat} CuO + H_2O$$

$$CuO + H_2SO_4 = CuSO_4 + H_2O$$

$$2CuSO_4 + 4 KI = 2CuI + I_2 + 2K_2SO_4$$

$$Na_2Cr_2O_7 + 7H_2SO_4 + 6 KI = Cr_2(SO_4)_3 + 3 I_2 + Na_2SO_4 + K_2SO_4 + 7H_2O$$

Procedure: 25 ml of the supplied solution is diluted to 250 ml in a measuring flask.

Separation: 25 ml of the stock solution is pipetted out into a 500 ml beaker. It is diluted to 50 ml and boiled. To this hot solution, 20 ml of 15% NaOH solution is slowly added with constant stirring. Boiling is continued until the precipitate turns black. The precipitate is allowed to settle down and filtered through Wheatman No. 41 filter paper. The precipitate is washed with hot water till free from dichromate. The precipitate and filtrate are separately treated for copper and dichromate estimation.

Estimation of copper: The precipitate in the beaker and in the filter paper is dissolved in dilute H_2SO_4. It is neutralised by dropwise addition of NH_4OH with constant stirring until a permanent turbidity appears. 5 ml or little more glacial acetic acid is added when turbidity completely disappears. The solution is cooled under tap and 2 g of potassium iodide dissolved in 20 ml water is added. The solution is vigorously shaken and the mouth of the beaker is covered with a watch-glass. The reaction mixture is allowed to stand for a few minutes when the solution turns dark brown. The liberated iodine is titrated with a standard solution of thiosulphate in presence of starch as indicator. Let the volume of ($N/10$) thiosulphate required is V ml.

Amount of copper in the mixture is

$$V \times S \times 0.006354 \times 40 \text{ g per litre,}$$

where S is the strength of thiosulphate ($N/10$) solution.

Estimation of Dichromate: The filtrate contains dichromate present in the mixture. it is acidified with 15 ml of (1:1) dilute HCl, and 2 g of potassium iodide dissolved in 20 ml of water is added. The liberated iodine is titrated against a standard solution of thiosulphate in presence of starch indicator. Let the volume of ($N/10$) thiosulphate solution consumed be V ml . Amount of chromium (VI) in the mixture is

$$V \times S \times 0.001734 \times 40 \text{ g per litre,}$$

3.5 Determination of Ferric Iron and Zinc in a Mixture

Principle: Zinc ion, if present, does not interfere in the estimation of Fe^{3+}. So ferric iron can be directly estimated by titration with standard solution of $K_2Cr_2O_7$ in the usual way. But the estimation of zinc requires the separation of iron (ic) which is actually done by precipitating it as $Fe(OH)_3$. After separation of ferric iron, zinc is estimated. For this purpose zinc may be precipitated either as ZnS and may be estimated iodimetrically or may be precipitated as $ZnNH_4PO_4$ and is estimated by acidimetry-alkalimetry method. The reactions involved in the process are as under:

$$2Fe^{3+} + Sn^{2+} = 2Fe^{2+} + Sn^{4+}$$

$$Cr_2O_7^- + 6Fe^{2+} + 14H^+ = 2Cr^{3+} + 6Fe^{3+} + 7H_2O$$

$$Zn^{2+} + H_2S = ZnS\downarrow + H_2\uparrow$$

$$ZnS + I_2 = ZnI_2 + S\downarrow$$

$$\text{or, } Zn^{2+} + (NH)_2HPO_4 + OH^- = ZnNH_4PO_4\downarrow + NH_4^+ + H_2O$$

$$2ZnNH_4PO_4 + 3H_2SO_4 = 2\,ZnSO_4 + (NH_4)_2SO_4 + 2H_3PO_4$$

Procedure: The solution supplied is diluted to 250 ml into a measuring flask.

Determination of Iron: 25 ml of stock solution is pipetted out into a 250 ml conical flask. 20 ml of conc. HCl is added to it and boiled. The hot solution is reduced by adding $SnCl_2$ solution drop wise with constant stirring until the solution becomes practically colourless. Finally 2-3 more drops of $SnCl_2$ solution are added and the solution is rapidly cooled. To this cold solution about 10 ml of $HgCl_2$ solution is added all at a time and is allowed to stand for 5 minutes when a silky white precipitate appears. Solution is diluted and to it about 25 ml of mixture of conc. H_2SO_4 and syrupy phosphoric is added. This solution is now titrated with a standard $(N/10)$ $K_2Cr_2O_7$ solution using diphenyl amine sulphonate solution as indicator in the usual way. Let the final burette reading is V ml.

Amount of ferric iron present in the mixture is

$$V \times S \times 0.0056 \times 40 \text{ g per litre,}$$

where S is the strength of $K_2Cr_2O_7$ solution $(N/10)$.

Estimation of Zinc

(a) **Separation of iron (ic):** 25 ml of the stock solution is pipetted out into a 500 ml beaker and ferric iron is precipitated as $Fe(OH)_3$ in hot condition by adding NH_4OH till the smell of NH_3 is felt. The solution is allowed to stand for settling down the precipitate. The precipitate is filtered and washed with hot water. The filtrate and washing containing zinc are collected in a beaker.

Precipitation of zinc as NH_4ZnPO_4: The volume of the filtrate in the beaker is reduced to 150 ml by boiling and the solution is made just acidic. The solution is heated just of boiling and to it 25-30 ml of 20% $(NH_4)_2HPO_4$ solution is slowly added. The solution is kept hot for about 20 minutes on placing it on a hot asbestos board when a crystalline precipitate settles down. It is allowed to stand for one hour more and then it is filtered using Whatman filter paper No. 41. The precipitate is washed with 1% cold solution of $(NH_4)_2HPO_4$ till it becomes free from chloride. Finally it is washed with 50% alcohol till it gets free from phsophate.

The precipitate is dissolved in measured excess of standard $(N/10)$ H_2SO_4 and finally excess H_2SO_4 is back titrated with a standard $(N/10)$ NaOH solution in presence of bromo-cresol green solution as indicator.

Amount of zinc present in the mixture is

$$(V_1-V_2) \times S \times 0.003269 \times 40 \text{ g per litre,}$$

where V_1 is the volume of $(N/10)$ NaOH in the blank titration with $(N/10)$ H_2SO_4 and V_2 is that required for back titration

Comments: (i) Zinc may be precipitated as ZnS and then be estimated iodimetrically as discussed in Art. 2.2.3.2.3.

(ii) Zinc may also be estimated by complexometric titration with EDTA (vide Art. 4.4).

3.6 Estimation of Ferrous Iron and Calcium in a Mixture

Principle: The quantitative analysis of the constituents of this mixture is based on the separation of both ferrous iron and calcium from the mixture. After separation, individual components are estimated. Ferrous iron is oxidised and is precipitated as $Fe(OH)_3$ while calcium is precipitated as calcium oxalate. The precipitate, $Fe(OH)_3$ is dissolved in hydrochloric acid and is estimated by a standard solution of $K_2Cr_2O_7$. Calcium oxalate is dissolved in sulphuric acid and the liberated oxalic acid is estimated by a standard solution of $KMnO_4$. Chemical reactions taking place in this analysis may be written as described below:

$$Fe^{2+} \xrightarrow{HNO_3} Fe^{3+}$$

$$Fe^{3+} + 3NH_4OH = Fe(OH)_3 + 3NH_4^{+}$$

$$Fe(OH)_3 + 3HCl = FeCl_3 + 3H_2O$$

$$2FeCl_3 + SnCl_2 = 2FeCl_2 + SnCl_4$$

$$Cr_2O_7^{-} + 6Fe^{2+} + 14H^{+} = 2Cr^{3+} + 6Fe^{3+} + 7H_2O$$

$$Ca^{2+} + (NH_4)_2C_2O_4 = CaC_2O_4 + 2NH_4^{+}$$

$$\text{Ammonium} \qquad \text{Calcium}$$
$$\text{oxalate} \qquad \text{oxalate}$$

$$CaC_2O_4 + H_2SO_4 = CaSO_4 + H_2C_2O_4$$

$$\text{Oxalic}$$
$$\text{acid}$$

$$2KMnO_4 + 16H^{+} + 5H_2C_2O_4 = 2Mn^{2+} + 10CO_2 + 8H_2O$$

Procedure: The supplied solution is diluted to 250 ml into measuring flask and 25 ml of the stock solution is pipetted out into 500 ml beaker and separation work for iron and calcium is undertaken.

Separation: The solution taken in a beaker is boiled with 2 ml of conc. HNO_3 for 5 minutes to oxidise ferrous iron into ferric iron. It is then diluted to 150 ml. To it 1 g of pure NH_4Cl is added and heated to boiling and next (1:1) NH_4OH solution is added till it smells of ammonia. It is boiled again and is allowed to settle down. It is filtered in hot condition through Whatman filter paper No. 41, and filtrate and washings are collected in another beaker.

Estimation of Iron: The precipitate of $Fe(OH)_3$ in the beaker and the filter paper is dissolved in (1:1) HCl and the ferric iron solution is estimated with a standard $(N/10)$ $K_2Cr_2O_7$ solution in the usual way.

Amount of iron present is $V \times S \times 0.0056 \times 40$ g per litre where V and S are the volume and strength of $(N/10)$ $K_2Cr_2O_7$ solution respectively.

Estimation of Calcium: The filtrate in the beaker contains calcium ions. The volume is reduced to 150 ml by careful evaporation. The solution is neutralised by the addition of 5 ml of concentrated HCl and boiled. To this hot solution about 20 ml of 10% ammonium oxalate is added. Next dilute NH_4OH solution is added till it smells of ammonia. The solution is allowed to stand for half an hour when precipitate of calcium oxalate appears. The precipitate is filtered and washed.

The precipitate is transferred to a 500 ml conical flask and is dissolved in 50 ml of moderately concentrated (8:1) H_2SO_4. The oxalic acid liberated is estimated with a standard solution of $KMnO_4$ (vide Art. 2.2.2.1.3). The amount of calcium is

$$V \times S \times 0.002 \times 40 \text{ g per litre,}$$

where V and S are the volume and strength of $(N/10)$ $KMnO_4$ solution respectively.

Chapter 4

Complexometric Titrations

The basis of complexometric estimation of metal ions through titrimetric method is the formation of complex by metal ions with polydentate ligands. However, for such type of titration certain conditions as mentioned below must be fulfilled.

(i) The complex must be very stable.

(ii) The ligand must have the capability of forming complex satisfying the coordination number of the metal ion and the complex so formed must be soluble.

(iii) The complex formation must take in a single step with high rate and

(iv) appropriate indicator to detect the end-point sharply must be available.

EDTA (Ethylene diamine tetra-acetic acid) has been found to satisfy all the above conditions and hence is frequently used in complexometric titrations. It is a white crystalline solid slightly soluble in water. Since it is tetra basic it is represented by the general formula, H_4Y. Its structure may be represented as

$$\text{HOOC}-H_2C \diagdown \atop \text{HOOC}-H_2C \diagup N-CH_2-CH_2-N \diagup CH_2-COOH \atop \diagdown CH_2-COOH$$

EDTA forms complexes with many metal ions. It may be mentioned that although it is tetra basic but readily forms disodium salt only, which indicates that out of four acidic hydrogens only two are strongly acidic and generally it behaves as a dibasic acid. Commercially available EDTA is its disodium salt, Na_2H_2Y. This disodium salt in aqueous readily ionises as

$$Na_2H_2Y \rightleftharpoons H_2Y^{2-} + 2Na^+$$
$$\text{ion}$$

The ion, H_2Y^{2-} formed is the active entity in forming complex as

$$\underset{\text{(Metal ion)}}{M^{n+}} + H_2Y^{2-} \rightleftharpoons M^{(n-4)+} + 2H^+$$

The above path of the reaction indicates that H^+ is released during complex formation. So it may be concluded that the pH of the medium plays a significant role in the formation of complex by EDTA. In fact, efficiency of complex formation by EDTA is affected by the change in pH of the solution. Schewarzenbach utilised the effects of pH in his titrimetric method for the estimating of metal ions during the addition of EDTA to a solution of metal ions. The concentration of EDTA ion (complexing species) is determined by the pH of the solution. Hence decrease in pH of the solution means decrease in the concentration of EDTA. So EDTA forms complexes most effectively in basic medium because in low pH ionisation increases and the efficiency is ultimately decreased in strongly acidic medium. The pH at which efficiency is lost is different for different metal ions. So the pH of solution under examination is kept constant within a certain limit of required pH by the addition of buffer solution.

4.1 Nature of Indicator to be Used in EDTA Titrations

In EDTA titrations metal indicators are used. These indicators are organic dye. The metal indicator first reacts with the metal ion to form coloured metal indicator complex which at the end of the reaction (at end-point) reacts with EDTA making free the indicator ion completely having different colours. This is the cause of change of colour. In order to fulfil such change in colour following conditions are to be fulfilled by the indicator.

(i) Colour reaction must be sensitive.

(ii) The difference in colour between metal-indicator complex and free indicator must be very wide.

(iii) The metal indicator complex must be very unstable.

(iv) The reaction between metal indicator complex and EDTA must be very rapid.

It has been observed that only a very few organic dyes fulfil such conditions. Eriochrome Black T and Muroxide are most commonly used such indicators. Structures of these two indicators may be written as under:

Eriochrome Black T

Muroxide

4.2 Preparation of Standard Solution of EDTA

Disodium salt of EDTA cannot be used as primary standard. Generally 0.01 M, 0.05 or 0.1 M solutions of EDTA are used. For 0.01 M solution approximately 0.93 g of disodium salt is weighed in a 250 ml measuring flask and is dissolved in de-ionised water.

4.3 Standardisation of EDTA Solution

(a) **Preparation of 0.01 M $ZnSO_4$ Solution**: EDTA solution is standardised by titration with a standard solution of $ZnSO_4$. About 1.61 g of $ZnSO_4$ is dissolved in one litre de-ionised water. This give 0.01 M solution of $ZnSO_4$.

(b) **Preparation of Buffer Solution**: Most of the EDTA titrations are carried out at pH 10. Commonly NH_4OH—NH_4Cl buffer is used. For the preparation of such buffer solution 54 g of NH_4Cl (solid) is dissolved in 200 ml of de-ionised water and to it 350 ml of 25% NH_4OH solution is added. Next it is diluted to one litre with de-ionised water.

(c) **Titration**: 10 ml of standard 0.01 M $ZnSO_4$ is pipetted out into a 250 conical falsk and to it 2 ml of buffer solution is added. It is diluted to 100 ml by adding de-ionised water. To this solution 0.5 g of Eriochrome Black T (commercial variety is known as solochrome Black T) is added when a wine red colour is developed. This solution is titrated with the standard EDTA solution taken in a burette until the colour changes to sky blue. The end-point is purely blue colour. The strength of EDTA is determined by using $S_1V_1 = S_2V_2$ formula.

4.4 Estimation of Zinc in a Solution of Zinc Salt

Previously described [Art. 4.3(c)] process is exactly followed to determine the quantity of zinc by the standard EDTA solution.

Calculations: 1 ml of 0.01 M EDTA = 0.00161 g of $ZnSO_4$ ≡ 0.0006538 g of Zn.

Amout of Zn = $0.0006538 \times V \times S$ g in 10 ml

$$≡ 0.0006538 \times V \times S \times 100 \text{ g per litre,}$$

where V and S are the volume and strength of EDTA solution respectively.

4.5 Estimation of Magnesium in Magnesium Salt Soltution

Procedure: 10 ml of magnesium salt solution is taken in a 250 ml conical flask and to it 2 ml of buffer solution is added, diluted to 100 ml by de-ionised water. To this solution 0.5 g of solochrome Black T indicator is added when a wine red colour is developed. It is then titrated with a standard EDTA solution taken in a burette, till the addition of a drop changes the colour from wine red to blue. Burette reading is noted.

Calculation: 1 ml solution of 0.01 M EDTA = 0.0002432 g of Mg.

Amount of magnesium = $0.0002432 \times V \times S$ g in 10 ml

$$= 0.0002432 \times V \times S \times 100 \text{ g per litre,}$$

where V and S represent respectively the volume and strength of EDTA solution used.

4.6 Estimation of Calcium in Calcium Salt Solution

10 ml of the solution is pipetted out into a 250 ml conical flask and following exactly the previous procedure calcium is estimated.

Calculations: 1 ml of 0.01 M EDTA = 0.0004 g of Ca

Amount of calcium = $0.0004 \times V \times S$ g in 10 ml

$$= 0.0004 \times V \times S \times 100 \text{ g per litre,}$$

where V and S represent the volume of EDTA and its strength respectively.

4.7 Estimation of Permanent and Temporary Hardness in Water

4.7.1 Determination of Total Hardness of Water

Principle: Hardness of water is primarily due to the dissolved salt of calcium and magnesium. Hence they may be estimated by using EDTA. Both these ions form complexes with EDTA. But an interesting observation has been noted that although Ca-EDTA complex is more stable than Mg complex but Ca-indicator complex is less stable than Mg-indicator complex. As a result, EDTA at first reacts with calcium ion, then with magnesium ion and lastly with magnesium-indicator complex setting free blue indicator ion when both calcium and magnesium are present in a mixture as in the case of hard water.

Due to this characteristic behaviour, change of colour from wine red to blue occurs at the end -point. Thus,

$$H_2Y^{2-} + Ca^{++} \rightleftharpoons CaY^{2-} + 2H^+$$
$$\text{EDTA}$$

$$H_2Y^{2-} + Mg^{++} \rightleftharpoons MgY^{2-} + 2H^+$$

$$MgI^- + H_2Y^{2-} \rightleftharpoons MgY^{2-} + HI^{2-} + H^+$$

Mg-indicator	Free
complex	indicator
(wine Red)	(Blue)

Procedure: 50 ml of hard water is pipetted out into a conical flask and to it 5 ml of dilute HCl is added. This mixture is boiled to remove any dissolved carbon dioxide. The solution is cooled and neutralised with NaOH and diluted to 100 ml. To it 0.5 g of solochrome Black T indicator is added when wine red colour is developed. It is then titrated with a standard EDTA solution taking EDTA in a burette, till the colour changes from wine red to blue. Burette reading is noted.

Calculations: Let the volume of $S(N/10)$ EDTA required be V ml for 50 ml of hard water.

$\therefore$ 50 ml of hard water contains $0.001 \times V$ g of $CaCO_3$

$$\equiv V \times 10^{-3} \text{ g of } CaCO_3.$$

Hardness of water is expressed in parts of $CaCO_3$ equivalent of calcium and magnesium salts per million parts of water, i.e., parts per million (ppm).

$\therefore$ 50 parts of hardwater contain $V \times 10^{-3}$ parts of $CaCO_3$

1   part of hardwater contains $\dfrac{V \times 10^{-3}}{50}$ parts of $CaCO_3$

$\therefore 10^6$ parts of hardwater contain $\dfrac{V \times 10^{-3} \times 10^6}{50}$ parts of $CaCO_3$

$$= \frac{V \times 10^2}{5} \text{ ppm.}$$

Thus, total hardness $= \dfrac{V \times 10^2}{5}$ ppm.

Determination of Permanent Hardness of Water

Principle: Permanent hardness is due to the presence of soluble sulphates of calcium and magnesium whereas temporary hardness originates from the presence of soluble bicarbonates of these two metal ions. When any hard water is boiled soluble bicarbonates of calcium and magnesium are converted into insoluble carbonates,

$$Ca(HCO_3)_2 \rightleftharpoons CaCO_3\downarrow + H_2O + CO_2$$

$$Mg(HCO_3)_2 \rightleftharpoons MgCO_3\downarrow + H_2O + CO_2$$

Now by filtration insoluble carbonates are separated out and the filtrate contains only soluble salts of calcium and magnesium, i.e., the hardness of water is now permanent.

Procedure: 250 ml of the previous hardwater is taken in a 500 ml beaker. It is then gently boiled, cooled and filtered. The filtrate is collected in a flask.

50 ml of the filtrate is taken in a 250 ml conical flask and is titrated with standard EDTA solution in presence of solochrome Black T as before till the end-point.

Calculations: Let the volume of $S(N/10)$ EDTA required be V_1 ml.

Hence 50 ml of hardwater contains

$V_1 \times 10^{-3}$ g of $CaCO_3$ due to permanent hardness.

Therefore, permanent hardness of the water is $\dfrac{V_1 \times 10^{-3} \times 10^6}{50}$ ppm.

$$= \frac{V_1 \times 10^2}{5} \text{ ppm.}$$

Estimation of Temporary Hardness: If amount of permanent hardness is deducted from the total hardness, temporary hardness will be obtained. Thus,

Temporary hardness $= \left(\dfrac{V \times 10^2}{5} - \dfrac{V_1 \times 10^2}{5} \right)$ ppm.

$$= \frac{(V - V_1)}{5} \times 10^2 \text{ ppm.}$$

Chapter 5

Gravimetric Analysis

Gravimetric analysis is based on the principle of precipitating quantitatively an element as its stable and pure salt from a solution of a known compound containing the element.

This technique of quantitative analysis primarily involves three major steps, viz., (i) preparation of a solution of weighed quantity of the sample. (ii) precipitation of the desired ion from a specific volume of the solution using appropriate chemical reagent and (iii) weighing of the precipitate formed after complete drying.

For successful completion of these three steps following operations are carried out.

(i) Weighing of the sample (ii) Preparation of the solution of the weighed sample (iii) Precipitation of the desired ion by using appropriate reagent (iv) Filtration of the precipitate formed (v) Drying of the precipitate and (vi) Weighing of the dry precipitate accurately after cooling it in a desiccator.

Two most common estimation of this category are described below in order to elaborate the different operations required to be carried out.

5.1 Estimation of Copper as Cuprous Thiocyanate in a Solution

Principle: Copper is quantitatively precipitated as cuprous thiocyanate in a faintly acidic solution by an alkali thiocyanate in presence of a reducing agent like sulphurous acid. Thus,

$$2Cu^{++} + HSO_3^- + H_2O \longrightarrow 2Cu^+ + HSO_4^- + 2H^+$$

$$Cu^+ + SCN^- \longrightarrow CuSCN\downarrow$$

White precipitate

Procedure: About 20 ml of the given salt solution is taken in a 500 ml beaker. To this 5-6 drops of dilute HCl and 3-4 ml of freshly prepared saturated solution of sulphurous acid are added. It is diluted to 150 ml with distilled water and heated at 80-90 °C. To this hot solution 30 ml of 10% solution of ammonium thiocyanate is slowly added with constant stirring. The mixture is allowed to stand for several hours, preferably overnight, when white precipitate appears. The supernatant liquid should be colourless with a smell of sulphur dioxide.

The precipitate is filtered through a weighed sintered glass crusible. The precipitate is washed 10-12 times with 10% ammonium thiocyanate solution containing 5-6 drops of sulphurous acid. The precipitate is finally washed with 20% alcohol to remove ammonium thiocyanate. The crucible and the precipitate are dried at 120-130 °C in an electric oven, cooled in a desiccator and weighed as CuSCN.

Calculations: Let the weight of the dry crucible before filtration be w g and the final weight after drying the precipitate is w_1 g.

∴ the amount of CuSCN formed is $(w_1 - w)$g.

Hence amount of copper present in 20 ml solution is

$$(w_1 - w) \times 0.5224 \text{ g,}$$

since of 1 g of CuSCN contains 0.5224 g of copper.

Comments

(i) The solution should be only faintly acidic because the precipitate dissolves with increase in acidity.

(ii) The solution should be free from any oxidising agent, such as HNO_3. If nitric acid is present in the solution, it is removed by boiling the solution to dryness and treating the dry residue with a few drops of conc. H_2SO_4 and further heating till the white dense fumes of sulphuric acid are evolved and finally the mass is extracted with water.

5.2 Estimation of Nickel as Nickel Dimethyl Glyoxime in a Solution

Working principle: Nickel is precipitated as nickel dimethyl glyoxime by adding an alcoholic solution of dimethyl glyoxime to ammoniacal solution of nickel salt. Reactions taking place in this process are as under:

$$NiSO_4 \quad + \quad \begin{matrix} HO-N{=}C-CH_3 \\ | \\ HO-N{=}C-CH_3 \end{matrix} \quad + 2NH_4OH$$

Nickel
sulphate

Dimethyl glyoxime

$$CH_3-C{=}N \quad\quad N{=}C-CH_3$$

Scarlet red

The precipitate formed is stable due to H-bond formation.

Procedure: 20 ml of the supplied solution is pipetted out into a 500 ml beaker and is diluted to 150 ml with distilled water. The solution is heated to 70-80 °C and a slight excess (30 ml) of 1% dimethyl glyoxime solution is added followed by immediate dropwise addition of dilute (1:1) ammonia solution till the smell of ammonia persists. The reaction mixture is then allowed to stand on a water bath for half an hour. At the end a drop of dimethyl glyoxime is added to ensure the complete precipitation. The solution is allowed to stand for an hour to cool and settle down.

The precipitate is filtered through a previously washed, dried and weighed sintered glass crucible. The precipitate is washed with hot water until it is free from chloride ions and dried at 120 °C in an electric oven. It is cooled in a desiccator and weight is taken.

Calculations: Let the weight of dry crucible before filtration be w g and that of after drying the precipitate be w_1 g.

∴ the ammount of nickel dimethyl glyoxime formed is

$$(w_1 - w) \text{ g.}$$

Hence, the amount of nickel is

$$(w_1 - w) \times 0.2032 \text{ g.}$$

(1 g of nickel dimethyl glyoxime contains 0.2032 g of nickel.)

Comments

(i) The precipitate is soluble in mineral acids and so it is precipitated in ammoniacal medium.

(ii) To much excess of reagent should be avoided because some quantity of the precipitate may dissolve in the alcohol present in the reagent. That is why only slight excess of the reagent has been used.

5.3 Estimation of Iron as Ferric Oxide

Principle: Solution of ferric salt on treatment with slight excess of ammonium hydroxide solution forms ferric hydroxide which on ignition yields ferric oxide.

$$FeCl_3 + 3NH_4OH = Fe(OH)_3 \downarrow + 3NH_4Cl$$

$$2Fe(OH)_3 = Fe_2O_3 \downarrow + H_2O$$

From the weight of ferric oxide the amount of iron may be estimated.

Procedure: The solution supplied is taken in a 500 ml beaker. It is diluted to 50 ml by adding distilled water. To it 10 ml of (1:1) hydrochloric acid, 2 ml of conc. HNO_3 are added and gently boiled till the colour of the solution becomes clear yellow. The solution is diluted to 100 ml with distilled water. The solution is heated to boiling by adding approximately 2 g of NH_4Cl and to hot solution (1:1) NH_4OH solution is slowly added with constant stirring until the solution smells of NH_3. The solution is boiled again for a minute or two and the precipitate is allowed to settle down for a few minutes when the supernatant liquid becomes colourless. The supernatant liquid is decanted off without disturbing the precipitate through an ashless quantitative filter paper (Whatman No. 41). About 100 ml of boiling 1% ammonium nitrate solution is added to the precipitate, stirred and allowed to settle. The supernatant liquid is filtered as before. This process of washing is repeated 3 to 4 times and the precipitate is transferred quantitatively on to the filter paper. The small particles that may be adhered to the side of the beaker are dislodged by scrubbing gently with a glass rod and transferred to the main precipitate. The precipitate is washed repeatedly with hot water and 1% solution of ammonium nitrate till the filtrate is free from chloride.

Now the funnel with the filter paper is dried in air-oven. The filter paper with the precipate is taken out from the funnel and is folded around the precipitate taking care that no particle is lost. The filter paper with the precipitate is placed on a weighed crucible. The crucible is placed on a wire gauze and is heated gently with a burner. When the filter paper has been completely burnt out the crucible is strongly heated for about 20 minutes. The erucible is cooled in a desiccator and is accurately weighed.

Calculations: Let the weight of the dry empty crucible be w_1 g and the final weight after drying the precipitate be w_2 g.

$\therefore$ The amount of $Fe_2O_3 = (w_2 - w_1)$ g.

Hence the weight of iron in solution is $(w_2 - w_1) \times 0.6994$ g,

Since 1 g of Fe_2O_3 contains 0.6994 g of Fe

Comments

(i) This process of analysis is not applicable in presence elements such as aluminium, chromium etc. that are precipitated by ammonium hydroxide.

(ii) The precipitation should be heated under perfect oxidising flame other wise partial reduction may occur.

(iii) The solution with the precipitate should not be heated for a long time because in longer heating precipitate may break and become colloidal.

5.4 Estimation of Silver as Silver Chloride

Principle: Silver is precipitated as silver chloride from silver salt solution by acidifying with dilute nitric acid and adding dilute hydrochloric acid. From the weight of washed and dried silver chloride, amount of silver may be determined. Reactions taking place are:

$$Ag\text{-salt} + HNO_3 = AgNO_3$$

$$AgNO_3 + HCl = AgCl\downarrow + HNO_3$$

Procedure: The supplied solution is quantitatively transferred to a 500 ml beaker and is diluted to 100 ml by adding distilled water. About 1 ml of chemically pure conc. HNO_3 is added to it. The solution is warmed up to 70 °C, about 5 ml of dilute HCl (0.2N) is added dropwise with constant stirring until the precipitation is complete. The precipitate is warmed for 5 minutes in a water bath and is allowed to cool in a dark place for at least half an hour. The supernatant liquid is tested by adding 0.2NHCl along with the walls of the beaker to ensure complete precipitation of Ag ions. The precipitation is allowed to settle down in dark for a few hours preferably overnight.

The supernatant liquid is poured through a cleaned, dried and weighed sintered glass crucible (G-3). The precipitate is washed several times with 0.01 (N) nitric acid till it is free from chloride ions. The precipitate is dried at 100-120 °C in an electric oven and cooled in a desiccator.

Calculations: Let the weight of emply crucible be w_1 g and the final weight after drying the precipitate be w_2 g.

$\therefore$ The amount of AgCl = $(w_2 - w_1)$ g.

Hence the weight of silver in the solution is $(w_2 - w_1) \times 0.7526$.

Since 1 g of AgCl contains 0.7526 g of Ag.

Comments

(i) Silver chloride undergoes decomposition in sunlight. So the experiment should be carried out in *subdued light* and the solution containing the precipitate should be kept in dark place and the container should be covered with a piece of black paper.

(ii) Washing with ordinary water may render the silver chloride colloidal in nature. So the solution must contain an electrolyte. For this reason, HNO_3 is preferably used.

5.5 Estimation of Chloride as Silver Chloride

Principle: Chloride ion may be estimated by precipitating it as silver chloride from its solution by the addition of silver nitrate solution. Thus,

$$\bar{Cl} + AgNO_3 = AgCl\downarrow + N\bar{O}_3$$

Procedure: The supplied solution is quantitatively transferred to a 500 ml beaker and is diluted to 100 ml by adding distilled water. It is acidified with 1 ml of dilute HNO_3 and cooled. To this cold solution $0.1N AgNO_3$ is added dropwise with constant stirring till the precipitation is complete. The solution is kept in the dark for 2-3 hours. It is then filtered through weighed glass crucible and the precipitate is washed with $0.01(N)HNO_3$ solution. The crucible along with the precipitate is dried at a temperature of 100-120 °C for an hour, cooled in a desiccator and weighed.

Calculations: Let the weight of clean empty and dry crucible be w_1 g and the final weight after drying the precipitate be w_2 g.

$\therefore$ The amount of AgCl = $(w_2 - w_1)$ g.

Hence the weight of chloride is

$$\frac{(w_2 - w_1) \times 35.46}{143.34} = (w_2 - w_1) \times 0.2474 \text{ g}.$$

5.6 Estimation of Sulphate as Barium Sulphate

Principle: Sulphate ion is precipitated as barium sulphate from its solution by acidifying with dilute HCl and adding aqueous solution of barium chloride solution. From the weight of washed and dried barium sulphate formed amount of sulphate ion may be calculated. Thus,

$$SO_4^{2-} + BaCl_2 = BaSO_4\downarrow + 2\bar{Cl}$$

Procedure: The supplied solution is quantitatively transferred to a 500 ml beaker and to it 4-5 drops of conc. HCl are added and diluted to 200 ml by adding distilled water. The solution is boiled and to this hot olution 5% $BaCl_2$ solution is added dropwise with constant stirring till the precipitation is complete. The precipitate is allowed to stand on an asbestos board over a small flame for half an hour.

The precipitate is filtered through Whatman No. 40 filter paper and washed with hot water.

The filter paper with precipitate is taken in a weighed crucible and is heated over a low flame and the heating is increased gradually till the filter paper chars and all carbon is volatilised. Finally it is strongly heated and ignited at a temperature of 1000 °C for half an hour, cooled in a desiccator and weighed.

Calculations: Let the weight of clean, dry and empty crucible be w_1 g and the final weight of the crucible after drying the precipitate be w_2 g,

$\therefore$ The amount of $BaSO_4 = (w_2 - w_1)$ g.

Hence the amount of sulphate in the supplied solution is

$$(w_2 - w_1) \times 0.4116 \text{ g.}$$

Since 1 g of $BaSO_4$ contains 0.4116 g of sulphate.

Comments: The same principle and procedure may be employed for the estimation of barium as barium sulphate. But in this case solution containing barium ion is to be acidified first with little HCl and then to be treated with H_2SO_4 when barium is quantitatively precipitated as barium sulphate. Thus,

$$Ba\text{-salt} + HCl = BaCl_2$$

$$BaCl_2 + H_2SO_4 = BaSO_4\!\downarrow + 2\,HCl$$

Calculations: The amount of $BaSO_4 = w_2 - w_1$ g where w_2 is the weight of crucible with the precipitate and w_1 is the weight of clean, dry and empty crucible.

Hence amount of barium in the supplied solution is $(w_2 - w_1) \times 0.5885$ g since 1 g of $BaSO_4$ contains 0.5885 g of barium.

5.7 Estimation of Manganese as Mn(NH₄) PO₄

Principle: The most commonly employed method of gravimetric analysis of manganese is its precipitation as manganese ammonium phosphate, $Mn(NH_4)PO_4$, H_2O and weighing this precipitate either as $Mn(NH_4)\,PO_4$ or as $Mn_2P_2O_7$. Reactions taking places are as under:

$$Mn^{2+} + N\overset{+}{H}_4 + HPO_4^{2-} + O\bar{H} = Mn(NH_4)PO_4\!\downarrow + H_2O$$

$$2\,Mn(NH_4)PO_4 = Mn_2P_2O_7 + 2\,NH_3 + H_2O$$

Procedure: The supplied solution is quantitatively transferred to a 500 ml beaker. The solution is made slightly acidic with HCl and is diluted to 150 ml. The solution is then made almost neutral with (1:1) NH_4OH solution. To this solution 2 g of solid NH_4Cl and 2 g of $(NH_4)_2\,PO_4$ are added. If any precipitate appears at this stage it is dissolved by adding a few drops of (1:3) HCl. The solution is now boiled and to it (1:3) NH_4OH solution is added dropwise with constant stirring until the precipitate begins to form. Heating is continued until crystalline precipitate of $Mn(NH_4)$ PO_4. H_2O appears. A few drops of NH_3 solution is added to ensure the complete precipitation. The heating is done at a temperature of 100 °C through out the experiment. The solution is allowed to stand for a few hours. The precipitate is filtered through Whatman filter No. 40, washed with dilute (1%) NH_4NO_3 solution to make it free from Cl^- ions. The filter paper containing the precipitate is placed in a clean, dry and weighed crucible and is converted to $Mn_2P_2O_7$ by igniting the crucible at about 1000 °C for half an hour, cooled in a desiccator and then weighed again.

Calculations: Let the weight of empty crucible be w_1 g and the final weight of the crucible after igniting the precipitate be w_2 g.

∴ The amount of $Mn_2P_2O_7$ obtained is $(w_2 - w_1)$ g.

Hence the amount of Mn present in the supplied solution is

$$(w_2 - w_1) \times 0.3870 \text{ g.}$$

Since 1 g of $Mn_2P_2O_7$ contains 0.3870 g of Mn.

5.8 Determination of Number of Water of Crystallisation in Hydrated Salts

Principle: Hydrated salts like $BaCl_2, 2H_2O, MgSO_4 . 7H_2O$, when heated at a temperature of above 100 °C loses all their water molecules and the corresponding anhydrous salts are formed which are thermally stable and non-volatile in nature. So if a known amount of such salt is ignited at a high temperature, from the loss in weight, the number of water of crystallisation may be determined. Thus,

$$MgSO_4 \cdot 7 H_2O = MgSO_4 + 7 H_2O\uparrow$$

$$BaCl_2 \cdot 2 H_2O = BaCl_2 + 2 H_2O\uparrow$$

Procedure: A silica crucible with lid is cleaned, dried and weighed. To this a known quantity of hydrated salt is taken and heated at a temperature of 120° for approximately an hour. The crucible is cooled in a desiccator covered by the lid and weighed.

Calculations: Let the weight of clean and dry empty crucible with lid be w_1 g and that of the crucible, sample and lid be w_2 g the final weight after heating be w_3 g.

∴ The weight of the hydrated salt taken is $(w_2 - w_1)$ g and weight of anhydrous salt in $(w_3 - w_1)$ g.

Hence weight of water of crystallisation is $(w_2 - w_1) - (w_3 - w_1)$ g $= (w_2 - w_3)$ g.

Ratio of Salt: $H_2O = \dfrac{(w_3 - w_1)}{M} : \dfrac{(w_2 - w_3)}{18}$

where M is the molecular weight of the anhydrous salt.

Comments: Same principle may be followed for determining ferric iron as Fe_2O_3 in ferric alum i.e.,

$$(NH_4)_2 SO_4, Fe_2(SO_4)_3 NH_4, 24 H_2O = Fe_2O_3\downarrow + 2 NH_3\uparrow + 4 SO_3\uparrow + 25 H_2O\uparrow$$

Similarly aluminium as Al_2O_3 may be determined in aluminium alum. Thus,

$$(NH_4)_2 SO_4, Al_2(SO_4)_3, 24 H_2O = Al_2O_3\downarrow + 2 NH_3\uparrow + 4 SO_3\uparrow + 25 H_2O\uparrow$$

Chapter 6

Records of Results

Experiment No: Date:

Determination of Amount of Ferrous Iron in Mohr's Salt by Standard $KMnO_4$ Solution

1. Standardisation of $KMnO_4$ by oxalic acid

Weight of oxalic acid taken for preparing 250 ml solution of $(N/10)$ order $= w$ g.

So its strength is $\dfrac{w}{1.575} = S(N/10)$.

2. Tiration of oxalic acid by $KMnO_4$ solution

Volume of oxalic acid taken	Volume of $KMnO_4$ solution required (Burette reading)	Average of burette readings
25 ml	V_2 ml	V ml
25 ml	V_3 ml	
25 ml	V_4 ml	

Hence, strength of $KMnO_4$ solution

$$25 \times S = V \times x_1$$

or, $x_1 = \dfrac{V}{25 \times S}$ $(N/10) = S_1(N/10)$.

3. Titration of Mohr's salt solution by the standard $KMnO_4$ solution

Volume of Mohr's salt solution taken	Volume of $KMnO_4$ solution required (Burette reading)	Average of burette readings
25 ml	V_5 ml	V_1 ml
25 ml	V_6 ml	
25 ml	V_7 ml	

Therefore, the amount of ferrous iron 25 ml Mohr's salt solution is

$$V_1 \times S_1 \times 0.005585 \text{ g}$$

or, ferrous iron present in one litre is

$$V_1 \times S_1 \times 0.005585 \times 40 \text{ g}.$$

Chapter 7

Questions and Answers for Viva Voce

1. **What are the different methods of quantitative analysis?**

   Ans. Generally there are two different methods of quantitative analysis viz., (i) volumetric and (ii) gravimetric methods.

2. **What is volumetric method of analysis?**

   Ans. In volumetric analysis, the concentration of a solution is determined by allowing a known volume of solution, to react quantitively with another solution of known strength.

3. **What are the conditions required for volumetric analysis?**

   Ans. The following conditions are to be fulfilled for volumetric analysis:

   (i) The reaction should occur easily with faster rate.

   (ii) There must be an appropriate indicator.

   (iii) The reaction should be complete and stoichiometric.

4. **What is a normal solution and a Molar solution.**

   Ans. Normality is the number of gram equivalents of solute present in one litre of its solution. When one gram molecular weight of a solute is dissolved in one litre of a solvent, molar solution of the solute is obtained.

5. **Calculate the equivalent weights of oxalic acid, potassium permanganate, and potassium dichromate.**

   Ans. See Art. 1.5.

6. **What is a standard solution?**

   Ans. A solution of known concentration is called a standard solution.

7. **What are primary and secondary solutions?**

   Ans. Primary standard solutions are those which can be prepared directly by accurately weighing the substance in chmical balance and dissolving it in known volume of solvent in a measuring flask. Examples, Na_2CO_3, oxalic acid, etc.

But secondary standard solution are those which cannot be prepared by direct weighing. They are usually prepared by standardising their approximately standard solutions against a suitable primary standard soltuion.

Examples, HCl, H_2SO_4, $KMnO_4$ etc.

8. How much oxalic acid is to be weighed for the preparation of $(N/10)$ solution?

Ans. 1.575 g is required for 250 ml solution.

9. How would you calculate the rider reading from a balance?

Ans. See Art. 1.4.1

10. What is a titrant?

Ans. The solution whose concentration is known is called titrant.

11. What is a titre?

Ans. The solution whose concentration is to be determined.

12. What is an indicator? Name an acid-base indicator stating the colour it exhibits in acid and alkaline medium.

Ans. An indicator is a chemical substance which can indicate the completion of a chemical reaction. Methyl orange is an acid-base indicator, it is pink in acid and yellow in alkali.

13. What is meant by the 40, 41, 42 of Whatman filter paper?

Ans. Porosity of the filter paper is indicated by the numbers.

14. Pick out the substances that may be used as primary standard.

$KMnO_4$, NaOH, $K_2Cr_2O_7$, H_2SO_4.

Ans. $K_2Cr_2O_7$

15. What is Zimmermann-Reinhardt solution?

Ans. Manganous sulphate solution containing sulphuric and phosphoric acids.

16. Why Reinhardt solution is used in the determination of iron of a given ferric iron solution with permanganate?

Ans. Reinhardt solution is used to prevent the oxidation of Cl^- ion to Cl_2 by MnO_4^-.

17. Why the decolouration of permanganate is slow in the beginning during the standardisation with oxalic acid?

Ans. Oxidation of oxalic acid by $KMnO_4$ is catalysed by manganous ion (Mn^{2+}). Since in the beginning, this ion is not formed, decolouration is slow.

18. Does it necessary to use Reinhardt solution in the estimation of ferric iron by dichromate?

Ans. No.

19. Which one is stronger oxidising agent—$KMnO_4$ or $K_2Cr_2O_7$?

Ans. $KMnO_4$.

20. Why dilute H_2SO_4 is added during the preparation of Mohr's salt solution?

Ans. To prevent hydrolysis.

21. Is it necessary to heat continuously during the oxalic acid-permanganate titration?

Ans. No, heating is needed at the initial stages, but as soon as Mn^{2+} ions are available, they act as auto-catalyst in the rest of the reaction.

22. Why is $KMnO_4$ solution not filtered through filter paper?

Ans. Filter paper contains organic matters which can reduce $KMnO_4$. $KMnO_4$ solution is filtered through glass wool.

23. How can it be known during estimation of iron the addition of stannous chloride is sufficient to reduce entire amount of ferric ion to ferrous ion?

Ans. Appearance of silky white precipitation on addition of mercuric chloride.

24. What is the formula of Mohr's salt?

Ans. $(NH_4)_2SO_4, FeSO_4, 6H_2O$. It is a double salt.

25. During the titration with permanganate why no indicator is used?

Ans. $KMnO_4$ itself acts as the self indicator for its pink colour.

26. What do you mean by available oxygen in pyrolusite?

Ans. Volume of O_2 liberated by MnO_2 of pyrolusite is known as available oxygen in pyrolusite.

27. Why is phosphoric acid is added before the titration of ferrous ion with dichromate in presence of barium diphenyl amine sulphonate?

Ans. Phosphoric acid is used to reduce the standard potential of Fe^{3+}/Fe^{2+} system and this makes the indicator suitable for the titration.

28. Why is $K_2Cr_2O_7$ accepted as a primary standard?

Ans. It is available in pure and stable form.

29. What are meant by the terms iodometry and iodimetry?

Ans. See Art. 2.2.3.

30. What is meant by available chlorine in bleaching powder? How is it estimated?

Ans. See Art. 2.2.3.1.8.

31. Why is ammonium thiocyanate added in the iodometric estimation of copper with thiosulphate?

Ans. Some amount of iodine is absorbed by cuprous iodide. Ammonium thiocyanate converts Cu_2I_2 into $Cu(SCN)_2$ which is more insoluble, and absorbed iodine is set free.

32. Why is iodometric titration is carried out in the cold?

Ans. To minimise the loss of iodine through volatilisation.

33. What is the commonly used indicator in iodometric titration?

Ans. Starch.

34. Which portion of starch gives blue colour with iodine?

Ans. Starch which is a polysaccharide consists of two components—amylose and amylopectin. Amylose forms a blue coloured complex with iodine.

35. Why the starch solution is added at the end of the titration?

Ans. Starch can absorb iodine. So to minimise the absorption of iodine starch is added at the end of titration.

36. Why the fresh solution of starch is used?

Ans. Starch solution is a very good nutrient medium for microorganism and so it rapidly decomposes.

37. When should the starch solution be added?

Ans. Starch solution should be added at the end of titration. Since at the end concentration of iodine is low, absorption of it becomes less.

38. How may the decomposition of starch be avoided?

Ans. If a few milligram of HgI_2 is added to starch-potassium iodide solution decomposition may be avoided.

39. What is the function of bifluoride in the titration of copper in the brass?

Ans. Iron is present in brass. So to suppress the interference of iron, bifluoride is added. Bifluoride forms complex with iron as $[FeF_6]^{3-}$.

40. What is the principle of quantitative analysis of iron and calcium mixture?

Ans. See Art. 3.6.

41. What is the role of NH_4HF_2 in the titration of ferrous iron with dichromate.

Ans. It reduces the standard potential of Fe^{3+}/Fe^{2+} system due to formation of FeF_6^{3-}. It also helps in detecting sharp end-point by masking yellow colour of Fe^{3+}.

42. What is the role of Na_2O_2 in the estimation of iron (III) and chromium (III)?

Ans. It oxidises $Cr(III)$ to CrO_4^{2-} and precipitates $Fe(OH)_3$.

43. Can cupric copper be directly estimated in presence of Fe^{3+}?

Ans. By adding NH_4HF_2, Cu^{2+} can be directly estimated.

44. What are meant by acidimetry and alkalimetry?

Ans. That branch of volumetric analysis which involves the reaction between acid and base.

45. What are the indicators commonly used in acidimetry-alkalimetry?

Ans. Phenolphthalein with strong base, methyl orange with weak base.

46. What do you mean by complexometric titration?

Ans. See Chapter 4.

47. What is the most common organic ligand used in complexometry?

Ans. Ethylene diamine tetra-acetic acid, abbreviated as EDTA. This short name is more popular. It is available as its disodium salt.

48. Why is the pH of the solution be kept within certain limit in complexometric titration with EDTA?

Ans. When EDTA forms, complex, H^+ ions are released, and since the reaction is reversible, increase in H^+ may decrease the stability of the complex and excess of EDTA may be required and error may result.

49. What is metal-indicators?

Ans. See Art. 4.1.

50. What is the cause of hardness of water?

Ans. See Art. 4.7.

51. How the hardness of water can be estimated by EDTA?

Ans. See Art. 4.7.

52. What is the unit of hardness?

Ans. Part(s) per million (ppm).

53. What do you mean by gravimetric analysis?

Ans. See Chapter 5.

54. What are the conditions to be fulfilled for fruitful gravimetric analysis?

Ans. See Chapter 5.

55. Why the solution should be faintly acidic during the precipitation of copper?

Ans. The precipitate is soluble in higher acidity.

56. Outline the principle of estimation of iron and zinc when they are present in a mixture?

Ans. See Art. 3.5.

57. Discuss the principle of estimation of iron and calcium in a mixture.

Ans. See Art. 3.6.

58. What is the principle of estimation of iron and chromium in a mixture?

Ans. See Art. 3.1.

59. Discuss the principle of estimation of iron and manganese present in a mixture.

Ans. See Art. 3.3.

60. What do you mean by precipitation titration?

Ans. In this type of titration the strength of a solution is determined by its complete precipitation with the help of a standard solution of another substance. Thus,

$$AgNO_3 + NaCl \longrightarrow AgCl + NaNO_3$$

$$AgNO_3 + KCNS \longrightarrow AgCNS + KNO_3$$

Inorganic Preparations

Part III

Chapter 1

Preparations

The preparation of chemical substances in the laboratory provides an excellent mean of acquiring practical knowledge on applied chemistry. Although laboratory preparations involve simple reactions but can provide fundamental working knowledge of industrial methods. So it is felt pertinent to discuss preparation of a few inorganic compounds.

1.1 Preparation of Sodium Trioxalato Ferrate

$$\{Na_3[Fe(C_2O_4)_3], 9H_2O\}$$

1.1.1 Reaction Involved in the Preparation

Hydrated ferric oxide when dissolved in aqueous solution of oxalic acid containing sodium hydroxide, sodium trioxalato ferrate is obtained as green crystals.

$$Fe_2O_3 + 6Na_2C_2O_4 = 2Na_3[Fe(C_2O_4)_3]$$

Green cystals

1.1.2 Chemicals Required for the Preparation

1. Ferric chloride   7.5 g
2. Sodium hydroxide   9.0 g
3. Oxalic acid   9.0 g

1.1.3 Procedure

(a) **Preparation of hydrated ferric oxide:** In a beaker 7.5 g of ferric chloride is dissolved in 5 ml of water. To it 6 g of sodium hydroxide dissolved in 5 ml of water is added little at a time with stirring. It is allowed to stand for 5 minutes. The precipitate of ferric hydroxide, $Fe(OH)_3$ formed, is filtered and washed 5-6 times with hot water.

(b) Preparation of sodium trioxalato ferrate: In a beaker 9.0 g of oxalic acid is taken and is dissolved in 30 ml of hot water. To it 3 g of sodium hydroxide is added and shaken well. To this hot alkaline solution ferric hydroxide (hydrated ferric oxide) prepared earlier is added in small portion with constant stirring when green solution of the desired compound is formed. The solution is filtered and the filtrate is concentrated in a silica dish on a water bath. Green crystals of sodium trioxalato ferrate are formed. It is filtered and dried by soaking through blotting paper.

The yield is 15 g.

The prepared sample is kept in labelled test tube.

1.2 Preparation of Copper Tetramine Sulphate

$$\{[Cu(NH_3)_4] SO_4.H_2O\}$$

1.2.1 Reactions Involved

When solution of ammonia is added to a solution of copper sulphate, cupric tetramine sulphate is formed.

$$CuSO_4 + 4NH_3 + H_2O = [Cu(NH_3)_4]SO_4.H_2O$$

1.2.2 Chemicals Required

1. Copper sulphate   5 g
2. Liquor ammonia   50 ml
3. Dilute sulphuric acid   10 ml
4. Rectified spirit   50 ml

1.2.3 Procedure

5 g of copper sulphate (finely powdered) is taken in a beaker and is dissolved in minimum quantity of water containing a few drops of H_2SO_4. To it liquor ammonia is added drop from a dropping funnel till the blue precipitate formed is dissolved with the formation of a deep blue coloured solution.

To this blue coloured solution 50 ml of rectified spirit is slowly added with constant stirring. The beaker is covered with a watch-glass and allowed to stand for 15 minutes. Long needle-shaped blue crystals of the desired compound are separated out. It is filtered and washed with a few drops of rectified spirit and dried in a desiccator.

The yield is 7 g.

The sample is kept as usual in a labelled test tube.

1.3 Preparation of Nickel Dimethyl Glyoxime

1.3.1 Reactions Involved

When an alcoholic solution of dimethyl glyoxime is added to an ammoniacal solution of nickel sulphate a scarlet red precipitate of nickel dimethyl glyoxime is formed.

$$NiSO_4 \ + \ 2 \quad \begin{array}{c} CH_3-C=N-OH \\ | \\ CH_3-C=N-OH \end{array} \quad + \ 2NH_4OH$$

1.3.2 Chemicals Required

Nickel sulphate	7 g
Ammonia solution (1:1)	50 ml
Dimethyl Glyoxime	2 g
Rectified spirit	250 ml

1.3.3 Procedure

7 g of Nickel sulphate is taken in a beaker and is dissolved in 10 ml of distilled water. This solution is diluted to 100 ml and is heated to 70-80 °C. To this hot solution 2 g of dimethyl glyoxime dissolved in 100 ml rectified spirit is added followed by immediate dropwise addition of dilute (1:1) ammonia solution till the smell of ammonia persists. The reaction is allowed to stand on a water bath for half an hour. The solution is cooled and allowed to settle down for an hour. The solid residue is filtered, washed with hot water and dried in vacuum desiccator. The product obtained is scarlet red crystals and is preserved in a well stoppered test tube.

Yield: 8 g.

1.4 Preparation of Mohr's Salt (Ferrous Ammonium Sulphate)

$$\{[FeSO_4, (NH_4)_2SO_4], 6H_2O\}$$

1.4.1 Reactions Involved

Mohr's salt is a double salt consisting of ferrous and ammonium sulphates. It is light green transparent crystals. It is prepared by mixing equimolecular amount of hydrated ferrous sulphate and ammonium sulphate in water containing little sulphuric acid.

$$FeSO_4 \cdot 7H_2O \ + \ (NH_4)_2SO_4 \longrightarrow FeSO_4 \cdot (NH_4)_2SO_4 \cdot 6H_2O \ + \ H_2O$$

1.4.2 Chemicals Required

1. Ferrous sulphate   7 g
2. Ammonium sulphate   4 g
3. Dilute sulphuric acid   2 ml

1.4.3 Procedure

7 g of ferrous sulphate and 4 g of ammonium sulphate are mixed together and the mixture is taken in a 500 ml beaker. This mixture is dissolved in 50 ml of water containing 2 ml of dilute sulphuric acid. It is warmed to get clear solution. It is filtered and concentrated by heating over a sand bath. The solution is stirred well during heating. The heating is continued till precipitation appears. The beaker, containing the reaction mixture, is now cooled under tap. After 15-20 minutes crystals of Mohr's salt seperate. The crystals are separated by decantation, washed with water, dried by spreading on a porous plate and kept in a stoppered test tube.

The yield = 10 g.

[N.B. Dilute sulphuric acid is added to prevent hydrolysis of ferrous sulphate.]

1.5 Preparation of Sodium Cobaltinitrite

$$\{Na_3[CO(NO_2)_6]\}$$

1.5.1 Reactions Involved

When a solution of sodium nitrite is added to a solution of cobalt nitrate in cold and the resulting mixture is acidified with glacial acetic acid, sodium cobalt nitrite is formed. Thus,

$$NaNO_2 + CH_3COOH \longrightarrow HNO_2 + CH_3COONa$$

$$CO(NO_3)_2 + 3NaNO_2 + 2HNO_2 \longrightarrow Na_3[CO(NO_2)_6] + NO\uparrow + H_2O$$

$$\text{(Yellow)}$$

1.5.2 Chemicals Required

1. Sodium nitrite   15 g
2. Cobalt nitrate   5 g
3. Glacial acetic acid   5 ml
4. Rectified spirit   25 ml

1.5.3 Procedure

15 g of sodium nitrite taken in a beaker is dissolved in 50 ml of warm water and cooled. To it 5 g of cobalt nitrate is added in portion with constant stirring until it is completely dissolved. 5 ml of glacial acetic acid mixed with equal volume of water is slowly added to the reaction solution with stirring. The solution is filtered and to the filtrate 20 ml of reactified spirit is added in small portion and it is left for several hours preferably overnight. The yellow precipitate of the desired compound is separated out. It is filtered, washed with small quantity of rectified spirit until the washings are colourless. The yellow crystalline sodium cobalt initrite is spread on a filter paper and dried in air. It is kept in well stoppered bottle and labelled test tube.

Yield : 15 g.

Chapter 2

Questions and Answers for Viva Voce

1. How will you prepare sodium trioxalato ferrate?
   Ans. See Art. 1.1.
2. Write down the reactions involved in the preparation of sodium tri oxalato ferrate.
   Ans. See Art. 1.1.
3. What are the chemical reactions involved in the preparation of copper tetramine sulphate.
   Ans. See Art. 1.2.
4. Describe the preparation of nickel dimethyl glyoxime.
   Ans. See Art. 1.3.
5. Write the formula of Mohr's salt. Is it a complex compound?
   Ans. See Art. 1.4. No, it is a double salt.
6. Write the reactions for the preparation of sodium cobaltinitrite.
   Ans. See Art. 1.5.1.

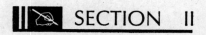

ORGANIC CHEMISTRY PRACTICAL

ORGANIC CHEMISTRY PRACTICAL

Introduction

Laboratory experiments on organic chemistry to be performed by the general and honours students of undergraduate level involves following types of works:

1. Qualitative Analysis of Single Organic Compound.
2. Preparative Chemistry Involving Typical Organic Reactions.
3. Quantitative Analysis.
4. Separation of Components of Organic Mixture and Isolation of Organic Compounds from Natural Source.

Before going into the detailed discussion on the above types of experiments it is felt pertinent to mention some useful aspects on organic laboratory experiments in general.

The aim of organic laboratory work is to train the students in the art of chemical reactions and to motivate them in the scientific principle on which the art is founded. However, it must be remembered in this context that since the organic chemicals are covalently bonded compounds they are not readily ionisable. As a result, organic reactions are much more time consuming than their inorganic counterparts which, in general, involve ionic compounds. So it is obvious that the processes to achieve the primary goal, organic laboratory experiments should be lengthy and time consuming. So each and every experiment must be performed with extreme patience and care. Otherwise inconclusive result may be obtained.

Another aspect which must be mentioned here is that for rapid and efficient performance of each experiment clear undrstanding of the principles of different laboratory techniques is essentially required. Once again, smooth and efficient performance of any experment is possible if it is properly planned in advance and is carried out purposefully during the laboratory work. Further, work in the laboratory should be carried out in open and inquiring mind and should be recorded what are actually observed. Again, every student should take care about the quality, quantity and the presentation of the work performed and all the observations and results should be recorded in a notebook.

Qualitative Analysis of Single Organic Compound

Part I

Chapter 1

General Discussion

The organic qualitative analysis is concerned with the identification of organic compounds. The process of identification involves the study of characteristic properties of organic compounds. It is known that the characteristic behaviours of organic compounds find their origin from the functional group(s) present in them. Again, the behaviour of functional groups depends upon the nature of element to which it is associated. It is thus obvious that the process of qualitative organic analysis involves a series of steps that help to establish the identity of the compound. This analysis begins with a preliminary tests which provide certain clue about the type and class of the compound under examination. In genral, following procedures are adapted for the systematic analysis of organic compounds:

1. **Study on Physical Properties**: The physical properties of organic compounds are ascertained by studying the following characteristics of the compound:

(a) **Physical state**: The physical state of the compound, i.e., whether it is solid or liquid, must be known as it helps in determining the subsequent step to be undertaken for the identification process.

(b) **Colour**: Among the huge number of organic compounds only a few are coloured. So it is natural that the colour of the compound may reveal the presence of certain groups like — NO_2(nitro), — NH_2 (amino), $>C=O$ (carbonyl), etc. These coloured groups are active towards ultraviolet light.

(c) **Odour**: A large number of organic compounds possess characteristic odour and so odour may be helpful in ascertaining the presence of certain functional groups.

(d) **Acid-base character**: Acid-base character is also an important physical property. It is usually studied in solution either with the help of litmus paper or pH-paper. From the change of colour of above papers the nature of the compound i.e., whether the compound belongs to acidic, basic or neutral group may be known. So it may be helpful in the identification of the functional group present.

(e) **Ignition:** This test helps to draw the general conclusion regarding the type of the compound. This test is carried out by taking a small quantity of the substance in a platinum spatula and is burnt on a naked flame. Aromatic compounds due to their higher content of carbon burn with a sooty flame but a yellowish flame is obtained when aliphatic compounds are burnt. Further a few organic compounds like sugars char and leave a black residue with characteristic odour.

(f) **Solubility:** In general, low molecular weight organic compounds are soluble in water and others dissolve in common organic solvents such as ethanol, ether, acetone, benzene, etc. Normally, solubility test of organic compounds are performed in (i) water (ii) 5% NaOH, (iii) 5% HCl and (iv) 5% NaHCO$_3$ solutions. By testing the solubility of the compound in these reagents, it is possible to ascertain whether the compound belongs to low molecular weight group, neutral, acidic or basic type. In this connection a solubility chart may be drawn which may act as a guideline in classifying the compounds.

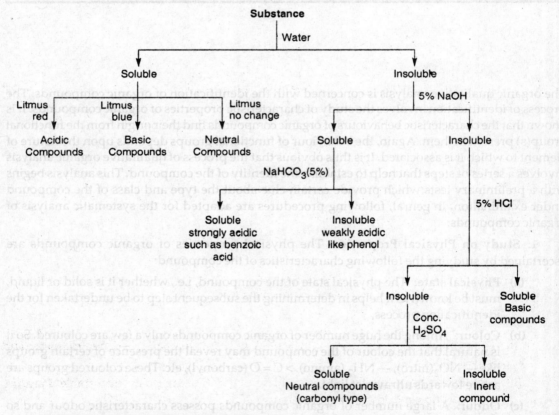

(g) **Melting and boiling points:** These two physical constants are important criteria not only for the identification but also for the purity of the substance. A pure compound exhibits a very sharp melting point or a boiling point as the case may be. The lack of sharp melting point or boiling point for a substance reveals its impurity. These physical constants are determined by the procedures depicted below.

(i) **Determination of melting point of a solid substance:** A little of the powdered solid sample is introduced into a capillary tube. This is carried out by inverting a capillary tube and a small portion of the sample is scooped up with the open end of the tube. Next the capillary tube is reverted and the solid is tamped into the bottom by gently tapping the tube on the desk holding the capillary tube with the thumb and forefinger. Finally the capillary tube is also dropped through a 2ft long glass tube for complete transfer of the solid sample into the bottom of the capillary tube. The capillary tube containing the sample is attached to a calibrated thermometer by moistening it with the liquid of the bath. The thermometer along with attached capillary tube is suspended in a bath of conc. H_2SO_4 as shown in the figure below.

The bath is slowly heated; the temperature at which melting just begins and becomes complete is noted. This is the melting point of the solid sample under examination.

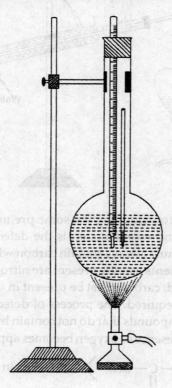

Comments

(i) The capillary tube should be thin-walled with approximately 1-2 mm diameter and sealed at one end.

(ii) Liquids are in use for the bath should be of high boiling points and stable. Paraffin, glycerol and conc. H_2SO_4 are commonly used.

(iii) Some substances decompose before melting. For such compounds the bath is heated slightly below the expected melting point and next the capillary tube containing the sample should be attached. Then further heating is continued.

(iv) For prolonged use, H_2SO_4 becomes coloured due to the presence of charred samples. To make it clear a few crystals of KNO_3 are dropped into the bath.

(ii) Determination of boiling point of a liquid substance: The apparaturs required for determining the boiling point is as shown in the figure below. The liquid is taken in the distilling flask and the thermometer is fitted at the mouth of the distilling flask through a cork in such a way that it just dips into the centre of the flask. A few pieces of porous beads are dropped into the liquid. The flask is connected to a water condenser and is gently heated by a small flame. The whole of the liquid, if it is pure, passes over at a constant temperature. This constant temperature is the required boiling point of the liquid under consideration.

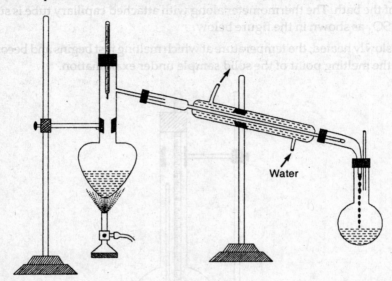

Water

2. Detection of eliments: After studying the some preliminary examinations of physical properties next most important and essential step is the detection of elements present in the compound. Organic compounds must always contain carbon whereas hydrogen and oxygen are often present. In addition, the elements usually present are nitrogen, sulphur, halogens (F, Cl, Br, I), phosphorous, etc. As mentioned, carbon must be present in organic compounds, detection of this element usually is not at all required. The process of detection of hydrogen is a very time consuming one and only a few compounds that do not contain hydrogen offer no difficulty in the detection of other elements. The presence of oxygen becomes apparent from the recognition of the

functional groups such as $-OH$, $-\underset{\underset{O}{\|}}{C}-OH$, $>C=O$, etc. In view of the above consideration

as well as from the limitations of the syllabus only those elements such as nitrogen, sulphur and halogens termed as *special elements* are normally detected for the purpose of identification of organic compounds. The detection of these *special elements* has immense importance in the identification of organic compound, particularly in the class determination. Thus, organic compounds may broadly be classified as (i) non-nitrogeneous and (ii) nitrogeneous. This classification will be of great help in selecting the procedure for ascertaining the nature of functional group; as for example, for non-nitrogeneous compounds tests for nitrogen containing functional group need not be performed, while when nitrogen is present, test for nitrogen containing group will highly enlighten regarding the identity of the compound.

3. Detection of functional group: Detection of functional group constitutes another vital step to establish the identity of the compound under examination. This step provides an insight into the form in which the different elements exist in the compound. The procedure involved in this step has clearly two distinct parts, viz, (i) detection of group(s) on the basis of some standard tests and (ii) confirmation of the presence of such group(s) by the preparation of derivatives. In this connection following guidlines are to be remembered.

(a) When special elements (mainly nitrogen, sulphur and halogens) are absent, i.e., the compound contains only carbon, hydrogen and oxygen, the expected types of compounds and the functional groups (functional group in the parenthesis) are as under:

    (i) Alcohols (R—OH)

    (ii) Phenols (Ar—OH)

    (iii) esters (—COOR)

    (iv) alkoxy (—O—R)

(b) When nitrogen is present along with common elements, the types of compound may be

    (i) amines (—NH$_2$)

    (ii) amides (—C—NH$_2$)
$$\underset{\displaystyle O}{\overset{\displaystyle \|}{}}$$

    (iii) anilides (—C—NH—Ar)
$$\underset{\displaystyle O}{\overset{\displaystyle \|}{}}$$

    (iv) nitro (—N=O)
$$\downarrow$$
$$O$$

(c) If sulphur is present along with other elements, the compound is expected to be

    (i) sulphonic acid (—SO$_3$H)

    (ii) sulphonamides (—S—NH$_2$)
$$\overset{\displaystyle O}{\underset{\displaystyle O}{\|\,\|}}$$

(d) If halogens are present the compound may be halogen substituted above types of compounds.

It is, thus, evident from the above discussions that in order to identify the organic compounds with certainty, steps depicted above should be systematically followed.

Chapter 2

Detection of Elements

For the detection of nitrogen, sulphur and halogens it is necessary to fuse the organic compound with sodium metal to prepare the sodium fusion extract by *Lassaigne's test* as discussed below.

2.1 Lassaigne's Test

A piece of metallic sodium (about 0.04 g) is taken in a clean and dry ignition tube (fusion tube) made of soft glass. It is carefully heated over a flame and a little of the organic compound under investigation is added over the molten sodium metal. The fusion tube is heated first gently and next strongly till red hot. Again, a little more substance is added and heated similarly till red hot. Immediately, the hot fusion tube is carefully immersed in 15 ml of distilled water taken in a porcelain mortar and broken by tapping. The broken glass piece and the fused mass is ground thoroughly by a pestle. The mixture is filtered to remove glass splinters. The filtrate is known as *sodium fusion extract*. Following experiments as presented in the tabular form below are carried out for the identification of nitrogen, sulphur and halogens.

Treatment of Sodium Fusion Extract

Experiments	Observations	Inference
(i) A portion of the filtrate is taken in a test tube and 3-4 drops of freshly prepared ferrous sulphate solution are added. The mixture is boiled about a minute and cooled. The cold solution is acidified with dilute H_2SO_4	(i) A prussian blue colouration or precipitate appears.	(i) Nitrogen present
(ii) A little of the filtrate is taken in a test tube and to it 1-2 drops of freshly prepared sodium nitro-prusside solution are added.	(ii) A violet colour appears.	(ii) Sulphur present.

Contd.

Experiments	Observations	Inference
(iii) 1 ml of the filtrate is taken in a test tube and is acidified with dilute acetic acid. To it 1-2 drops of saturated solution of lead acetate is added.	(iii) A black precipitate is formed	(iii) Sulphur present.
(iv) A little of the filtrate is taken in a test tube and is acidified with dilute HNO_3, boiled and to this acidified solution several drops of $AgNO_3$ solution are added.	(iva) A white or yellow precipitate appears.	(iva) Halogens – chlorine, bromine and iodine are present.
	(ivb) The white precipitate formed is soluble in dilute NH_4OH but reappears on acidification with dilute HNO_3.	(ivb) Chlorine present.
	(ivc) The yellow precipitate is difficultly dissolved in dilute NH_4OH but insoluble in dilute HNO_3.	(ivc) Bromine.
	(ivd) The yellow precipitate is insoluble in NH_4OH and in dilute HNO_3.	(ivd) Iodine.
(va) Another part of the filtrate is acidified with dilute HCl or H_2SO_4 and to it 1-2 ml of carbon tetra-chloride is added. Now strong chlorine water is added dropwise with shaking.	(va) Carbon tetra chloride layer turns	
	(va)(i) Violet	(va)(i) Iodine.
	(va)(ii) Brown or reddish brown.	(va)(ii) Bromine.
(vb) If carbon tetrachloride layer becomes violet after addition of chlorine water the process of dropwise addition of chlorine water is continued till the violet colour disappears.	(vb)(i) Violet colour disappears but a reddish brown colour appears.	(vb)(i) Both iodine and bromine present.
	(vb)(ii) Carbon tetrachloride layer becomes colourless.	(vb)(ii) Iodine present but bromine absent.
	(vb)(iii) No violet or brown colour at all.	(vb)(iii) Iodine and bromine are absent but chlorine may present.

Comments

(i) During detection of nitrogen, after addition of ferrous sulphate solution, the solution may be acidified with conc. HCl followed by addition of a few drops of $FeCl_3$ solution instead of acidification with dilute H_2SO_4.

(ii) If no green precipitate or colouration appears on adding ferrous sulphate solution, a few drops of dilute NaOH solution may be added.

(iii) If a black precipitate appears after addition of ferrous sulphate solution, the reaction mixture is boiled by adding a little more ferrous sulphate solution, cooled and filtered to remove the black precipitate of FeS. With the filtrate, test for nitrogen is performed.

(iv) When both nitrogen and sulphur are present in the sample, it becomes difficult to detect nitrogen and sulphur because of the incomplete fusion. But in such situation *sulphocyanide test* may be performed. This test is carried by acidifying 1-2 ml of sodium extract with dilute HCl followed by addition of 1-2 drops of $FeCl_3$ solution when the development of blood red colouration indicates the presence of both nitrogen and sulphur.

(v) Presence of halogen may be confirmed by *performing flame test* which is commonly known as *Beilstein test*. This is performed as follows:

Beilstein test: A thick copper wire of about 4" length fitted with a cork at one end and bent at other end is taken. The bent end is strongly heated in the oxidising flame of the burner until the bent end of the wire ceases to impart any colour to the flame. It is cooled and a small portion of the sample is placed on the bent end and heated over the outer edge of the flame. Appearance of a green colour of the flame indicates the presence of *halogens*.

It may be remembered that this test is very sensitive and it has been observed that in some cases compounds having no halogen may respond to this test. Hence this test cannot be considered as a confirmatory test. However, if there is no colour, this test may be accepted as an evidence for the absence of halogen.

(vi) The sodium extract of the sample may also be prepared by Middleton's method as described below:

Middleton's test: In this test pure zinc dust and pure anhydrous sodium carbonate in the ratio 2:1 is mixed together. A small portion of the solid sample is taken in a fusion tube and it is covered with the 3 cm thick layer of fusion mixture just prepared (Zn-dust and Na_2CO_3 mixture) and is shaken well and a little more fusion mixture is added. The reaction mixture is gently heated, starting the heating from upper portion of the fusion tube. Gradually the heating is extended to the bottom portion. Finally, fusion tube is strongly heated until it becomes red hot. The hot fusion tube is plunged into 20 ml of water taken in a porcelain mortar, ground and filtered. With the filtrate, tests for different elements are performed as in the case of Lassigne's method. *In this method presence of sulphur does not interfere in the test of nitrogen due to the formation of water insoluble ZnS which remains in the residue.* The residue on the filter paper is treated with dilute HCl when smell of rotten egg for H_2S is evolved if sulphur is present.

2.2 Chemical Reactions Involved in the above Tests for Detection of Special Elements

2.2.1 Lassigne's Test

In this method sodium metal combines with the elements present in the sample and converts them into water soluble salts as shown below:

$$C + N + Na \longrightarrow NaCN$$

$$S + 2Na \longrightarrow Na_2S$$

$$X + Na \longrightarrow NaX$$
(Halogens)

$$C + N + S + Na \longrightarrow NaSCN \quad \text{(incomplete fusion)}$$

Sodium
sulphocyanide

2.2.1.1 Tests for Nitrogen

NaCN formed is allowed to react with $FeSO_4$ solution when sodium ferrocyanide is formed. On boiling the alkaline solution some ferric ions are formed due to oxidation by air. Both ferrous and ferric hydroxides are dissolved on adding dilute H_2SO_4. Ferrocyanide formed reacts with ferric ions to produce Prussian blue colour or precipitate.

$$2NaCN + FeSO_4 \longrightarrow Fe(CN)_2 + Na_2SO_4; \quad 4NaCN + Fe(CN)_2 \longrightarrow Na_4[Fe(CN)_6]$$
$$\text{Sodium ferrocyanide}$$

$$4FeSO_4 + 2H_2SO_4 + O_2 \longrightarrow 2Fe_2(SO_4)_3 + 2H_2O \quad \text{(Air oxidation in presence of } H_2SO_4\text{)}$$

$$3Na_4[Fe(CN)_6] + 2Fe_2(SO_4)_3 \longrightarrow Fe_4[Fe(CN)_6] + 6Na_2SO_4$$
$$\text{Ferroso ferri}$$
$$\text{cyanide}$$
$$\text{(Prussian blue)}$$

2.2.1.2 Tests for Sulphur

(a) Nitroprusside test: Na_2S formed during sodium extract reacts with sodium nitroprusside to form sodium sulphonitroprusside.

$$Na_2S + Na_2[Fe(CN)_6NO] \longrightarrow Na_4[Fe(CN)_6NOS]$$
$$\text{Sodium nitroprusside} \qquad\qquad \text{Sodium sulpho-}$$
$$\text{nitroprusside}$$
$$\text{(Violet)}$$

(b) Lead acetate test: Na_2S formed on treatment with acetic acid yields H_2S which reacts with lead acetate solution to afford insoluble PbS.

$$Na_2S + 2CH_3COOH \longrightarrow 2CH_3COONa + H_2S$$

$$(CH_3COO)_2Pb + H_2S \longrightarrow 2CH_3COOH + PbS$$
$$\text{(Black)}$$

(c) When both nitrogen and sulphur present: It has been mentioned [comment (iv)] that when both nitrogen and sulphur are present in the sample sodium sulphocyanide is formed instead of sodium sulphide due to incomplete fusion. In this case sodium extract is acidified with dilute HCl and a few drops of $FeCl_3$ solution are added. Thus,

$$C + N + S + Na \longrightarrow NaCNS$$
$$\text{Sodium sulphocyanide}$$

$$3NaCNS + FeCl_3 \longrightarrow Fe(CNS)_3 + 3NaCl$$
$$\text{Ferric}$$
$$\text{sulphocyanide}$$
$$\text{(Blood red colour)}$$

2.2.1.3 Tests for Halogens

(a) AgNO$_3$ test: Sodium halide, NaX, formed during fusion, reacts with AgNO$_3$ solution to form insoluble silver halide.

$$NaX + AgNO_3 \xrightarrow[HNO_3]{dil.} AgX\downarrow + NaNO_3$$

AgX is insoluble in HNO$_3$. *Acidification of the extract is essential because* it is alkaline and when AgNO$_3$ is added to it Ag(OH) may be precipitated even if halogens are absent. But in acidic solution formation of Ag(OH) is not possible. Further, *if nitrogen or sulphur be present boiling with dilute HNO$_3$ is required to drive away* **HCN** or **H$_2$S** otherwise **AgCN** and **Ag$_2$S** *may be precipitated which may create confusion.*

$$NaCN + HNO_3 \longrightarrow HCN\uparrow + NaNO_3; \quad Na_2S + 2HNO_3 \longrightarrow H_2S\uparrow + 2NaNO_3$$

In the case of chlorine AgCl is formed which is soluble in NH$_4$OH due to the formation of argento ammonium chloride which is soluble in NH$_4$OH solution.

$$NaCl + AgNO_3 \longrightarrow AgCl\downarrow \xrightarrow{NH_4OH} Ag(NH_3)_2Cl$$
$$\text{Soluble}$$

AgBr reacts similarly but the corresponding salt is soluble in excess NH$_4$OH while AgI does not form such salt, i.e.,

$$NaBr + AgNO_3 \longrightarrow AgBr \xrightarrow{NH_4OH} Ag(NH_3)_2Br$$
$$\text{(Soluble in excess NH}_4\text{OH)}$$

$$NaI + AgNO_3 \longrightarrow AgI \xrightarrow{NH_4OH} \text{No reaction}$$

(b) Chlorine-water test: Sodium bromide and sodium iodide formed during fusion, on reaction with aquous chlorine solution liberate bromine and iodine having characteristic colour.

$$2NaBr + Cl_2 \longrightarrow 2NaCl + Br_2$$
$$\text{(Brown)}$$

$$2NaI + Cl_2 \longrightarrow 2NaCl + I_2$$
$$\text{(Violet)}$$

I$_2$ liberated, with excess of chlorine water forms colourless hydroiodic acid.

$$I_2 + 5Cl_2 + 6H_2O \longrightarrow 2HIO_3 + 10HCl$$
$$\text{(Colourless)}$$

Chapter 3

Detection of Functional Groups

As mentioned before (vide Chapter 1, item 2) that the organic compounds may broadly be classified into two types on the basis of presence or absence of elements particularly nitrogen such as nitrogenous and non-nitrogenous compounds. Further, the form in which the elements are present in the compound is manifested by the nature of functional groups. It is, therefore, obvious that functional groups may also primarily be classified into similar two such categories, i.e., non-nitrogenous and nitrogenous functional groups. For identification of functional group(s) present in an organic compound in a systematic manner, it is convenient to perform the chemical tests of individual groups by following two different approaches for two different categories of commonly encountered functional groups.

3.1 Detection of Non-nitrogenous Functional Groups

Non-nitrogenous functional groups frequently observed in organic compounds are —OH (phenolic or alcoholic), > C=O (carbonyl, aldehydic and Ketonic), —COOH(Carboxylic), > C=C < (unsaturation) and —COOR (ester) groups. These functional groups are detected by following the procedures as tabulated below (Tables 3.1-3.6). The tests are performed with the aqueous or alcoholic solution as the case may be.

Table 3.1: Test for carboxylic group (—COOH)

Experiments	Observations	Inference
1. Litmus test: 2 ml of aqueous or alcoholic solution of the original sample is taken in a test tube and is tested with a blue litmus paper.	1. Blue litmus turns red.	1. — COOH or phenolic group is present.
2. Bicarbonate test: To another portion of 2 ml of aqueous or alcoholic solution an aqueous solution of $NaHCO_3$ is added drop by drop.	2. Effervescence of CO_2 occurs.	2. — COOH group present.

Contd.

Experiments	Observations	Inference
3. Phenolphthalein test: In a test tube 5 ml of NaOH solution is taken and to it 1-2 drops of phenolphthalein is added when a pink colour appears. To this pink solution solution original sample solution is added drop by drop.	3. Pink colour disappears.	3. — COOH group present.
4. Esterification test: A few portion of the solid sample is taken in a test tube and to it 2 ml of ethyl alcohol and 2-3 drops of concentrated H_2SO_4 are added and is heated on a water bath for 5 minutes. The product is then poured into a large volume of water taken in a beaker.	4. Characteristic fruity smell is obtained.	4. — COOH group confirmed.

Reactions involved in the above test:

(i) **Bicarbonate test:** $RCOOH + NaHCO_3 = RCOONa + CO_2\uparrow + H_2O$

(ii) **Esterification test:** $R—COOH + C_2H_5OH + H_2SO_4 = R—COOC_2H_5 + H_2O + H_2SO_4$

Ester
(Fruity smell)

Table 3.2: Test for carbonyl group (> C = O)

Experiments	Observations	Inference
1. Sodium bisulphite test: About 2 ml of saturated solution of $NaHSO_3$ is taken in a test tube and to it about 0.05 g of the original solid sample is added and shaken very vigorously.	1. Colourless crystalline precipitate appears.	1. Carbonyl group (aldehyde or ketone) is present.
2. 2:4-Dinitrophenyl hydrazine test (D.N.P.H. test): About 0.05 g of the solid original sample is added to 3 ml of saturated ethanolic solution of 2:4-Dinitrophenyl Hydrazine taken in test tube and shaken well. The test tube is gently heated on a water bath for 2-3 minutes and allowed to stand for 5 minutes. If no precipitate appears, 1 or 2-drops water is added warmed and cooled.	2. Yellow, orange or red precipitate or colouration.	2. Carbonyl group (aldehyde or ketone) is confirmed.

Distinction between an aldehydic and a ketonic group: If a carbonyl group is detected, in a compound it may be either an aldehydic ($R - C - H$) or a ketonic ($\underset{R}{\overset{R}{>}}C = O$) group. Distinction
between these two functional groups are made by the tests as tabulated in *Table 3.2A*

Table 3.2A: Distinction between aldehyde and ketone

Experiments	Observations	Inference
1. **Schiff's test**: To 2-3 ml of schiff's reagent about 0.05 g of the sample is added, shaken well and allowed to stand.	1. Pink colour develops	1. Aldehyde may be present.
2. **Tollen's test**: In a test tube Tollen's reagent is prepared by adding 1 ml of aqueous NaOH to 1 ml of aqueous $AgNO_3$ solution and then adding dilute NH_4OH solution drop by drop until the precipitate of Ag_2O just dissolves. To this reagent solution about 0.05 g of the sample is added, shaken well and warmed on a water bath.	2. A shining mirror is formed on the inner wall of the test tube or a grey precipitate is formed.	2. Aldehyde confirmed.
3. **Fehling's test**: Equal volumes of Fehling' solution nos. 1 and 2 are mixed in a test tube and to it about 0.05 g of the sample is added, shaken and warmed on a water bath.	3. A red precipitate is formed.	3. Aldehyde confirmed.

Comments

(i) **Ketones do not respond to these tests**. So negative respond to these test indicates the ketonic nature of the carbonyl group.

(ii) During Schiff's test mixture should not be heated. Development of pink colour is very slow. Heating may decompose the reagent and the solution becomes colourless.

(iii) α-hydroxy ketone may respond to this tests due to tautomeric effect.

$$R - \underset{\underset{O}{\|}}{C} - \underset{\underset{OH}{|}}{CH_2} \;\rightleftharpoons\; R - \underset{\underset{OH}{|}}{C} = CH - OH \;\rightleftharpoons\; R - \underset{\underset{OH}{|}}{CH} - \underset{\underset{H}{|}}{C} = O$$

α-hydroxy ketone   α-hydroxy aldehyde

Reactions involved

(i) Bisulphite test

$$R - \underset{\underset{O}{\|}}{C} - R' \quad + \quad NaHSO_3 \longrightarrow R - \underset{\underset{OH}{|}}{\overset{\overset{H}{|}}{C}} - SO_3Na$$

R or R′ may be H   White precipitate

(ii)

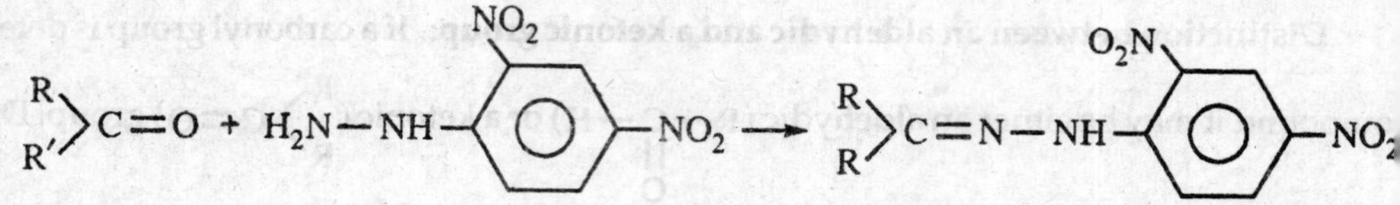

$$R_{R'}C=O + H_2N-NH-\underset{NO_2}{\overset{NO_2}{\bigcirc}}-NO_2 \longrightarrow R_{R}C=N-NH-\underset{}{\overset{O_2N}{\bigcirc}}-NO_2$$

D.N.P.H.

2:4-Dinitrophenyl hydrazone

(iii) **Schiff's test**

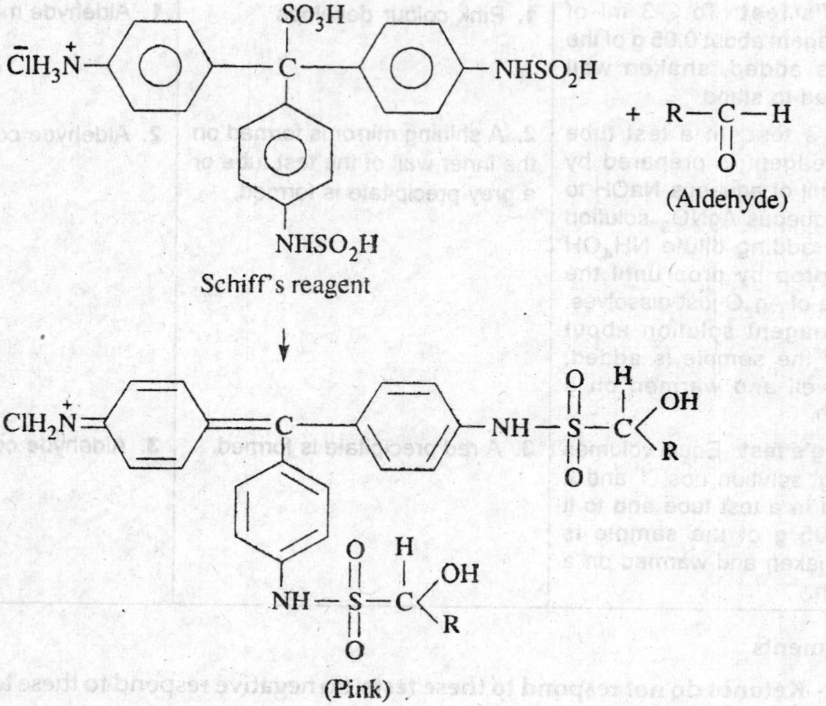

Schiff's reagent

+ R—C—H
      ||
      O

(Aldehyde)

(Pink)

(iv) **Tollen's test**

$$R-\underset{O}{\overset{}{C}}-H + 2Ag(NH_3)_2NO_3 + H_2O \longrightarrow 2Ag\downarrow + RCOONH_4 + 2NH_4NO_3 + NH_3$$

Aldehyde

(v) **Fehling's test:** Fehling's no 1 is a solution of $CuSO_4$ in water containing a few drops o conc. H_2SO_4 while Fehling solution no. 2 is a solution of sodium potassium tartarate in NaOH solution. The mixture of these two solutions in equal volume is known as Fehling's solutior Aldehydic group reduces cupric ion into cuprous ion, i.e.,

$$R-\underset{O}{\overset{}{C}}-H + Cu^{++} + NaOH + H_2O \longrightarrow \underset{Red}{Cu_2O\downarrow} + R-COONa + 2H_2O$$

Function of sodium potassium tartarate salt, known as Rochelle salt, is to stabilise cuprou ion through the formation of a complex.

Table 3.3: Test for phenolic hydroxyl group (Ar—OH)

Experiments	Observations	Inference
1. FeCl₃-test: Aqueous or alcoholic solution (2 ml) of the sample is taken in a test tube and to it 2 drops of FeCl₃ solution is added.	1. Violet, blue or green colour appears.	1. Phenolic —OH group is present.
2. Back dye test: 1 ml of aniline is diazotised with NaNO₂ solution is presence of HCl under cold condition in a test tube. In another test tube, solution of sample in NaOH is taken. To this alkaline solution diazotised aniline is added by cooling under tap.	2. Red or reddish dye.	2. Phenolic —OH group confirmed.
3. Leibermann's test: (a) 1 ml of the solution of the sample is taken in a test tube and to it a few crystals (0.02 g) of NaNO₂ is added. It is now gently warmed, cooled and then 1 ml of conc. H₂SO₄ is added.	3.(a) Green or blue colour appears.	3.(a) Phenolic —OH group.
(b) The above reaction mixture (a) is diluted carefully with water.	(b) Colour changes to red.	(b) Phenolic —OH group.
(c) To the diluted solution (b) excess solution of NaOH is added.	(c) Blue or green colour returns.	(c) Phenolic —OH group.

Comments

(i) Phenolic hydroxyl is acidic and so it responds to *Litmus test*.

(ii) Some phenols do not respond to FeCl₃ test. Some examples of such phenols are α and β-naphthols. In these cases original sample is dissolved in conc. KOH solution and CHCl₃ and is warmed, appearance of blue colour indicates β-naphthol. But α-naphthol requires the presence of copper powder in that solution to give blue colour.

Reactions involved:

(i) **FeCl₃ test**: FeCl₃ is a mild oxidising agent. So in some cases it act as oxidising agent and oxidises phenolic compounds to a product which is coloured. In other cases a complex may be formed. Thus,

(a)

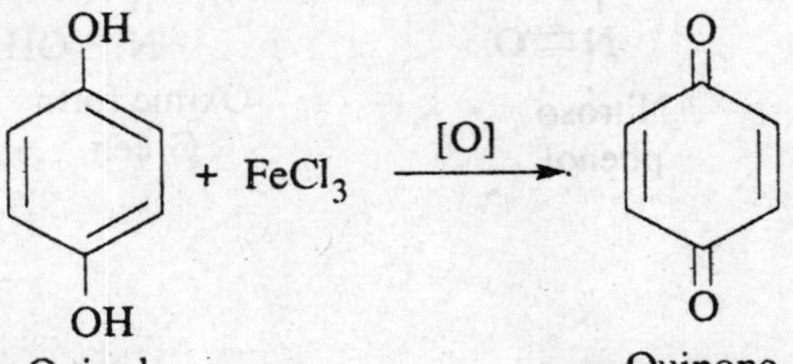

Quinol   Quinone (yellow)

(b)

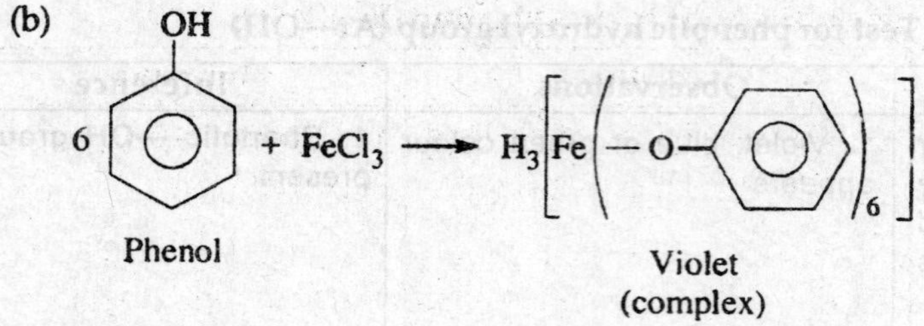

6 Phenol + FeCl$_3$ $\longrightarrow$ H$_3$[Fe(—O—⟨⟩)$_6$] + HCl

Phenol

Violet
(complex)

(ii) Back dye test

ArNH$_2$ + HCl + NaNO$_2$ $\longrightarrow$ Ar—N=N—Cl

Aniline   Diazo compound

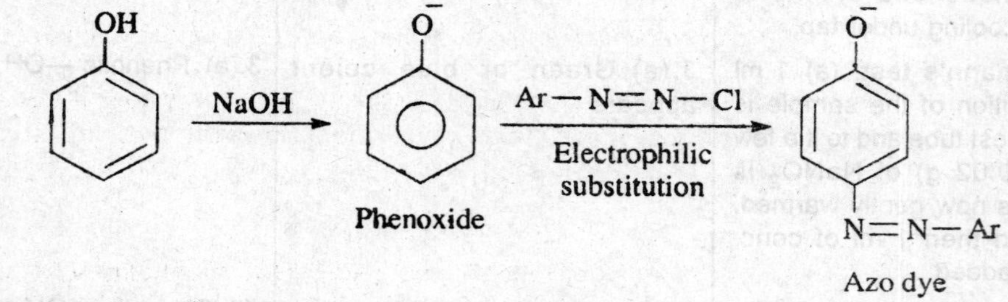

$\xrightarrow{\text{NaOH}}$ $\xrightarrow[\substack{\text{Electrophilic} \\ \text{substitution}}]{\text{Ar—N=N—Cl}}$

Phenoxide

Azo dye

In alkaline solution phenoxide ion is formed which is more electron rich than free phenol and so reaction with diazocompound (an electrophilic substitution reaction) will be favoured.

(iii) Liebermann's test

NaNO$_2$ + HCl $\longrightarrow$ HNO$_2$ + NaCl

HNO$_2$ ≡ H—O—N=O $\xrightarrow[-H_2O]{H^+}$ $\overset{+}{N}$=O

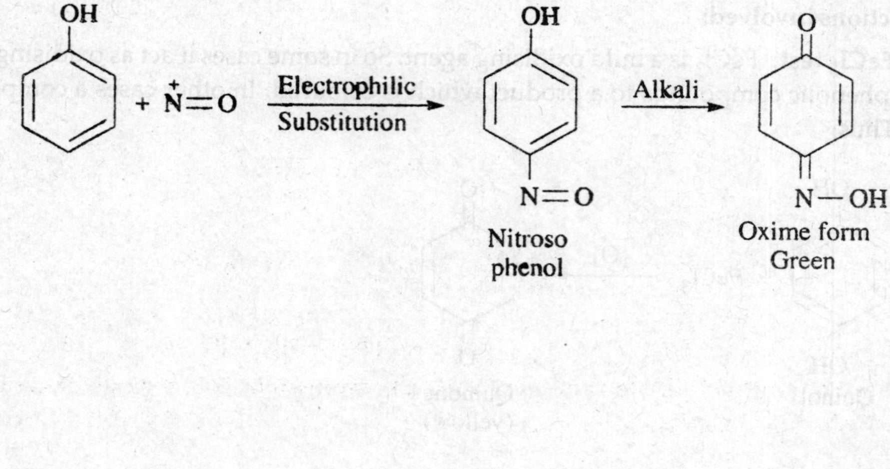

+ $\overset{+}{N}$=O $\xrightarrow[\text{Substitution}]{\text{Electrophilic}}$ $\xrightarrow{\text{Alkali}}$

Nitroso
phenol

N—OH
Oxime form
Green

Table 3.4: Test for alcoholic hydroxyl group (R—OH)

Experiments	Observations	Inference
1. Sodium metal test: A small portion of the original sample is dissolved in dry benzene and to it a very thin piece of sodium metal is added to it.	**1.** Effervescence of a gas (hydrogen) occurs.	**1.** Alcoholic —OH group may be present.
2. Acetate test: About of 0.5 g of the sample is taken in a dry test tube and to it 4 ml of mixture of acetic anhydride and two drops of conc. H_2SO_4 are added. The test tube is warmed on water bath for 5 minutes. Next the reaction mixture is poured into cold water taken in a beaker and stired.	**2.** A precipitate or a separate liquid layer with pleasant smell appears.	**2.** Alcoholic or phenolic —OH group may be present.
3.(a) Xanthate test: A few drops of solution of the sample is taken in a test and to it 2 drops of carbon disulphide and a few crystals of NaOH are added.	**3.(a)** Yellow precipitate or colour appears.	**3.(a)** Alcoholic —OH group is present.
(b) The mixture is shaken well for 2-3 minutes. To this solution 2 drops of 10% ammonium molybdate solution is added, acidified with 2(N) H_2SO_4 and finally 2-3 ml of chloroform is added and shaken.	**(b)** Violet or reddish blue colour appears in chloroform layer.	**(b)** Alcoholic—OH group is present.

Reactions taking place:

(i) Sodium metal test

$$2R—OH + 2Na \longrightarrow 2R—ONa + H_2\uparrow$$

(ii) Acetate test

$$R—OH + (CH_3—CO)_2O \longrightarrow R—O—\underset{\underset{O}{\|}}{C}—CH_3 + CH_3COOH$$

Acetic anhydride

(iii) Xanthate test

$$R—OH + NaOH \longrightarrow R—ONa + H_2O$$

$$\underset{\underset{S}{\|}}{\overset{\overset{S}{\|}}{C}} + R—ONa \longrightarrow S=\underset{\underset{SNa}{|}}{C}—O—R$$

Yellow precipitate (xanthate)

With ammonium molybdate xanthate forms a complex which is a violet or reddish blue oloured compound.

Table 3.5: Test for ester group (—COOR)

Experiments	Observations	Inference
1.(a) **Hydrolysis test**: 0.2 g of the sample is taken in a test tube and is dissolved in 2 ml of ethanol. To it two drops of phenolphthalein is added and 2-3 drops of NaOH are added and warmed on a water bath.	1.(a) Pink colour disappears.	1.(a) —COOR group may be present.
(b) About 0.1 g of the sample is taken in a test tube and to it 5 ml of 20% aqueous KOH solution is added and is heated on a water bath for 15-20 minutes. Next the clear solution is acidified with dilute H_2SO_4.	**(b)** Copious white precipitate.	**(b)** Ester group is present.
2. **Hydroxamic acid test**: About 0.1 g of the sample is taken in a test tube and to it 1 ml of hydroxylamine hydrochloride solution in ethanol is added. The solution is made alkaline with 10% NaOH solution. The mixture is heated just to boiling. The solution is cooled and acidified with dilute HCl. Next 1-2 drops of $FeCl_3$ solution is added.	2. Reddish-violet colour develops.	2. Ester confirmed.

Comments

(i) Anhydrides and lactones also respond to hydrolysis test.

(ii) Before performing hydroxamic acid test a blank test without using hydroxyl amine hydrochloride must be done. If *only yellow* colour appears in the blank test, this test is to be performed.

(iii) Majority of the esters are liquid, and soluble in water with characteristic pleasant smell of fruits. So smell of the sample should be ascertained.

Chemical reactions involved in the above tests:

1. Hydrolysis test

(a) $$R-\underset{\underset{O}{\|}}{C}-OR' + H_2O \underset{}{\overset{Alkali}{\rightleftharpoons}} R-\underset{\underset{O}{\|}}{C}-OH + R'-OH$$

Ester   Acid   Alcohol

$$R-\underset{\underset{O}{\|}}{C}-OH + H_2O \rightleftharpoons R-\underset{\underset{O}{\|}}{C}-O^- + H_3O^+$$

Acid anion

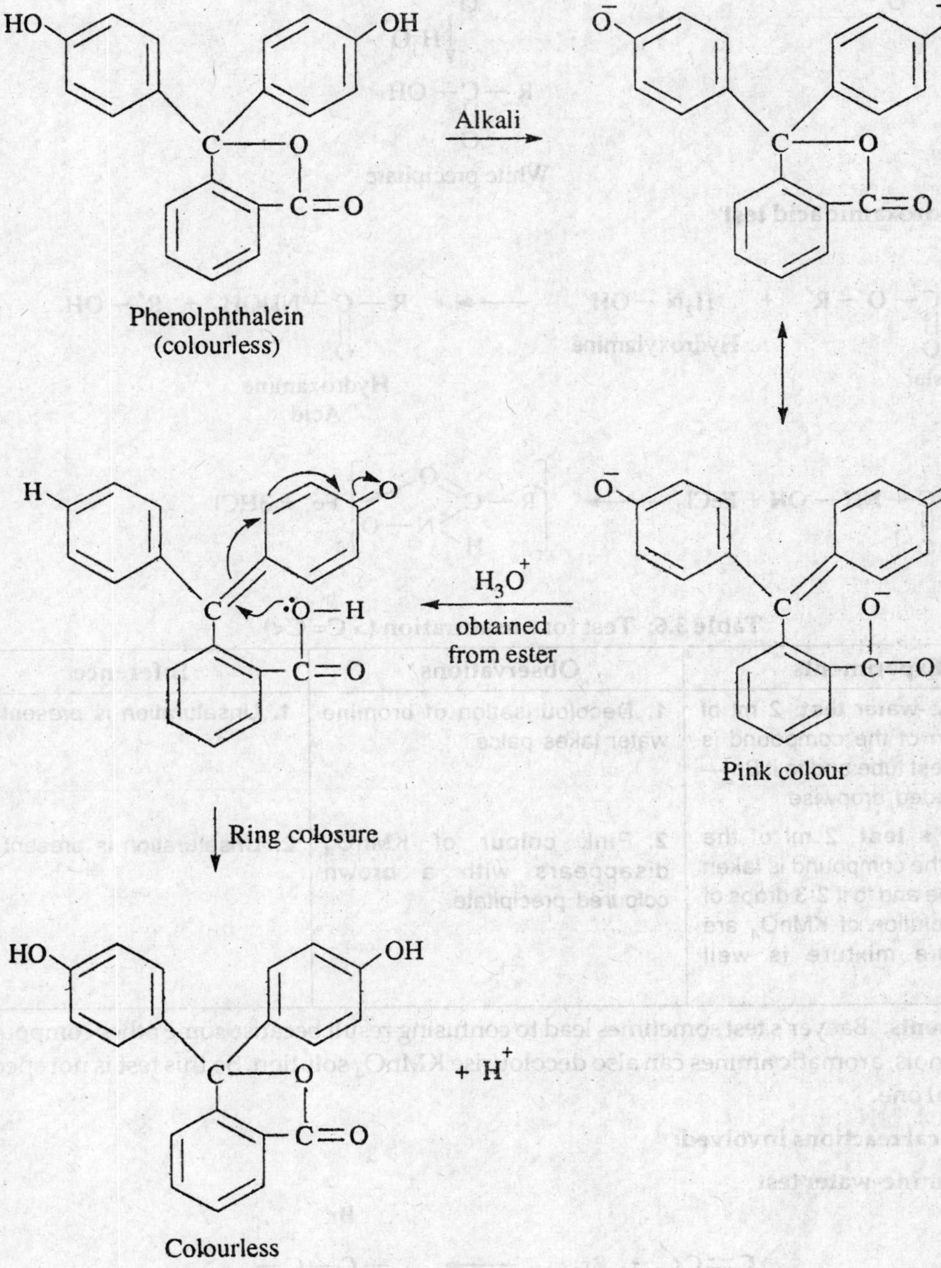

Phenolphthalein
(colourless)

Alkali →

← H_3O^+
obtained
from ester

Pink colour

Ring colosure

$+ H^+$

Colourless

(b)
$$R-\underset{\underset{O}{\|}}{C}-O-R' + H_2O \longrightarrow R-\underset{\underset{O}{\|}}{C}-\bar{O} + R'-OH$$

$$\downarrow H_3O^+$$

$$R-\underset{\underset{O}{\|}}{C}-OH$$

White precipitate

2. Hydroxamic acid test

$$\underset{\underset{Ester}{}}{R-\underset{\underset{O}{\|}}{C}-O-R'} + \underset{Hydroxylamine}{H_2N-OH} \longrightarrow R-\underset{\underset{O}{\|}}{C}-NHOH + R'-OH$$

Hydroxamine
Acid

$$R-\underset{\underset{O}{\|}}{C}-NH-OH + FeCl_3 \longrightarrow \left[R-C\underset{H}{\overset{O}{<}}\underset{}{\diagdown}_{N-O}\right]_3 Fe + 3HCl$$

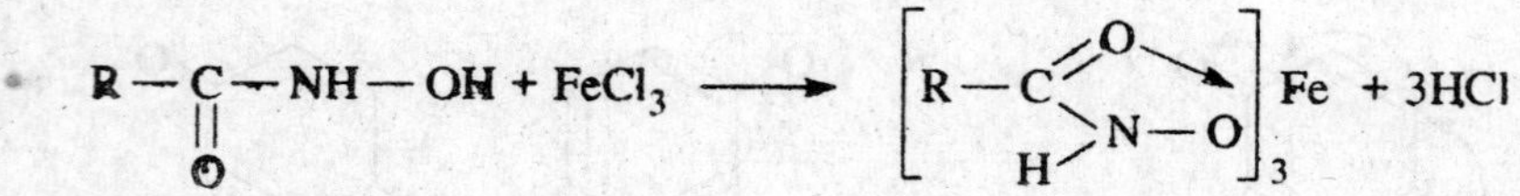

Table 3.6: Test for unsaturation (> C= C<)

Experiments	Observations	Inference
1. Bromine-water test: 2 ml of the solution of the compound is taken in a test tube and to it Br_2—water is added dropwise.	1. Decolourisation of bromine water takes palce.	1. Unsaturation is present.
2. Baeyer's test 2 ml of the solution of the compound is taken in a test tube and to it 2-3 drops of aqueous solution of $KMnO_4$ are added. The mixture is well shaken.	2. Pink colour of $KMnO_4$ disappears with a brown coloured precipitate.	2. Unsaturation is present.

Comments: Baeyer's test sometimes lead to confusing result because some other compounds such as phenols, aromatic amines can also decolourise $KMnO_4$ solution. So this test is not specific but a general one.

Chemical reactions involved:

1. Bromine-water test

$$>C=C< + Br_2 \longrightarrow -\underset{\underset{Br}{|}}{\overset{Br}{|}}{C}-\underset{}{C}-$$

2. Baeyer test

$$3>C=C< + 2KMnO_4 + 4H_2O \longrightarrow 3>\underset{\underset{OH}{|}}{C}-\underset{\underset{OH}{|}}{C}< + 2MnO_2 + 2KOH$$

Brown

3.2 Detection of Nitrogenous Functional Groups

Nitrogenous functional groups commonly encountered in organic compounds are —NH_2 (amino), — NO_2 (nitro), —$\underset{\underset{O}{||}}{C}$— NH_2 (amide) and —$\underset{\underset{O}{||}}{C}$— NH — Ar (anilido) groups. The most common tests for the detection of these functionalities are expressed in the following tabular forms (Tables 3.7-3.10):

Table 3.7: Test for amino group (—NH_2)

Experiments	Observations	Inference
1. Carbylamine test: A small portion of the sample is taken in a dry test tube and to it 2-3 drops of $CHCl_3$ and 1 ml of alcoholic KOH are added. The reaction mixture is warmed gently.	**1.** An obnoxious odour of isocyanide is produced.	**1.** Amino (—NH_2) group present.
2. Dye test: About 0.5 g of the sample is dissolved in 2 NHCl in a test tube. The solution is cooled in ice to about 5 °C. In another test tube 10% aqueous $NaNO_2$ solution is cooled. In a third test tube an alkaline solution of β-naphthol is cooled. When the solutions are cooled, cold $NaNO_2$ solution is added to cold 2(N) HCl solution of the sample, and shaken well. This mixed solution is now added to the cold alkaline β-naphthol solution.	**2.** An immediate brilliant scarlet red dye is formed.	**2.** Amino group confirmed.

Comments

(i) Carbylamine or isocyanide is highly *poisonous* and so it should not be inhaled directly. It is better to perform this test in a fume chamber. Before pouring into the sink, the test tube containing the reaction mixture should be acidified with dilute HCl. This converts isocyanide into the corresponding hydrochloride of the amine.

(ii) Brown or reddish purple or violet dye indicates the presence of two amino groups. Further, if the dye formed is soluble, then most probably sulphonic acid (—SO_3H) or phenolic OH is present along with aromatic amine. This test is applicable to aromatic amines only.

(iii) Some acyl derivatives of amines, such as acetanilide, respond to carbylamine test.

Reactions taking place:

(i) Carbylamine test

$$R — NH_2 + CHCl_3 + 3KOH \longrightarrow R — NC + 3KCl + 3H_2O$$

Isocyanide
(obnoxious smell)

(ii) **Dye test**

$$Ar\!-\!NH_2 + NaNO_2 + HCl \longrightarrow Ar\!-\!N\!=\!N\!-\!Cl$$
Aromatic diazonium
chloride

Na-salt of β-naphthol + $Ar\!-\!N\!=\!N\!-\!Cl \longrightarrow$ Scarlet red dye

Alkaline solution of B-naphthol is taken to form anion which is more electron rich and hence favours coupling at ortho position (electrophilic substitution).

Table 3.8: Test for nitro group (—NO₂)

Experiments	Observations	Inference
1. Mulliken and Barker's test: A little amount of the sample is dissolved in 0.5 ml of alcohol. To it a small amount of solid NH_4Cl (or 2 ml of 10% $CaCl_2$ solution) and a pinch of Zn-dust are added. The mixture is boiled for 2-3 minutes, cooled, and allowed to stand for 5 minutes. It is now filtered. With the filtrate following tests are performed:		
(a) A portion of the filtrate is added to ammoniacal $AgNO_3$ solution (Tollen's reagent) and warmed.	**1. (a)** A black or grey precipitate or a shining mirror on the inner side of the test tube.	**(a)** Nitro group (—NO₂) is present.
(b) Another portion of the filtrate is treated with Fehling's solutions (equal volume of 1 and 2 solutions).	**1. (b)** Red precipitate is formed.	**(b)** Nitro group (—NO₂) is present.
2. Diazo reaction and coupling: A little of the sample is taken in a test tube and to it 5 ml of conc. HCl and a few pieces of metallic tin are added. The mixture is boiled gently for 2-3 minutes, cooled under tap and supernatant liquid is decanted. To the liquid 2 ml cold solution of $NaNO_2$ is added and cooled again. This cold solution is added to a cold alkaline solution of β-naphthol.	**2.** A brilliant scarlet red dye is formed.	**2.** Nitro group is present.
3. Ferrous hydroxide test: About 25 mg of the sample is taken in a test tube and it is mixed with 2 ml of freshly prepared 5% solution of ferrous ammonium sulphate. To the mixture 1 drop of (N) H_2SO_4 followed by 1 ml of 2(N) KOH solution in methanol are added. The mouth of the test tube is stoppered quickly, and vigoroulsy shaken.	**3.** A reddish brown precipitate is obtained.	**3.** Nitro group is present.

Comments: Diazo test after reduction of nitro group cannot be performed, if —NH_2 or —NHCOR group is already present.

Chemical reactions:

1. **Mulliken and Barker test**

$$ArNO_2 \xrightarrow{\text{Zn/NH}_4\text{Cl}} ArNHOH + H_2O$$

$$\text{Hydroxyl amine}$$

$$ArNHOH + Ag_2O \text{ (Tollen's reagent)} \longrightarrow Ag\downarrow + ArNO + H_2O$$

$$ArNHOH + CuO \text{ (Fehling's solution)} \longrightarrow Cu_2O + ArNO + H_2O$$

2. **Diazo test**

$$ArNO_2 \xrightarrow{\text{S/HCl}} ArNH_2 \cdot HCi$$

The amino group produced now forms brilliant red dye as in the case of amine.

3. **Ferrous hydroxide test**

$$ArNO_2 + 6Fe(OH)_2 + 4H_2O \longrightarrow RNH_2 + 6Fe(OH)_3$$

$$\text{Brown}$$

Table 3.9: Test for amide group ($-\underset{\underset{O}{\|}}{C}-NH_2$)

Experiments	Observations	Inference
1. Hydrolysis test: A small portion (0.2 g) of the sample is taken in a test tube. To it 2 ml of 50% NaOH solution is added and heated.	1. Evolution of ammonia with characteristic smell which turns $Hg_2(NO_3)_2$ paper black.	**1.** Amide group ($-\underset{\underset{O}{\|}}{C}-NH_2$) is present.
2. Hydroxamic acid test: About 0.1 g of the sample is taken in a test tube. 2 ml of 1(N) hydroxyl amine hydrochloride solution, and 2 ml of 1(N) KOH solution are added to the sample and the mixture is boiled for 5 minutes. It is cooled, and to it a few drops of ferric chloride solution is added.	**2.** Red colouration develops.	**2.** Amide group is present.
3. Nitrous acid test: To a portion of aqueous solution of the sample taken in a test tube a few drops of cold solution of $NaNO_2$ and HCl are added.	**3.** Evolution of nitrogen occurs.	**3.** Amide group ($-\underset{\underset{O}{\|}}{C}-NH_2$) is present.

Chemical reactions:

1. **Hydrolysis test**

$$R-\underset{\underset{O}{\|}}{C}-NH_2 + NaOH \xrightarrow{\text{heat}} R-\underset{\underset{O}{\|}}{C}-OH + NH_3\uparrow$$

2. Hydroxamic acid test

$$R-\underset{\underset{O}{\|}}{C}-NH_2 + NH_2OH \longrightarrow R-\underset{\underset{O}{\|}}{C}-NH-OH + NH_3$$

Hydroxamic acid

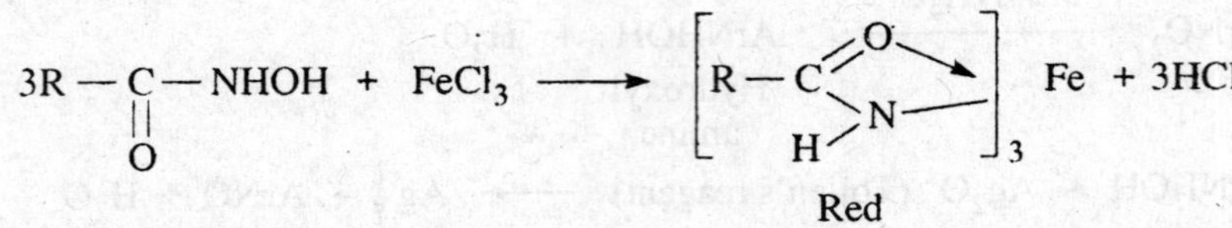

$$3R-\underset{\underset{O}{\|}}{C}-NHOH + FeCl_3 \longrightarrow \left[R-\underset{\underset{H}{N}}{C\overset{O}{\diagdown}} \right]_3 Fe + 3HCl$$

Red

3. Nitrous acid test

$$NaNO_2 + HCl \longrightarrow HNO_2 + NaCl$$

$$R-\underset{\underset{O}{\|}}{C}-NH_2 + HO-N=O \longrightarrow R-\underset{\underset{O}{\|}}{C}-OH + N_2\uparrow + H_2O$$

Table 3.10: Test for anilide group $(-\underset{\underset{O}{\|}}{C}-NH-Ar)$

Experiments	Observations	Inference
1. Hydrolysis test: About 0.05 g of the solid sample is taken in a test tube and to it 5 ml of conc. HCl is added. Boiled for 5 minutes, cooled, diluted and diazo reaction is performed with the solution in the usual way.	1. Brilliant scarlet or red precipitate.	1. Anilide group $(-\underset{\underset{O}{\|}}{C}-NH-Ar)$ is present.

Chemical reactions:

$$R-\underset{\underset{O}{\|}}{C}-NH-Ar + H_2O \longrightarrow R-\underset{\underset{O}{\|}}{C}-OH + ArNH_2$$

Primary amine

Primary amine formed responds to diazo reaction

$$ArNH_2 + HNO_2 (NaNO_2 + HCl) \longrightarrow Ar-N=N-Cl$$

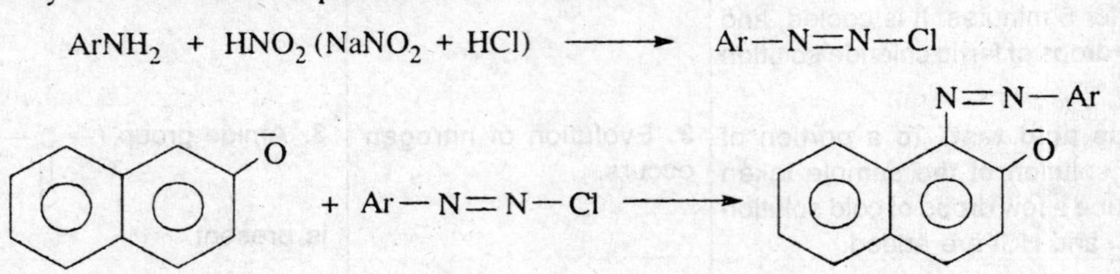

Alkaline solution
of β-naphthol

Dye

Chapter 4

Preparation of Derivatives for Identification of Organic Compounds

Determination of melting and boiling points of the compound and preparation of its suitable derivatives are the two most important methods which are usually adapted as the confirmatory evidences for the identification of an organic compound. But very often the observed melting and boiling points differ considerably from their reported values. So in order to confirm a compound it is always necessary to prepare a suitable solid derivative having melting point preferably in the range 100-250 °C.

It may be mentioned in this connection that the type of derivative to be suitable for a particular compound depends upon the class to which it belongs. Again it may so happen that more than one derivatives may be prepared for a particular ompound but it is always desirable that such a derivative is to be prepared which creates least confusion. Some of the typical derivatives generally prepared for different classes of compounds are listed in the tabular form below.

Derivative	Class of Compound
1. Acetyl, benzoyl and bromo drivatives	1. Phenols, amines, alcohols
2. Amide	2. Carboxylic acids
3. D.N.P.H, Oxime, Semicarbazone, etc.	3. Carbonyl compounds (aldehyde and ketone)
4. Hydrolysis product	4. Esters, amides and anilides
5. Reduction product	5. Nitro compounds
6. Picrate	6. Hydrocarbons, aromatic amines, phenols, etc.

4.1 Preparation of Some Common Derivatives

Preparation of some of the common derivatives which are generally employed for the identification of organic compounds are discussed below:

4.1.1 Preparation of Acetyl Derivative

1 g of the sample is taken in a dry test tube and is dissolved in 5 ml of acetic anhydride. A few drops of conc. H_2SO_4 or a little sodium acetate are added to the solution of the sample. The test tube with the reaction mixture is warmed for 5 minutes with constant shaking. The reaction mixture is cooled and poured into 25 ml of ice cold water taken in a 100 ml beaker with constant stirring. The solid precipitate is filtered, washed with little cold water and crystallised from rectified spirit. The derivative is dried on blotting paper and its melting point is determined.

Reactions:

Acetyl derivative

Acetyl derivative

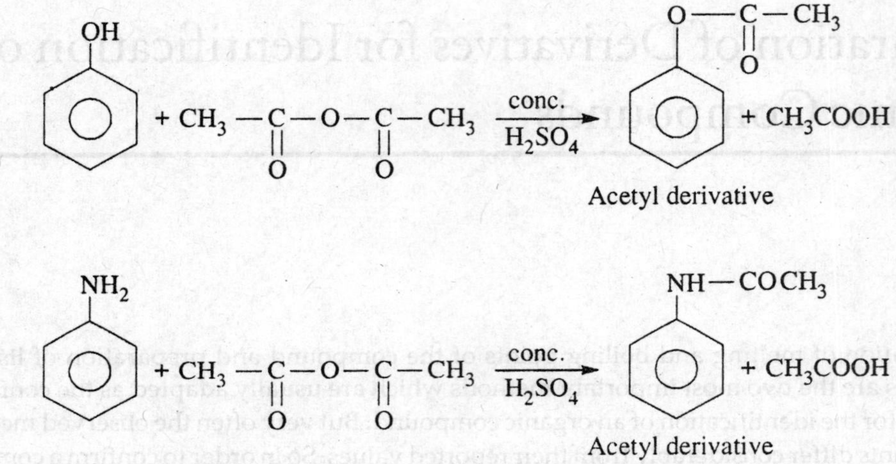

Comments: Acetylation may also be carried with acetyl chloride. In this case a saturated solution of the sample (1 g) is prepared with acetone as a solvent in a 100 ml conical flask. To it 2 ml of acetyl chloride and 25 ml of 25% NaOH solution are added and the mouth of the flask is closed with a cork. The conical flask is vigorously shaken till the smell of acetyl chloride disappears. A little NaOH solution is added and shaken again. The acetyl derivative separates as a white solid. It is filtered, washed first with cold dilute HCl and next with cold water. The solid derivative is crystallised from rectified spirit and its melting point is determined.

Reactions:

(i)

Acetyl derivative

(ii)

Acetyl derivative

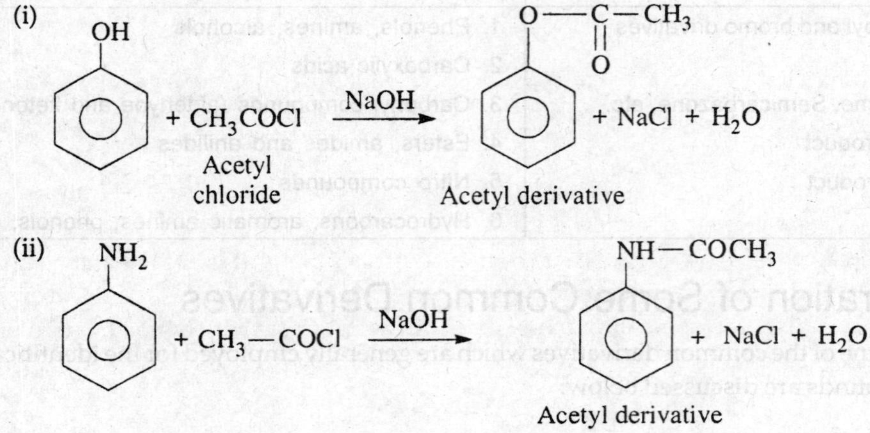

4.1.2 Preparation of Benzoyl Derivative

In a conical flask 1 g of the sample is taken and a saturated solution is prepared using acetone as a solvent. To it 5 ml of benzoyl chloride and 20 ml of 25% NaOH solution are added. The conical flask is corked up and is vigorously shaken. The flask is repeatedly cooled under tap. Finally a little more NaOH solution is added and shaking is continued till the disappearance of the smell of benzoyl chloride. The precipitate formed is filtered and washed first with cold dilute HCl and then with cold water. The solid benzoyl derivative is crystallised with reactified spirit, dried by blotting paper and melting point is determined.

Reactions:

(i)

$$+ \text{PhCOCl} + \text{NaOH} \longrightarrow \quad + \text{NaCl} + H_2O$$

Benzoyl chloride   Benzoyl derivative

(ii)

$$+ \text{PhCOCl} + \text{NaOH} \longrightarrow \quad + \text{NaCl} + H_2O$$

Benzoyl derivative

4.1.3 Preparation of Bromo Derivative

1 g of the original sample is taken in a test tube and is dissolved in 2-3 ml of glacial acetic acid. To it bromine solution in glacial acetic acid (1:3) is added drop by drop with constant shaking till the very light yellow colour appears. The reaction mixture is warmed for 5 minutes on a water bath and cooled. The cold solution is poured into 50 ml of cold water taken in a small beaker when solid bromo derivative separates out. It is filtered, washed with cold water, crystallised from rectified spirit, and its melting point is determined.

4.1.4 Preparation of 2, 4-Dinitrophenyl Hydrazone (D.N.P.H.) Derivative

In a test tube small portion (0.5 g) of the sample is taken. To it 5 ml of 1% 2, 4-dinitrophenyl hydrazine and 3-4 drops of conc. HCl are added. The mixture is heated on a water bath for 5 minutes. A few drops of water are added to it when turbidity appears. It is heated again till clear solution is obtained. The reaction mixture is cooled under tap when crystals of D.N.P.H. derivative separates. It is filtered, dried over blotting paper, crystallised from reactified spirit, and melting point is determined.

Reactions:

$$\ce{>C=O + H2N-NH-}\overset{O_2N}{\underset{}{\langle \bigcirc \rangle}}\ce{-NO2 ->} \ce{>C=N-NH-}\overset{O_2N}{\underset{}{\langle \bigcirc \rangle}}\ce{-NO2}$$

(Aldehyde or   2, 4-Dinitrophenyl hydrazine   2, 4-Dinitrophenyl hydrazone
ketone)

4.1.5 Preparation of Oxime Derivative

1 g of the sample is taken in a small (250 ml) round bottom flask fitted with an air condenser and is dissolved in 10 ml of 50% alcohol. To it about 2 g of solid hydroxylamine hydrochloride and 2 g of powdered sodium acetate are taken and the the mixture is gently refluxed for 15 minutes with occassional shaking until no precipitation appears when a drop of the solution is added to 5 ml of 1% NaOH solution. The solution is cooled and diluted with cold water when solid derivative separates out. It is filtered, washed with cold water and crystallised from rectified spirit. It is dried as usual by blotting paper, and melting point is determined.

Reactions:

$$\ce{>C=O} \quad + \quad \ce{H2N OH} \quad \longrightarrow \quad \ce{>C=N-OH + H2O}$$

(Aldehyde or   Hydroxyl   Oxime
ketone)   amine

4.1.6 Preparation of Amides

1 g of the sample is taken in a porcelain disc kept in a fume chamber. To it 5 g of PCl_5 is added and the sample is ground with a pestle until the mixture becomes liquid. Now 2 ml of liquor NH_3 is added to the liquid mixture in small portion. When the vigorous reaction ceases the mixture is stirred, cooled and filtered. The solid amide obtained is dried by blotting paper and its melting point is determined.

Reactions:

$$\ce{R-\underset{O}{\overset{||}{C}}-OH + PCl5 ->} \ce{R-\underset{O}{\overset{||}{C}}-Cl + POCl3 + H2O}$$

Carboxylic   Acid chloride
acid

$$\ce{R-\underset{O}{\overset{||}{C}}-Cl + NH3 ->} \ce{R-\underset{O}{\overset{||}{C}}-NH2 + HCl}$$

Amide

4.1.7 Preparation of Derivatives for Amides and Esters (Hydrolysis Product)

Derivatives of amides and esters are prepared by their hydrolysis to corresponding acids. The hydrolysis is carried out either with alkali or with acid.

1 g of the sample is taken in a 100 ml conical flask and to it 25 ml of 20% NaOH solution or 25 ml of 70% H_2SO_4 is added. The reaction mixture is boiled for 20 minutes and cooled. If the hydrolysis has been carried out with NaOH, the cold solution is acidified with dilute HCl when the insoluble acid is precipitated. It is filtered, washed with water, crystallised from rectified spirit, dried, and melting point is determined.

Reactions:

$$R-\underset{\underset{O}{\|}}{C}-NH_2 \xrightarrow{H_2O} R-\underset{\underset{O}{\|}}{C}-OH + NH_3$$

Amide   Acid

$$R-\underset{\underset{O}{\|}}{C}-OR' \xrightarrow{H_2O} R-\underset{\underset{O}{\|}}{C}-OH \quad + \quad R'-OH$$

Ester   Acid   Alcohol or phenol

4.1.8 Preparation of Derivatives by Reduction

When the given sample contains only nitro group ($-NO_2$) as its functional group, its derivative is prepared by the reduction of the nitro group to amine. This reduction is usually carried by the following method.

A solution of polysulphide is prepared by dissolving 5 g of pure $Na_2S, 9H_2O$ in 20 ml of water and 1 g of powdered sulphur is added to it. It is warmed till clear solution of sodium polysulphide is obtained.

In a small conical flask, 3 g of the sample (say m-Dinitrobenzene) is taken and is dissolved in 25 ml of alcohol and boiled. To this hot solution polysulphide solution prepared is added drop by drop in boiling condition with constant stirring for 10-15 minutes. The solution is cooled, filtered and washed with water. The solid is now dissolved in dilute HCl by boiling, cooled, filtered when sulphur, if any, and unreacted sample are separated out. Excess of NH_4OH is added to the filtrate to precipitate nitroamine. It is filtered and crystallised from boiling water, dried and melting point is noted.

m-Dinitrobenzene m-Nitroaniline

4.1.9 Preparation of Picrate Derivative

1 g of the sample is dissolved in benzene in a dry test tube to make a saturated solution. To this solution 2 ml of saturated solution of picric acid in benzene is added and shaken well. The reaction mixture is allowed to stand for a few minutes, filtered and the pricrate formed is washed carefully with little cold benzene, dried by blotting paper, and its melting point is noted.

Reactions:

Picric acid   Charge transfer complex

Chapter **5**

Classified List of Some Very Common Organic Compounds and Their Simple Derivatives

A. Hydrocarbons
Liquid

B.P. (in°C)	Name	Derivatives
80	Benzene, 	m-Dinitrobenzene, M.P. 90 °C
110	Toluene, 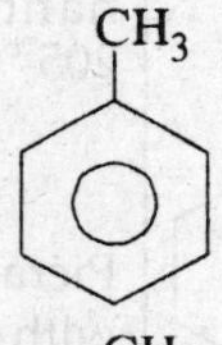	Benzoic acid, M.P. 121 °C by oxidation with KMnO$_4$
137	p-xylene, 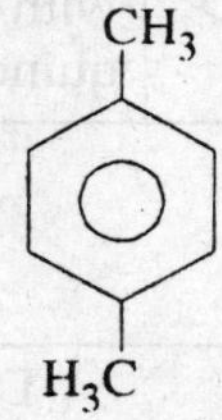	Terephthalic acid
139	m-xylene, 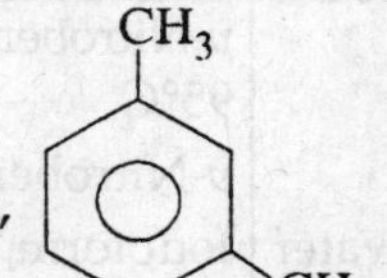	iso-phthalic acid, M.P. > 300 °C
142	o-xylene, 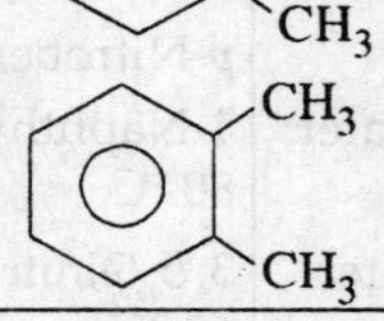	Phthalic acid, M.P. 121 °C

187

Solid

M.P. (in °C)	Name	Derivatives
70	Diphenyl,	On oxidation with dichromate in glacial acetic acid forms benzoic acid, M.P. 121 °C
80	Naphthalene,	Picrate, M.P. 150 °C
95	Acetaphthene,	Picrate, M.P. 161 °C
100	Phenanthrene, Insoluble in water	Picrate, M.P. 143 °C, oxid^n with AcOH/CrO$_3$ phenanthraquinone, M.P. 205 °C
216	Anthracene, Insoluble in water	Picrate, M.P. 138 °C, oxid^n with CrO$_3$/AcOH anthraquinone, M.P. 280 °C

B. Alcohols

Liquid

M.P. (in °C)	Name	Derivatives
65	Methyl alcohol, CH_3OH, soluble in water	p-Nitrobenzoyl derivative, M.P. 95°C
78	Ethyl alcohol, C_2H_5OH, soluble in water	p-Nitrobenzoate, M.P. 56 °C
82	Iso-Propyl alcohol, $(CH_3)_2CHOH$, solutble in water	Iodoform, M.P. 119°C
83	t-Butyl alcohol, $(CH_3)_3COH$, soluble in water	p-Nitrobenzoate, M.P. 80 °C
97	n-Propyl alcohol, $CH_3(CH_2)_2OH$, soluble in water	1-Naphthyl carbamate, M.P. 80 °C
117	n-Butyl alcohol, $CH_3(CH_2)_3OH$, soluble in water	3, 5-Dinitrobenzoate, M.P. 63 °C

Contd.

M.P. (in °C)	Name	Derivatives
160	Cyclohexanol, , sparingly soluble in water	Adipic acid, M.P. 150 °C
205	Benzyl alcohol, , soluble in water	Benzoic acid, M.P. 121 °C
290	Glycerol, $\begin{array}{l} CH_2-OH \\ CH-OH \\ CH_2-OH \end{array}$, soluble in water	Tribenzoate, M.P. 76 °C

C. Phenols

Liquid

B.P. (in °C)	Name	Derivative
181	Phenol,	Tribromophenol, M.P. 94 °C Acetate, M.P. 196 °C
196	Salicylaldehyde,	Salicyclic acid, M.P. 155 °C
224	Methyl salicylate,	Acetyl derivative, M.P. 48 °C Benzoyl derivative, M.P. 82 °C
234	Ethyl salicylate,	Acetyl derivative, M.P. 272 °C

Contd.

Solid

M.P. (in °C)	Name	Derivative
94	α-Naphthol, (structure) , insoluble in water	Picrate, M.P. 189 °C
104	Catechol, (structure) , soluble in water, gives green colour with FeCl₃	Diacetate, M.P. 63 °C tetrabromo derivative, M.P. 192 °C
118	Resorcinol, (structure) , soluble in water gives bluish violet colour with FeCl₃	Dibenzoate, M.P. 117 °C
122	β-Naphthol, (structure) , insoluble in water	Benzoate, M.P. 107 °C
133	Pyrogallol, (structure) , insoluble in water yellow colour with FeCl₃	Tribenzoate, M.P. 89 °C triacetate, M.P. 261 °C
169	Hydroquinone, (structure) , soluble in water	Benzoquinone, M.P. 116 °C
218	Pholroglucinol, (structure) , soluble in water	Tribromo derivative, M.P. 151 °C 151 °C triacetate, M.P. 105 °C

D. Carbonyl compounds (Aldehydes and ketones)

Liquid

B.P. (in °C)	Name	Derivative
56	Acetone, CH_3COCH_3, soluble in water	Iodoform 199 °C
80	Methyl ethyl ketone, $CH_3 - COCH_2CH_3$, soluble in water responds to iodoform tert	Semicarbazone, M.P. 140 °C
98	Formaldehyde, HCHO, soluble in water	2, 4-Dinitro phenylhydrazone, M.P. 155 °C
130	Mesityl oxide, $CH_3COCH = C(CH_3)_2$, sparingly soluble in water	Semicarbazone, M.P. 156 °C
164	Diacetone alcohol, $(CH_3)_2 C(OH) CH_2COCH_3$	2, 4-Dinitrophenyl hydrazone, M.P. 235 °C
178	Benzaldehyde, ![CHO benzene ring], sparingly soluble in water	Benzoic acid, M.P. 121 °C
196	Salicylaldehyde, ![CHO OH benzene ring], sapringly soluble in water	Salicylic acid, M.P. 155 °C
202	Acetophenone, ![COCH3 benzene ring], sparingly soluble in water	Semicarbazone, M.P. 105 °C

Solid

M.P. (in °C)	Name	Derivative
48	Benzophenone, Ph — C — Ph, insoluble in water （‖O)	Benzoic acid, M.P. 121 °C
		D.N.P.H. 229 °C
80	Vanillin, (CHO, OH, OCH$_3$ on benzene ring), slightly soluble in water, smell of vanila, gives colour (blue) with FeCl$_3$	Vanillic acid, M.P. 207 °C
95	Benzil, Ph — C — C — Ph, pale yellow in colour, （‖O ‖O） insoluble in water	Benzilic acid, M.P. 150 °C
130	Benzoin, Ph — C — CH — Ph, （‖O ｜OH） insoluble in water, responds to Fehling's test	Benzil, M.P. 95 °C, benzoic acid, M.P. 121 °C

E. Carboxylic acids

Liquid

B.P. (in °C)	Name	Derivative
100	Formic acid, HCOOH, soluble in water, decolourises KMnO$_4$	Anilide, M.P. 47 °C
118	Acetic acid, CH$_3$COOH, soluble in water	Amide, M.P. 82, Anilide, M.P. 115 °C
141	Propionic acid, CH$_3$—CH$_2$—COOH, soluble in water	Amide, M.P. 79 °C
163	n-Butyric acid, CH$_3$(CH$_2$)$_2$—COOH, soluble in water	Amide, M.P. 114 °C

Solid

M.P. (in °C)	Name	Derivative
63	Chloroacetic acid, ClCH$_2$COOH, soluble in water	Amide, M.P. 119 °C
76	Phenylacetic acid, PhCH$_2$COOH, soluble in water	Benzoic acid, M.P. 121 °C
97	Glutaric acid, (CH$_2$)$_3$ (COOH)$_2$, soluble in water	Amide, M.P. 174 °C

Contd.

100	Citric acid, $\begin{array}{l}CH_2-COOH\\C(OH)-COOH,\\CH_2-COOH\end{array}$ soluble in water	Methyl ester, M.P. 79 °C
101	Oxalic acid, $\begin{array}{l}COOH\\COOH\end{array}$ 2H$_2$O, soluble in water	Anilide, M.P. 245 °C
101	Methyl salicylic acid, (ring with OCH$_3$ and COOH), sparingly soluble in water	Amide, M.P. 128 °C
102	o-Toluic acid, (ring with COOH and CH$_3$), sparingly soluble in water	Phthalic acid, M.P. 195 °C
109	m-Toluic acid, (ring with COOH and CH$_3$), sparingly soluble in water	Amide, M.P. 94 °C
213	p-Hydroxy benzoic acid, (ring with OH and COOH), gives violet colour with FeCl$_3$	Acetyl derivative, M.P. 185 °C
121	Benzoic acid, (ring with COOH), soluble in hot water	Amide, M.P. 128 °C

Contd.

126	Phenyl glycine, Ph—NH—CH$_2$—COOH, soluble in hot water	Acety derivative, M.P. 195 °C
133	Cinnamic acid, Ph—CH=CH—COOH, sparingly soluble in water, decolourises Br$_2$-water	Amide, 141 °C
135	Acetyl salicylic acid, (Aspirin), sparingly soluble in water	Salicylic acid, M.P. 155 °C
137	o-Chloro Benzoic acid, , soluble in hot water	Amide, M.P. 139 °C
150	Benzilic acid, (Ph)$_2$C(OH) COOH, soluble in hot water	Amide, M.P. 154 °C
151	Adipic acid, (CH$_2$)$_4$ (COOH)$_2$, sparingly soluble in water	Amide, M.P. 220 °C
155	Salicylic acid, , soluble in water, gives violet colour with FeCl$_3$	Amide, M.P. 139 °C
177	p-Toluic acid, , soluble in hot water	Amide, M.P. 158 °C
184	Anisic acid, , sparingly soluble in water	Amide, M.P. 162 °C

Contd.

195	Phthalic acid, , soluble in hot water	Phthalimide, M.P. 238 °C
200	*m*-Hydroxy benzoic acid, , slightly soluble in water	Acetyl derivative, M.P. 127 °C
207	Vanillic acid, , sparingly soluble in water	Acetyl derivative, M.P. 142 °C
236	*p*-Chloro benzoic acid, , sparingly soluble in water	Amide, M.P. 179 °C

F. Esters

Liquid

B.P. (in °C)	Name	Derivative
181	Ethyl acetoacetate, $CH_3—COCH_2COOC_2H_5$, sparingly soluble in water	Semicarbazone, M.P. 129 °C
186	Ethyl oxalate, $\begin{array}{l} COOC_2H_5 \\ | \\ COOC_2H_5 \end{array}$, slightly soluble in water	Oxamate, M.P. 114 °C
198	Ethyl malonate, $CH_2(COOC_2H_5)_2$, insoluble in water	Malonic acid, M.P. 133 °C

213	Ethyl benzoate, 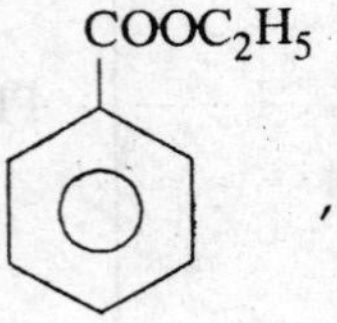 $COOC_2H_5$, insoluble in water	Benzoic acid, 121 °C
224	Methyl salicylate, 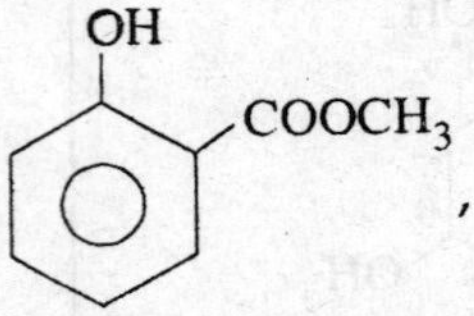 OH $COOCH_3$, insoluble in water, smell of oil of winter green, gives violet colour with $FeCl_3$	Salicylic acid, M.P. 155 °C
298	Ethyl phthalate, 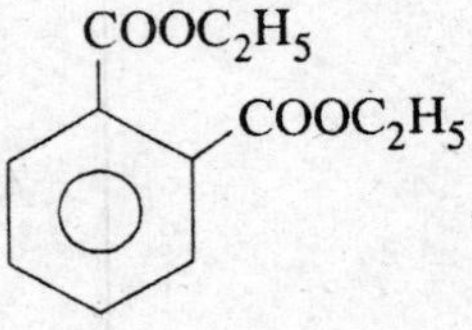 $COOC_2H_5$ $COOC_2H_5$, insoluble in water	Phthalic acid, M.P. 195 °C

Solid

M.P. (in °C)	Name	Derivative
42	Salol, 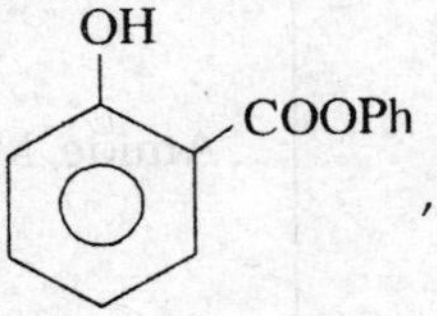 OH COOPh , insoluble in water	Acetyl derivative, M.P. 79 °C
116	Ethyl-*p*-hydroxy benzoate, 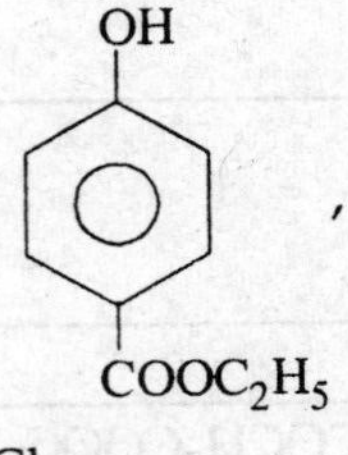 OH $COOC_2H_5$, gives violet colour with $FeCl_3$	p-Hydroxy benzoic acid, M.P. 213 °C
131	Methyl-*p*-hydroxy benzoate, 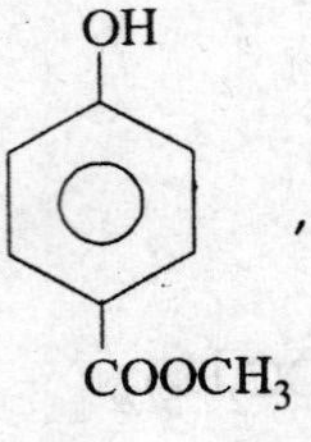 OH $COOCH_3$, gives violet colour with $FeCl_3$	Benzoyl derivative, M.P. 135 °C

G. Amines

Liquid

B.P. (in °C)	Name	Derivative
183	Aniline, NH_2–C$_6$H$_5$, sparingly soluble in water	Tribromo derivative, M.P. 118 °C
		Acetyl derivative, M.P. 114 °C
185	Benzyl amine, CH_2NH_2–C$_6$H$_5$, sparingly soluble in water	Acetyl derivative, M.P. 60 °C
193	Methyl aniline, $NHCH_3$–C$_6$H$_5$, insoluble in water in water	Acetyl derivative, M.P. 102 °C
193	Dimethyl aniline, $N(CH_3)_2$–C$_6$H$_5$, insoluble	p-Bromo Derivative, M.P. 55 °C
197	o-Toluidine, CH_3, NH_2 substituted benzene, sparingly soluble in water	Acetyl derivative, M.P. 112 °C
199	m-Toluidine, CH_3, NH_2 substituted benzene, sparingly soluble in water	Benzoyl derivative, M.P. 125 °C
218	o-Anisidine, OCH_3, NH_2 substituted benzene, sparingly soluble in water	Acetyl derivative, M.P. 84 °C

Solid

M.P. (in °C)	Name	Derivative
45	p-Toluidine, 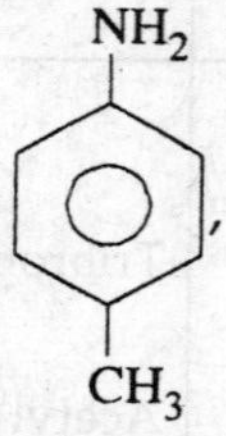 ![NH2 benzene ring with CH3] when dissolved in 1:1 H_2SO_4 and HNO_3 blue-violet-red-brown colour is obtained	Acetyl derivative, M.P. 148 °C
54	Diphenyl amine, $(Ph)_2NH$, gives blue colour with HNO_2	Acetyl derivative, M.P. 101 °C Benzoyl derivative, M.P. 180 °C
57	p-Anisidine, 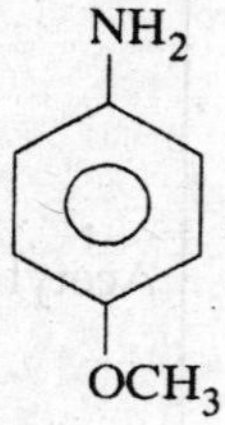 ![NH2 benzene ring with OCH3] sparingly soluble in water	Acetyl derivative, M.P. 127 °C Benzoyl derivative, M.P. 154 °C
63	m-Phenylene diamine, 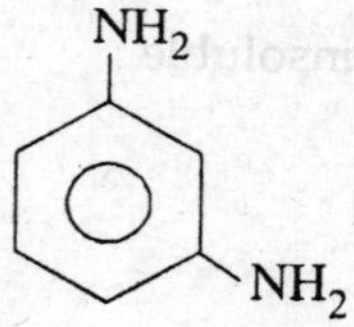 ![NH2 benzene ring with NH2 meta] soluble in hot water	Tribromo derivative, M.P. 158 °C Diacetyl derivative, M.P. 240 °C
71	o-Nitro aniline, 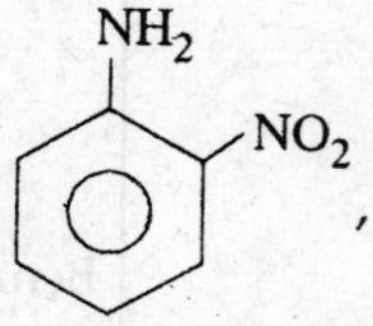 ![NH2 benzene ring with NO2 ortho] soluble in hot water it is orange in colour	Acetyl derivative, M.P. 92 °C Benzoyl derivative, M.P. 94 °C
102	o-Phenylene diamine, 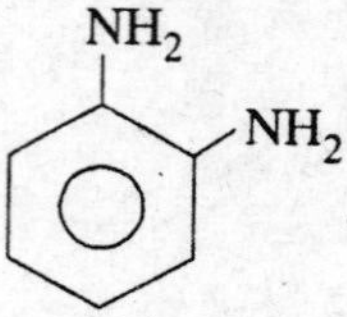 ![NH2 benzene ring with NH2 ortho] soluble in hot water	Diacetyl derivative, M.P. 185 °C

Contd.

111	β-Naphthylamine, sparingly soluble in water	Acetyl derivative, M.P. 132 °C Benzoyd derivative, M.P. 162 °C
114	m-Nitro aniline, yellow coloured and soluble in hot water	Acetyl derivative, M.P. 155 °C
122	m-Aminophenol, sparingly soluble in water	Acetyl derivative M.P. 101 °C Benzoyl derivative, M.P. 153 °C
128	Benzidine, sparingly soluble in hot water	Acetyl derivative, M.P. 317 °C Benzoyl derivative, M.P. 350 °C
140	p-Phenylene diamine, soluble in hot water	Acetyl derivative, M.P. 304 °C Benzoyl derivative, M.P. >300 °C
144	Anthranilic acid, soluble in water	Acetyl derivative, M.P. 180 °C Benzoyl derivative, M.P. 178 °C

Contd.

| 147 | p-Nitro aniline, | Acetyl derivative, M.P. 214 °C |

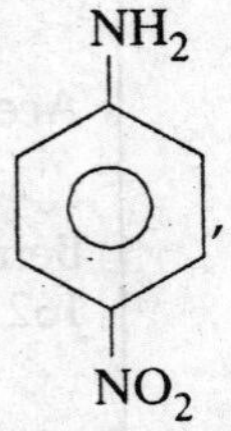

soluble in hot water yellow in colour

Benzoyl derivative, M.P. 200 °C

| 174 | o-Amino phenol, | Acetyl derivative, M.P. 200 °C |

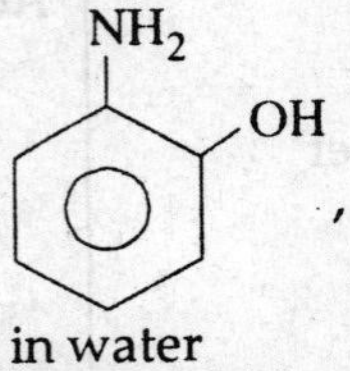

sparingly soluble in water
dark brown precipitate with FeCl$_3$

Benzoyl derivative, M.P. 180 °C

| 174 | m-Amino benzoic acid, | Amide, M.P. 75 °C |

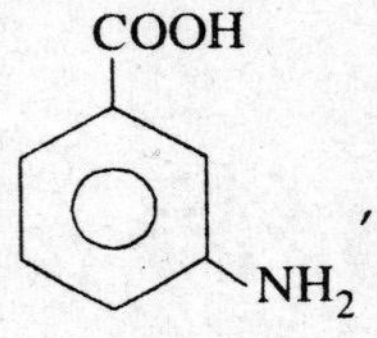

soluble in hot water

Actyl derivative, M.P. 250 °C

| 184 | p-Amino phenol, | Acetyl derivative, M.P. 250 °C |

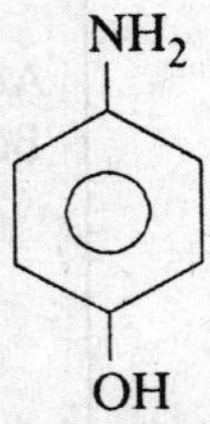

sparingly soluble in water

Benzoyl derivative, M.P. 234 °C

| 186 | p-Amino benzoic acid, | Amide, M.P. 180 °C |

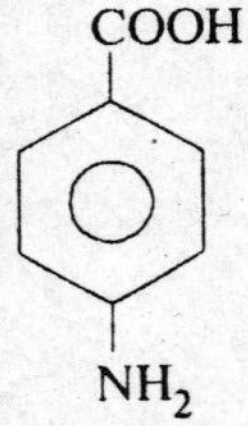

souble in hot water

Acetyl derivative M.P. 252 °C

| >300 | 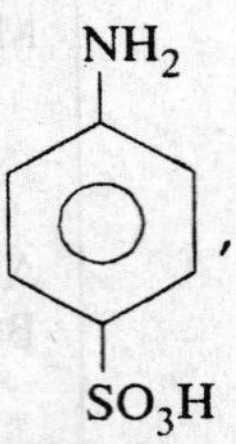 Sulphanilic acid, | Bromo derivative, M.P. 120 °C |

sparingly soluble in water

H. Amide

Solid

M.P. (in °C)	Name	Derivative
82	Acetamide, CH_3CONH_2, soluble in water	Acetanilide, M.P. 114 °C
114	Acetanilide, NHCONH₂ ⬡ , soluble in hot water	p-Nitro derivative M.P. 210 °C
125	Succinimide, $\begin{array}{c} CH_2-CO \\ \vert \qquad\quad \rangle O, \\ CH_2-CO \end{array}$ soluble in water	Succinic acid, M.P. 184 °C
128	Benzamide, CONH₂ ⬡ , sparingly soluble in water	Benzoic acid, M.P. 121 °C; Benzanilide, M.P. 160 °C
132	Urea, $CO(NH_2)_2$, soluble in water	Nitrate, M.P. 162 °C; Oxalate, M.P. 170 °C
138	Salicylamide, OH ⬡ CONH₂ , sparingly soluble in water, gives colour (violet) with $FeCl_3$	Acetyl derivative, M.P. 143 °C
161	Benzanilide, CONH—Ph ⬡ , insoluble in water	Bromo derivative, M.P. 204 °C
167	p-Bromo acetanilide, NHCOCH₃ ⬡ Br , insoluble in water	Nitro derivative, M.P. 104 °C; p-bromo aniline, M.P. 66 °C

Contd.

233	Phthalimide, [structure: benzene ring fused with CO-NH-CO ring] NH,	Phthalic acid, M.P. 195 °C
	insoluble in water	
238	Carbazole, [structure: carbazole ring system with N-H],	Picrate, M.P. 182 °C
	insoluble in water, with a drop of conc. H_2SO_4, gives yellow colour which turns to green on addition of $NaNO_2$ solution (2%)	

Nitro Compound   Liquid

B.P. (in °C)	Name	Derivative
210	Nitrobenzene, [structure: benzene with NO_2], insoluble in water	m-Nitroaniline, M.P. 90 °C
220	o-Nitrotoluene, [structure: toluene with CH_3 and NO_2 ortho], insoluble in water	o-Nitrobenzoic acid, M.P. 147 °C
230	m-Nitrotoluene, [structure: toluene with CH_3 and NO_2 meta], insoluble in water	m-Nitrobenzoic acid, M.P. 140 °C

Solid

M.P. (in °C)	Name	Derivative
44	o-Nitrophenol, [structure: phenol with OH and NO_2 ortho], soluble in hot water	Acetate, M.P. 40 °C

Contd.

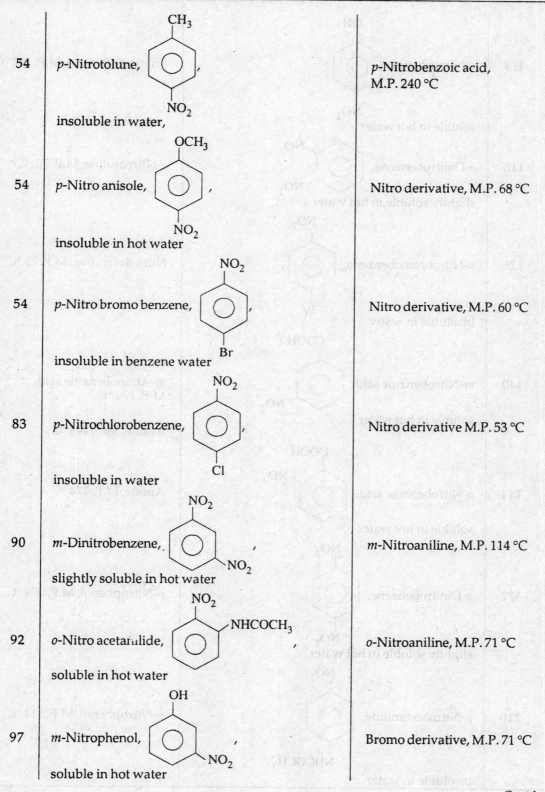

54	*p*-Nitrotolune, insoluble in water,	*p*-Nitrobenzoic acid, M.P. 240 °C
54	*p*-Nitro anisole, insoluble in hot water	Nitro derivative, M.P. 68 °C
54	*p*-Nitro bromo benzene, insoluble in benzene water	Nitro derivative, M.P. 60 °C
83	*p*-Nitrochlorobenzene, insoluble in water	Nitro derivative M.P. 53 °C
90	*m*-Dinitrobenzene, slightly soluble in hot water	*m*-Nitroaniline, M.P. 114 °C
92	*o*-Nitro acetanilide, soluble in hot water	*o*-Nitroaniline, M.P. 71 °C
97	*m*-Nitrophenol, soluble in hot water	Bromo derivative, M.P. 71 °C

Contd.

114	*p*-Nitrophenol, soluble in hot water	Bromo derivative, M.P. 142 °C
118	*o*-Dinitrobenzene, slightly soluble in hot water	*o*-Nitroaniline, M.P. 70 °C
126	*p*-Nitrobromobenzene, insoluble in water	Nitro derivative, M.P. 72 °C
140	*m*-Nitrobenzoic acid, soluble in hot water	*m*-Aminobenzine acid, M.P. 174 °C Amide, M.P. 143 °C
144	*o*-Nitrobenzoic acid, soluble in hot water	Amide, M.P. 174 °C
172	*p*-Dinitrobenzene, slightly soluble in hot water	*p*-Nitrophenol, M.P. 174 °C
210	*p*-Nitroacetanilide, insoluble in water	*p*-Nitrophenol, M.P. 114 °C

Chapter 6

Outline of Reporting a Qualitative Organic Analysis with Classified Tests

A. For general course

Date: Sample No.:

1. Physical Properties

 (a) Physical state

 (b) Colour

 (c) Odour

 (d) Litmus or pH paper test

 (e) Ignition test

 (f) Solubility in (i) hot and cold water, (ii) dilute acid, (iii) dilute alkali and (iv) alcohol.

 (g) Melting point [(as in Ig(i)]

2. Detection of Elements

Lassigne's experiment: A portion of the substance supplied is fused with a small piece of metallic sodium in a fusion tube till red hot and the hot fusion tube is poured into 30-40 ml of distilled water taken in a mortar and broken and ground by a pestle. Next, the solution is filtered and following tests are performed with the filtrate.

Experiments	Observations	Inference
(a) To a portion of the filtrate 3-4 drops of freshly prepared ferrous sulphate solution are added and boiled for a minute. The solution is cooled. The cold solution is acidified with dilute H_2SO_4	**(a)** Prussian blue colour is developed or No colouration	**(a)** Nitrogen present or Nitrogen absent
(b) To another portion of the filtrate taken in a test tube, 1-2 drops of freshly prepared sodium nitroprusside solution is added.	**(b)** Violet colour appears or No violet colouration.	**(b)** Sulphur present or Sulphur absent
(c) Another portion of the filtrate is taken in a test tube and is acidified with dilute HNO_3, boiled and a few drops of $AgNo_3$ solution is added to it.	**(c)** A white / yellow precipitate appears or No precipitate appears	**(c)** Halogens are present or Halogens are absent

Conclusion: From above experiments it is thus seen that the compounds contain N/S/halogen or no special elements (N, S and halogens).

3. Detection of Functional Group

To detect the functional groups following tests are performed:

A. Detection of non-nitrogeneous functional group

Experiments	Observations	Inference
(a) 2 ml of aqueous or alcoholic solution of the sample is taken in a test tube and tested with a blue litmus paper.	**(a)** Blue litmus paper turns red or No change in the colour of litmus paper.	**(a)** Acidic nature, COOH or phenolic OH or Neutral substance, may be >C=O group.
(b) To another portion of 2 ml solution an aqueous solution of $NaHCO_3$ is added drop by drop.	**(b)** Effervescence of CO_2 occurs or No effervescence.	**(b)** —COOH group is present or —COOH group is absent
(c) In a test tube, 5 ml of NaOH solution is taken and to it 1-2 drops of phenolphthalein is added when pink colour develops. To this pink solution sample solution is added drop by drop.	**(c)** Pink colour disappears or Pink colour is not discharged.	**(c)** —COOH group is present or —COOH group is absent.
(d) A few portion of the solid sample is taken in a test tube and to it 2-3 ml of ethyl alcohol and 1-2 drops of conc. H_2SO_4 are added and heated on a water bath.	**(d)** Characteristic fruity smell is obtained or No fruity smell is obtained.	**(d)** —COOH group is confirmed or —COOH group is absent.
(e) 2 ml of solution of the sample is taken in a test tube and to it 2 drops of $FeCl_3$ solution are added.	**(e)** Violet / blue / green colour appears	**(e)** Phenolic OH group is present

Contd.

Experiments	Observations	Inference
	or	or
	No characteristic colour.	Phenolic OH group is absent.
(f) 1 ml solution of the aniline is diazotised with $NaNO_2$ solution in presence of dilute HCl under cold condition. In another test tube solution of sample in NaOH is taken and to it diazotised solution of the aniline is added cooling under tap.	(f) A reddish dye is formed or No dye is formed.	(f) Phenolic OH is confirmed or Phenolic OH group is absent.
(g) About 0.05 g of the solid sample is added to 3 ml of saturated solution of 2:4-Dinitrophenyl hydrazine, shaken and warmed on a water bath for 2-3 minutes. The solution is allowed to stand for 5 minutes, 1 or 2 drops of water are added, warmed and cooled.	(g) Yellow / orange / red precipitate or colouration or No colouration nor precipitation.	(g) >C=O group is present or >C=O group is absent.
(h) To 1 ml of Tollen's reagent (ammoniacal $AgNO_3$ solution) 0.05 g of the sample is added, warmed on a water bath and cooled.	(h) A shining mirror is formed on the inner wall or grey precipitate is formed or No such mirror or precipitate is formed.	(h) Aldehydic group is present or Aldehydic group is absent.
(i) Equal volumes of Fehling's solution nos. 1 and 2 (1 ml each) is mixed in a test tube and to it 0.05 g of the sample is added, shaken and warmed on a water bath.	(i) Red precipitate is formed or No precipitate.	(i) Aldehydic group is present or Aldehydic group is absent.

B. Detection of nitrogeneous functional group

Experiments	Observations	Inference
(j) A small portion of the sample is taken in a dry test tube and to it 2-3 drops of $CHCl_3$ and 1 ml of alcoholic KOH are added. The reaction mixture is warmed gently.	(j) An obnoxious smell of isocyanide is obtained or No bad smell is obtained.	(j) —NH_2 group is present or —NH_2 group is absent.
(k) About 0.05g of the sample is dissolved in 2(N) HCl and is cooled in ice. To it 2 ml of cold 10% $NaNO_2$ solution is added and cooled again. This cold solution is added to alkaline solution of β-naphthol taken in another test tube,	(k) A brilliant scarlet red dye is formed or No dye is formed.	(k) —NH_2 group is confirmed or —NH_2 group is absent.
(l) A little of the sample is dissolved in 5 ml alcohol. To it small amount of solid NH_4Cl and a pinch of Zn-dust are added. The mixture is boiled for 2-3 minutes, cooled and allowed to stand for 5 minutes. Next it is filtered. To the filtrate Tollen's reagent is added and warmed on a water bath.	(l) A black / grey precipitate or a shining mirror is formed on the inner side of the test tube or No such observation.	(l) Nitro group is present or —NO_2 group is absent.

Contd.

Experiments	Observations	Inference
(m) A little of the sample is taken in a test tube and to it a few pieces of metallic tin and 5 ml of conc. HCl are added. The mixture is boiled for 2-3 minutes, cooled under tap and the supernatant liquid is decanted. To this liquid 2 ml of $NaNO_2$ solution is added and cooled. This cold solution is added to an alkaline solution of β-naphthol taken in another test tube.	**(m)** A brilliant red dye is formed or No dye is formed.	**(m)** —NO_2 group is present or —NO_2 group is absent.

Notes

(i) If nitrogen is found to be absent during element detection, tests for nitrogenous group need not be performed.

(ii) If the sample does not contain carbonyl group (>C=O) tests for aldehydes need not be performed.

(iii) If —NH_2 group is present dye test (**m**) for nitro group cannot be performed.

(iv) During reporting of the result only definite observation is to be reported, i.e., there should *not be any observation in 'or' manner.*

Final conclusion: The supplied sample contains .... elements(s) and .... as functional group.

N.B. General students are required to detect elements (N, S, halogens) in the organic compound and to detect the presence of any one out of five (phenolic OH, —COOH >C=O (aldehyde or ketone) —NH_2 and —NO_2) functional groups only in the sample and to observe its physical characteristics according to the syllabus for many universities.

B. For Honours or Major Course

Date: Sample No.:

1. Physical Properties

(a) Physical state

(b) Colour

(c) Odour

(d) Litmus or pH paper Test

(e) Ignition Test

(f) Solubility in (i) hot and cold water, (ii) dilute acid, (iii) dilute alkali and (iv) alcohol.

(g) Melting point / Boiling point [As in Ig(i) and (ii)]

2. Detection of Elements

Lassigne's experiment: A small portion of the sample is fused with a small piece of metallic sodium in a fusion tube till red hot and the hot fusion tube is plunged into 30-40 ml of distilled water taken in a mortar, broken and ground by a pestle. The solution is filtered and with the filtrate following tests are performed:

Experiments	Observations	Inference
(a) To a portion of the filtrate 3-4 drops of freshly prepared ferrous sulphate solution are added and boiled for a minute. The solution is cooled and is acidified with dilute H_2SO_4.	**(a)** Prussian blue / green is developed or No colouration.	**(a)** Nitrogen is present or Nitrogen is absent.
(b) To another portion of the filtrate 1-2 drops of freshly prepared sodium nitroprusside solution is added.	**(b)** Violet colour appears or No violet colouration.	**(b)** Sulphur is present or Sulphur is absent.
(c) 1 ml of the filtrate taken in a test tube is acidified with dilute acetic acid and to it 1-2 drops of saturated lead acetate solution is added.	**(c)** A black precipitate is formed or No black precipitate.	**(c)** Sulphur is present or Sulphur is absent.
(d) Another portion of the filtrate taken in a test tube is acidified with dilute HNO_3, boiled and a few drops of $AgNO_3$ solution is added.	**(d)(i)** A white / yellow precipitate appears or No such precipitate.	**(d)(i)** Halogens are present or Halogens are absent.
	(ii) White precipitate is soluble in NH_4OH but reappears on acidification with dilute HNO_3 or	**(ii)** Chlorine is present.
	(iii) The yellow precipitate is difficultly soluble in NH_4OH but insoluble in dilute HNO_3 or	**(iii)** Bromine is present.
	(iv) Yellow precipitate is insoluble both in NH_4OH and dilute HNO_3.	**(iv)** Iodine is present.
(e) Another portion of the filtrate is acidified with dilute HCl or H_2SO_4 and to it 1-2 drops of CCl_4 is added. Next, strong chlorine solution is added. dropwise with shaking. **(e)(i)** CCl_4 layer becomes violet after addition of chlorine water, the addition of chlorine water is continued till violet colour disappears.	**(e)(i)** CCl_4 layer turns violet or	**(e)(i)** Iodine is present.
	(ii) CCl_4 turns Brown / reddish brown.	**(ii)** Bromine is present.
	Reddish brown colour appears or	Both iodine and bromine are present or
	CCl_4 layer becomes colourless or	Only iodine is present but bromine is absent or
	No violet or brown colouration.	Both iodine and bromine are absent but chlorine may be present.

Beilstein test: A long copper wire fitted with a cork at one end is strongly heated in an oxidising flame of the burner until it ceases to impart any colour to the flame. It is cooled and a small portion of the sample is placed on the wire and heated over the outer edge of the flame. The colour of the flame is noted.

Observations	Inference
Colour of the flame becomes green or No characteristic colour of the flame.	Halogens are present. or Halogens are absent.

Conclusion: From the above elemental analysis it is seen that the sample contains .... as its special elements.

3. Detection of Functional Group

For the detection of functional groups following tests are performed:

A. Detection of non-nitrogenous functional group

Experiments	Observations	Inference
(a) 2 ml of aqueous or alcoholic solution of the sample taken in a test tube is tested with a blue litmus paper.	**(a)** Blue litmus paper turns red or No change in the colour of litmus paper.	**(a)** Acidic nature — COOH or phenolic —OH or Neutral substance, may be >C=O group.
(b) To another portion of 2 ml solution, an aqueous solution of $NaHCO_3$ is added drop by drop.	**(b)** Effervescence of CO_2 occurs. or No effervescence.	**(b)** —COOH group is present or —COOH is absent.
(c) In a test tube 5 ml of NaOH solution is taken and to it 1-2 drops of phenolphthalein is added when pink colour develops. To this pink solution sample solution is added dropwise.	**(c)** Pink colour disappears or Pink colour is not discharged.	**(c)** —COOH group is present or —COOH group is absent.
(d) A small portion of the solid sample is taken in a test tube and 2-3 ml of ethyl alcohol and 1-2 drops of conc. H_2SO_4 are added and heated on a water bath.	**(d)** Characteristic fruity smell is obtained or No fruity smell.	**(d)** —COOH group is confirmed or —COOH group is absent.
(e) 2 ml of the sample solution is taken in a test tube and to it 2 drops of $FeCl_3$ solution are added.	**(e)** Violet / blue /green colour appears.	**(e)** Phenolic —OH group is present

Contd.

Experiments	Observations	Inference
	or	or
	No characteristic colour.	Phenolic OH group is absent.
(f) 1 ml of the aniline solution is diazotised with $NaNO_2$ in presence of dilute HCl under cold condition. In another test tube, alkaline solution of sample is taken and to it diazotised cold solution of the aniline is added cooling under tap.	**(f)** A reddish dye is formed or No dye is formed.	**(f)** Phenolic —OH group is confirmed or Phenolic —OH group is absent.
(g)(i) 1 ml of the solution of the sample is taken in a test tube and to it 0.02 g of crystalline $NaNO_2$ is added, gently warmed and cooled.	**(g)(i)** Green / blue colour or No such colour.	**(g)(i)** Phenolic —OH group is present or Phenolic group is absent.
(ii) The above mixture is diluted carefully with water.	**(ii)** Colour changes to red or No response.	**(ii)** Phenolic —OH group is present or Phenolic —OH group is absent.
(iii) To this dilute solution (ii), excess of NaOH solution is added.	**(iii)** Blue / green colour returns or No such change.	**(iii)** Phenolic —OH group is present or Phenolic —OH group is absent.
(h)(i) About 0.05 g of the solid sample is added to 3 ml of saturated solution of 2:4-Dinitrophenyl hydrazine, shaken and warmed on a water bath for 2-3 minutes. The solution is allowed to stand for 5 minutes, 1 or 2 drops of water is added, warmed and cooled.	**(h)(i)** Yellow / orange / red precipitate or colouration or No colouration nor any precipitation.	**(h)(i)** >C=O group is present or >C=O group is absent.
(ii) To 1 ml of Tollen's solution (ammoniacal $AgNO_3$ solution) 0.05 g of the sample is added, warmed on a water bath and cooled.	**(ii)** A shining mirror is formed on the inner wall of the test tube or grey precipitate or No such mirror or precipitate.	**(ii)** Aldehydic group is present or Aldehydic group is absent.
(iii) Equal volumes of Fehling's solution nos. 1 and 2 (1 ml each) is mixed in a test tube and to it 0.05 g of the sample is added and warmed on a water bath.	**(iii)** Red precipitate is formed or No precipitate is formed.	**(iii)** Aldehydic group is present or Aldehydic group is absent.
(i) A small portion of original sample is dissolved in dry benzene and to it a small piece of metallic sodium is added.	**(i)** Effervescence of a gas (hydrogen) occurs.	**(i)** Alcoholic —OH group may be.

Contd.

Experiments	Observations	Inference
	or	or
	No such effervescence.	Alcoholic —OH group is absent.
(j)(i) A few drops solution of the sample is taken in a test tube and to it 2 drops of CS_2 and a few crystals of NaOH are added, shaken for 2-3 minutes.	(j)(i) Yellow precipitate / colour or No colour / precipitate.	(j)(i) Alcoholic OH group is present or Alcoholic —OH group is absent.
(ii) To above solution (i) 2 drops of 10% ammonium molybdate solution is added, acidified with 2(N) H_2SO_4 and 2-3 ml of chloroform is added.	(ii) Violet / reddish blue colouration on chloroform layer or No colouration.	(ii) Alcoholic —OH group is present or Alcoholic —OH group is absent.
(k) 0.2 g of the sample taken in a test tube is dissolved in ethanol and to it 1-2 drops of phenolphthalein and 2-3 drops of NaOH are added.	(k) Pink colour disappears or Pink colour does not disappear.	(k) Ester group is present or Ester group is absent.
(l) About 0.1 g of the sample is taken in a test tube and to it 5 ml of 20% KOH solution is added and heated on a water bath for 15 minutes. The solution is acidified with dilute H_2SO_4.	(l) a white precipitate appears or No precipitate.	(l) Ester group is present or Ester group is absent.
(m) About 0.1 g of the sample is taken in a test tube and to it 1 ml of hydroxylamine hydrochloride solution in ethanol is added. The solution is made alkaline with 10% NaOH solution. The mixture is boiled, cooled and acidified with dilute HCl. To this solution 1-2 drops of $FeCl_3$ solution is added.	(m) Reddish violet colour appears or No colouration.	(m) Ester group is present or Ester group is absent.

B. Test for nitrogeneous functional group

Experiments	Observations	Inference
(n) A small portion of the sample is taken in a dry test tube and to it 2-3 drops of $CHCl_3$ and 1 ml of alcoholic KOH solution are added. The reaction mixture is warmed gently.	(n) An obnoxious smell of isocyanide is obtained or No bad smell is obtained.	(n) —NH_2 group is present or —NH_2 group is absent.
(o) About 0.05 g of the sample is dissolved in 2(N) HCl and is cooled in ice. To it 2 ml of cold 10% $NaNO_2$ solution is added and cooled again. This cold solution is added to an alkaline solution of β-naphthol taken in another test tube.	(o) A brilliant scarlet red dye is formed or No dye is formed.	(o) —NH_2 group is confirmed or —NH_2 group is absent.

Contd.

Experiments	Observations	Inference
(p)(i) A little of the sample is dissolved in ethyl alcohol (5 ml). To it small amount of solid NH_4Cl and a pinch of Zn-dust are added. The mixture is boiled for 2-3 minutes, cooled, allowed to stand for 5 minutes, and filtered. To one part of the filtrate Tollen's reagent is added and warmed on a water bath.	**(p)(i)** A black / grey precipitate or a shining mirror is formed on the inner wall of the test tube or No such observation.	**(p)(i)** $-NO_2$ group is present or $-NO_2$ group is absent.
(ii) To another part of the filtrate Fehling's solutions (1 and 2) are added and warmed on a water bath.	**(ii)** Red precipitate or No precipitate.	**(ii)** $-NO_2$ is present or $-NO_2$ group is absent.
(q) About 0.025 g of the sample is taken in a test tube and it is mixed with 2 ml of freshly prepared 5% solution of ferrous ammonium sulphate. To this mixture 1 drop of 2(N) H_2SO_4 followed by 1 ml of 2(N) KOH solution in methanol are added. The mouth of the test tube is stoppered quickly, and vigorously shaken.	**(q)** A reddish brown precipitate is obtained or No reddish brown precipitate is obtained.	**(q)** $-NO_2$ group is present or $-NO_2$ group is absent
(r) A little of the sample is taken in a test tube and to it 4 ml of conc. HCl and a few pieces of tin metal are added. The mixture is boiled gently for 2-3 minutes, cooled under tap and the supernatant liquid is decanted. The liquid is diazotised by 2 ml solution of $NaNO_2$, cooled again and is added to an alkaline solution of β-naphthol taken in a test tube. **N.B.** If $-NH_2$ group is present, this test is not applicable.	**(r)** A brilliant red dye is formed or No dye is formed.	**(r)** $-NO_2$ group is present or $-NO_2$ group is absent.
(s) A small portion of the sample is taken in a test tube. To it 2 ml of 50% NaOH solution is added and heated.	**(s)** Ammonia gas evolves which turns $Hg_2(NO_3)_2$ paper black or No smell of ammonia.	**(s)** Amide group is present or Amide group is absent.
(t) A small portion of the sample is taken in a test tube. To it 2 ml of hydroxylamine hydrochloride solution (1N) and 2 ml of 1(N) KOH solution are added and the mixture is heated for 5 minutes. It is cooled and to it a few drops of $FeCl_3$ solution is added.	**(t)** Red colour appears or No such colour develops.	**(t)** Amide group is present or Amide group is absent.
(u) About 0.5 g of the sample is taken in a test tube and to it 5 ml of conc. HCl is added. The mixture is boiled, cooled, diluted and diazo reaction (dye formation) is performed in the usual way.	**(u)** A brilliant red scarlet or red precipitate or No such precipitation.	**(u)** Anilide group is present or Anilide group is absent.

N.B. If nitrogen is found to be absent during detection of elements, tests for nitrogenous functional groups need not to be performed.

Conclusion: From above analytical experiments it appears that the given sample contains (i) .... special elements (or no special elements) and (ii) ....—........ as functional group(s).

4. Preparation of Derivatives

.... derivative has been prepared (short description of particular derivative is to be given) and its melting point has been noted as .... °C.

5. Final Conclusion

From the above analytical tests the given sample appears to be .... which has been confirmed from literature search. Thus,

　　　M.P. of the sample .... °C

　　　M.P. of the derivative prepared .... °C

　　　Reported melting point of .... °C

　　　Reported melting point of .... derivative of .... °C

　　　Thus, the given sample is ....

Chapter 7

Questions and Answers for Viva Voce

1. **What happens when an organic compound is fused with metallic sodium?**

   Ans. Organic compound decomposes with the formation of following compounds.

   $$Na + C + N \longrightarrow NaCN$$
   $$2Na + S \longrightarrow Na_2S$$
   $$Na + X \longrightarrow NaX \quad (X = halogen)$$
   $$C + N + S + Na \longrightarrow NaSCN, \text{ if incomplete fusion occurs.}$$

2. **What is the name of the method for detecting elements in organic compounds?**

   Ans. Lassigne's method.

3. **What colour is given by nitrogen containing compound when the filtrate of sodium fusion is tested? Write down the reaction.**

   Ans. Prussian blue colour or precipitation.

   $$2NaCN + FeSO_4 = Fe(CN)_2 + Na_2SO_4; 4NaCN + Fe(CN)_2 \longrightarrow Na_4[Fe(CN)_6]$$
   $$FeSO_4 + 2H_2SO_4 + O_2 \longrightarrow 2Fe_2(SO_4)_3 + 2H_2O \text{ (Air oxidation)}$$
   $$3Na_4[Fe(CN)_6] + 2Fe_2(SO_4)_3 \longrightarrow Fe_4[Fe(CN)_6] + 6Na_2SO_4$$
   $$\text{(Prussian blue)}$$

4. **What colour is obtained in Beilstein test? Is it reliable?**

   Ans. Green. Not reliable.

5. **What colour is obtained when sodium nitroprusside solution is added to fusion extract? Write down the reaction.**

   Ans. Violet.

   $$Na_2S + Na_2[Fe(CN)_6] NO \longrightarrow Na_4[Fe(CN)_6NOS]$$
   $$\text{Sodium nitroprusside} \qquad\qquad \text{Violet}$$

6. **How bromine and iodine in organic compound are tested?**

   Ans. See Art. 2.1.

215

7. Why a green colour is sometimes obtained in Lassigne's test for nitrogen?

   Ans. Due to incomplete fusion there is formation of sodium sulphocyanide, NaCNS.

8. Why is the solution finally acidified during the detection of nitrogen in Lassigne's test?

   Ans. Prussian blue formed is unstable in alkaline medium but stable in acidic medium.

9. What is the functional group present in an alcohol?

   Ans. Alcoholic hydroxyl.

10. What is the colour given by a phenolic OH group in ferric chloride test? Write down the reaction.

    Ans. See Art. 3.1, table 3.3.

11. What is the back dye test?

    Ans. See Art. 3.1, table 3.3.

12. Which is more acidic—phenols or carboxylic acid?

    Ans. Carboxylic acid.

13. How carboxylic group is detected?

    Ans. By sodium bicarbonate test.

14. How carbonyl group is detected?

    Ans. By using 2, 4-Dinitrophenyl hydrazine (D.N.P.H.).

15. Why D.N.P.H. is usually used as a reagent for detecting carbonyl group?

    Ans. Because this reagent normally forms crystalline derivative.

16. There are two types of carbonyl compounds. What are those?

    Ans. Aldehyde ($R - \overset{\underset{\|}{O}}{C} - H$) and ketone ($\overset{R}{\underset{R}{>}}C = O$).

17. How aldehydes and ketones are differentiated?

    Ans. By Tollen's test and Fehling's solution test.

18. What property has been utilised in differentiating between aldehyde and ketone?

    Ans. Reducing property of aldehyde. Generally aldehydes possess reducing property but ketone does not have such property.

19. What is Tollen's reagent?

    Ans. Ammoniacal $AgNO_3$ solution.

20. What happens in Tollen's test?

    Ans. Metallic silver is precipitated.

    $$R - \overset{\underset{\|}{O}}{C} - H + 2Ag(NH_3)_2NO_3 + H_2O \longrightarrow 2Ag\downarrow + RCOONH_4 + NH_3 + 2NH_4NO_3$$

21. What is Fehling's solution?

    Ans. It is a mixture of two solutions—Fehling's nos. 1 and 2. Fehling's no. 1 contains aqueous $CuSO_4$ solution containing a few drops of H_2SO_4 and Fehling's no. 2 is an alkaline solution of sodium potassium tartarate (Rochelle salt).

22. What happens when Fehling's solution is added to an aldehyde?

Ans. A red precipitate of Cu_2O is obtained.

$$R - \underset{\underset{O}{\|}}{C} - H + Cu^{++} + NaOH + H_2O \longrightarrow Cu_2O\downarrow + R - COONa + H_2O$$

23. What is Rochelle salt? What is its function?

Ans. It is sodium potassium tartarate. Its function is to stabilise cuprous ion by complex formation as shown below.

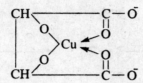

Tartarate coppercomplex

24. What is Schiff's reagent? What happens when this reagent is used for detection of aldehydic group.

Ans. Schiff's reagent is magenta solution rendered colourless by SO_2. Aldehyde generally gives pink magenta colour.

25. How amino group is detected?

Ans. (i) Carbylamine test and (ii) Dye test.

26. What happens in carbylamine and Dye test?

Ans. See Art. 3.2, table 3.7.

27. Name a test by which nitro group is detected?

Ans. Mulliken and Barker test.

28. What happens in Mulliken and Barker test?

Ans. See Art. 3.2, table 3.8.

29. How is amide detected?

Ans. On heating with NaOH, ammonia is evolved.

30. How is anilide group detected?

Ans. See Art. 3. 2, table 3.10.

31. How is ester group detected?

Ans. See Art. 3. 2, table 3.5.

32. What is Hydroxamic acid test?

Ans. See Art. 3. 2, table 3.5.

Organic Preparations

Part II

Chapter 1

Preparation of Organic Compounds

1. Introduction

The study of organic chemistry is really both an art and a science. The primary objective of the preparative organic chemistry is both to train in the art and to create awareness in the scientific principles on which the art is founded. In this connection it may be mentioned that it may perhaps be possible in the earliest stages of laboratory work to get the result without a clear understanding regarding the cause and nature of the work. But truly speaking, rapid, efficient and meaningful achievement always requires a real understanding of the principles, techniques and procedures of the laboratory experiment to be performed. In order to achieve such goal careful planning of the work in advance as well as motivation in the experiment are urgently needed. With these objective the preparations of some organic compounds involving the applications of typical reactions are described in sequel.

1.1 Preparation of p-Nitro Acetanilide

Principle: The preparation of p-nitro acetanilide is based on the nitration of acetanilide with a mixture of concentrated sulphuric acid and concentrated nitric acid (nitrating mixture). Both para and ortho nitro derivatives are formed but para isomer is formed as the major product. The ortho isomer is highly soluble in ethanol while para isomer remains practically insoluble in this solvent. Thus, p-nitro acetanilide is isolated by crystallisation from ethanol. The reaction taking place is given below:

Reaction:

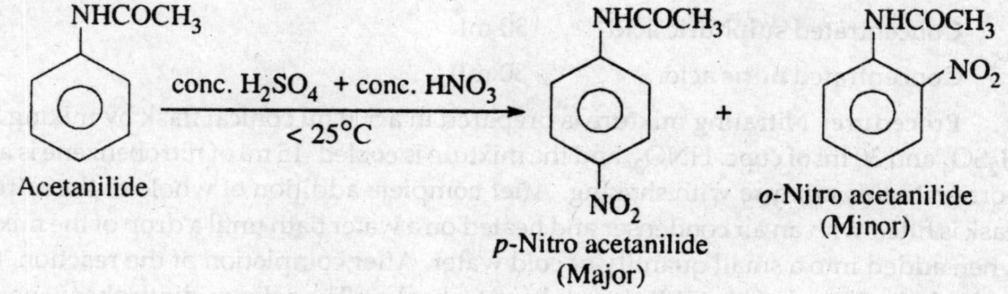

NHCOCH$_3$ $\xrightarrow[< 25°C]{\text{conc. H}_2\text{SO}_4 + \text{conc. HNO}_3}$ NHCOCH$_3$ ... NO$_2$ +   NHCOCH$_3$ ... NO$_2$

Acetanilide

p-Nitro acetanilide
(Major)

o-Nitro acetanilide
(Minor)

Chemicals required:

Acetanilide	10 g
Glacial acetic acid	10 ml
Conc. H$_2$SO$_4$	20 ml
Conc. HNO$_3$	4 ml

Procedure: 10 g of acetanilide is dissolved in 10 ml of glacial acetic acid in a 500 ml beaker by gentle warming, if needed. The mixture is cooled to room temperature and 16 ml of conc. H$_2$SO$_4$ acid is added in portion by stirring with a glass rod. The mixture becomes hot and clear. The solution is cooled by keeping the beaker in a bath of freezing mixture of ice and salt. The solution is stirred and the nitrating mixture prepared by mixing 4 ml of conc. HNO$_3$, and 4 ml of conc. H$_2$SO$_4$ is added dropwise through a dropping funnel. The temperature of the reaction mixture is kept below 10 °C. After completion of addition of whole of the nitrating mixture the beaker is removed from the freezing mixture bath and is allowed to stand for half an hour at room temperature. Next the reaction mixture is poured into 100 g of ice taken in another beaker when *p*-nitro acetanilide separates out. It is filtered, washed with cold water to remove excess of acid. The solid is crystallised from ethyl alcohol and dried by blotting paper. Melting point and yield are noted.

Yield : 10 g

M.P. : 215 °C

Comments: Direct nitration of aniline is not possible because the amino group is oxidised. So the protection of amino group is necessary by acetylation.

1.2 Preparation of *meta*-Dinitrobenzene

Principle: Preparation of *m*-dinitrobenzene is based on the nitration of nitrobenzene by nitrating mixture in the usual procedure.

Reaction:

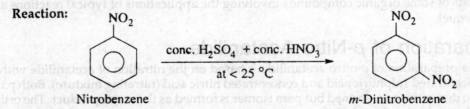

Nitrobenzene   *m*-Dinitrobenzene

Chemicals required:

Nitrobenzene	15 ml
Concentrated sulphuric acid	30 ml
Concentrated nitric acid	30 ml

Procedure: Nitrating mixture is prepared in a 500 ml conical flask by mixing 30 ml of conc. H$_2$SO$_4$ and 30 ml of conc. HNO$_3$, and the mixture is cooled. 15 ml of nitrobenzene is added in small portion to this mixture with shaking. After complete addition of whole of the nitrobenzene, the flask is fitted with an air condenser and heated on a water bath until a drop of the mixture solidifies when added into a small quantity of cold water. After completion of the reaction, the mixture is poured into 250 ml of ice cold water taken in a beaker. The solid *m*-dinitrobenzene separates out, filtered, washed with cold water and crystallised from methyl alcohol. It is dried by blotting paper and its yield and melting points are recorded.

Yield : 15 g

M.P. : 90 °C

1.3 Preparation of Acetanilide

Principle: Acetanilide is prepared by direct acetylation of aniline according to the following reaction. Acetylating agent usually used is acetic anhydride.

Reaction:

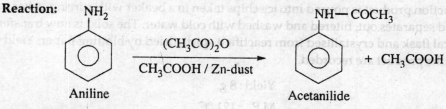

Aniline   Acetanilide

Chemicals required:

Aniline	15 ml
Acetic anhydride	15 ml
Glacial Acetic acid	15 ml
Zn-dust	0.1 g

Procedure: 15 ml of aniline is taken in a 500 conical falsk and is dissolved in 15 ml of glacial acetic acid. To it 0.1 g of Zn-dust is added. The conical flask is fitted with an air condenser and is gently warmed for half an four over a low flame. The hot reaction mixture is then poured into 250 ml ice cold water taken in a beaker with constant stirring by a glass rod. The solid product is filtered at the pump, washed with cold water and crystallised from hot water. If needed, a little amount of alcohol may be added to the hot water to dissolve the crude product. It is filtered, and dried in an oven. Its melting point and yield are noted.

Yield : 15 g

M.P. : 114 °C

1.4 Preparation of Quinol Diacetate

Principle: Quino diacetate is prepared by acetylation of quinol with acetyl chloride in presence of basic catalyst, pyridine.

Reaction:

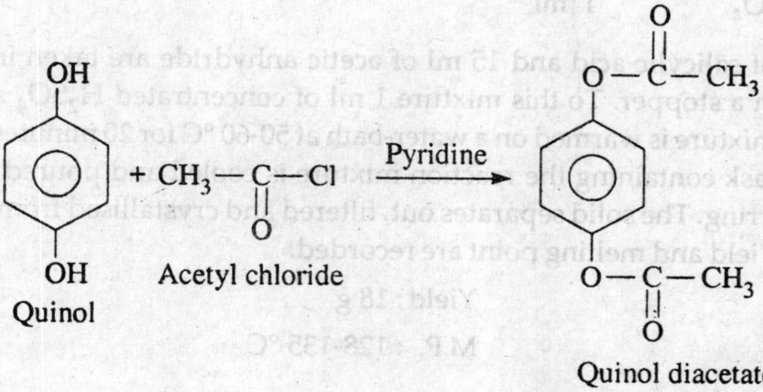

Quinol   Acetyl chloride   Quinol diacetate

Chemicals required:

Acetyl chloride   40 ml

Quinol   6 g

Pyridine   5 ml

Procedure: 6 g of quinol is dissolved in 5 ml of pyridine in a 250 ml conical flask (preferably dry) fitted with a rubber cork and a calcium chloride guard tube. The reaction flask is chilled in a freezing mixture. Acetyl chloride is added in small portion with shaking, and after complete addition of acetylchloride, the reaction flask is kept at room temperature for an hour with occasional shaking. The reaction product is poured into ice chips taken in a beaker with stirring. After a few minutes, the solid separates out, filtered and washed with cold water. The solid is now transferred to a 250 ml conical flask and crystallised from reactified spirit, dried by blotting paper. Yield and melting point of the product are recorded.

Yield : 8 g

M.P. : 121 °C

1.5 Preparation of Acetyl Salicylic Acid (Aspirin)

Principle: Acetyl salicylic acid (Aspirin) is generally prepared by acetylation of salicylic acid with acetic anhydride in presence of concentrated sulphuric acid. Thus,

Reaction:

Salicylic acid $+ (CH_3CO)_2O \xrightarrow{\text{Conc. } H_2SO_4}$ Acetyl salicylic acid (Aspirin) $+ CH_3COOH$

Chemicals required:

Pure Salicylic acid   15 g

Acetic Anhydride   15 ml

Concentrated H_2SO_4 1 ml

Procedure: 15 g of salicylic acid and 15 ml of acetic anhydride are taken in a 250 ml dry conical flask fitted with a stopper. To this mixture 1 ml of concentrated H_2SO_4 are added and shaken vigrously. The mixture is warmed on a water-bath at 50-60 °C for 20 minutes with constant shaking. The conical flask containing the reaction mixture is cooled and poured into 250 ml of water with constant stirring. The solid separates out, filtered and crystallised from 1:1 mixture of acetic acid and water. Yield and melting point are recorded.

Yield : 18 g

M.P. : 128-135 °C

1.6 Preparation of Phenyl Benzoate

Principle: Preparation of phenyl benzoate is carried out according to the method proposed by *Schotten and Baumann*. This process of benzoylation is one of the most important synthetic process for the preparation of large number of organic compounds. Both phenols and amines can be benzoylated by this process.

Reaction:

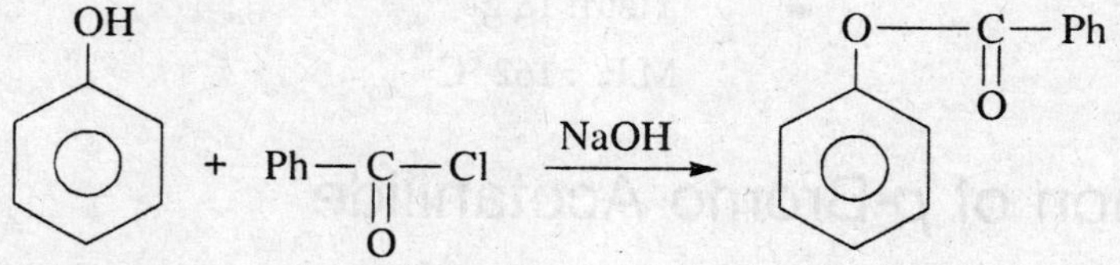

Phenol   Benzoyl   Phenyl benzoate
chloride

Chemicals required:

Phenol	10 g
Benzoyl chloride	20 ml
Sodium hydroxide (10%)	200 ml

Procedure: 10 g of phenol and 200 ml of 10% NaOH solution are taken in a 250 ml conical flask fitted with stopper and shaken well to dissolve phenol. To it 20 ml of pure benzoyl chloride is added, stoppered well and vigorously shaken for half an hour. If the smell of benzoyl chloride persists, little more 10% NaOH is added and vigorously shaken again till a solid is obtained. The crude product is filtered at the pump, washed with water and finally crystallised from rectified spirit. Yield and melting point of the dry sample are as recorded below:

Yield : 15 g

M.P. : 60 °C

1.7 Preparation of Benzanilide

Principle: Benzanilide is prepared by Schotten-Baumann process. Aniline is benzoylated with benzoyl chloride in presence of sodium hydroxide solution according to the reaction below:

Reaction:

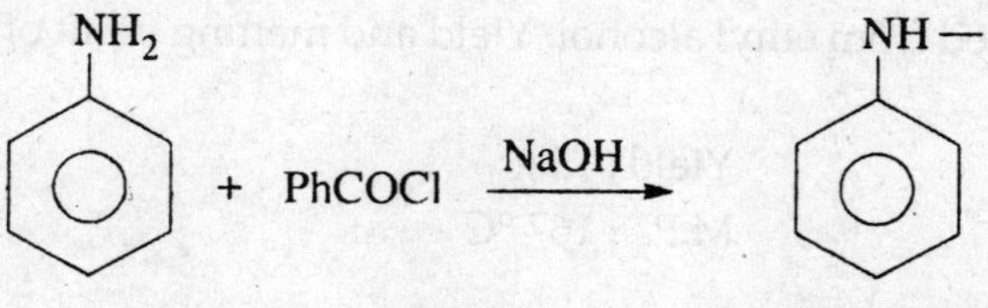

Benzanilide

Chemicals required:

Pure aniline	10 ml
Benzoyl chloride	15 ml
Sodium hydroxide (10%)	100 ml

Procedure: 10 ml of pure aniline and 100 ml of 10% NaOH solution is taken in a 500 ml conical flask fitted with a stopper and shaken vigorously. To this mixture 15 ml of benzoyl chloride is added and shaken vigorously for half an hour. When no smell of benzoyl chloride is detected, the reaction mixture is diluted with 50 ml of water when solid product separates out. It is filtered under suction, washed with dilute HCl and crystallised from rectified spirit. Yield and melting point of the dry sample are noted.

Yield: 18 g

M.P. : 162 °C

1.8 Preparation of *p*-Bromo Acetanilide

Principle: Para-bromoacetanilide is usually prepared by bromination of acetanilide by a solution of bromine in acetic acid. The reaction occurs smoothly according to the following reaction.

Reaction:

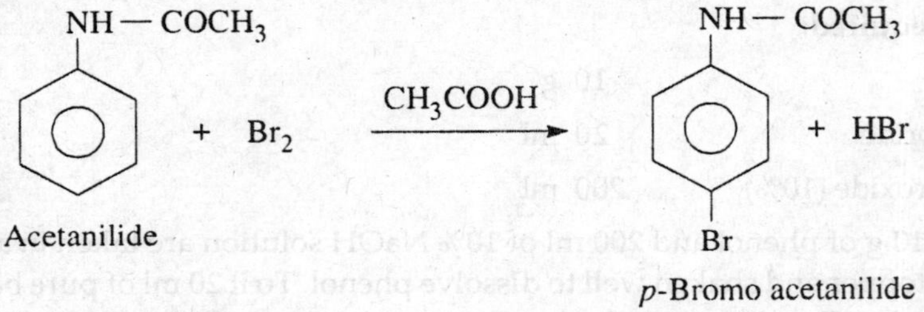

Acetanilide $\quad\quad\quad\quad$ *p*-Bromo acetanilide

Chemicals required:

Acetanilide	12	g
Bromine	5.5	ml
Glacial acetic acid	70	ml

Procedure: In 250 ml conical flask fitted with a cork 12 g of acetanilide is taken and is dissolved in 50 ml of glacial acetic acid and warmed gently, if necessary. To this solution 5.5 ml of bromine in 20 ml glacial acetic acid is slowly added with continuous shaking. The temperature of the reaction is kept below 40 °C by cooling under tap. The reaction mixture is allowed to stand for 20 minutes with occasional shaking. The orange or any colour if persists due to excess bromine, sodium bisulphite solution is added till the colour is discharged. It is now diluted by adding 150 ml of cold water when solid bromo compound separates out. It is filtered under suction, washed with water and crystallised from ethyl alcohol. Yield and melting point of the dry sample are recorded.

Yield : 15 g

M.P. : 167 °C

1.9 Preparation of Iodoform

Principle: Iodoform is prepared with the help of **Haloform reaction**. The haloform reaction is carried out with the solution of halogens in alkali (hypohalides). When it reacts with compounds containing keto-methyl group ($-\underset{\underset{O}{\|}}{C}-CH_3$) or such compounds like ethyl alcohol (CH_3CH_2OH), isopropanol ($CH_3CHOHCH_3$), etc. which may be converted to keto-methyl group containing compounds under the influence of mild oxidising property of hapohalides haloform is formed. Since the final product formed in this reaction is haloform, the reaction is named *Haloform reaction*.

Reaction:

$$CH_3 - \underset{\underset{O}{\|}}{C} - CH_3 \xrightarrow[\text{NaOH}]{X_2 \text{ in}} \underset{\text{Haloform}}{CHX_3} + CH_3COONa$$

Acetone

$$CH_3 - \underset{\underset{O}{\|}}{C}H_2OH \xrightarrow[\text{NaOH}]{X_2 \text{ in}} CH_3 - \underset{\underset{O}{\|}}{C} - H \xrightarrow[\text{NaOH}]{X_2} \underset{\text{Haloform}}{CHX_3} + HCOONa$$

Ethyl alcohol

Generally iodoform which is a solid substance is prepared either from acetone or from ethyl alcohol.

(a) Preparation from acetone

Chemicals required:

Potassium Iodide	25	g
Solid Iodine	12.5	g
Acetone	5	ml
Sodium hydroxide (10%)	20	ml

Procedure: To a solution of acetone (5 ml) in 25 ml water and 20 ml of 10% NaOH solution in a conical flask, a solution of iodine (prepared by dissolving 12.5 g of solid iodine in an aqueous solution of 25 g KI in 50 ml water) is added in small portion till the colour of iodine persists. The mixture is heated at 60 °C on a water bath. More iodine solution is added, if colour disappears. Heating at 60 °C is continued till yellow precipitate of iodoform settles down. It is filtered and crystallised from methanol-water mixture (1:1). Melting point and yield of the product are recorded.

Yield : 5 g

M.P. : 199 °C

(b) Preparation from ethyl alcohol

Chemicals required:

Ethyl alcohol	5	ml
Sodium hydroxide solution 10%	25	ml
Iodine solution	10	g of I_2 dissolved in 20 g of KI in 50 ml water

Procedure: Ethyl alcohol (5 ml) is taken in a 250 ml conical flask and to it 10% NaOH (25 ml) is added. Iodine solution is now added to this alkaline solution in small quantities at a time with shaking the contents. The reaction mixture is heated at 80 °C on a water bath for 5 minutes and then cooled. Iodoform separates out, filtered and crystallised from dilute alcohol (1:1). Melting point and yield of the dry sample are recorded.

Yield : 3 g

M.P. : 119 °C

1.10 Preparation of β-Naphthyl Benzoate (by Esterification Process)

β-Naphthyl benzoate is prepared according to Schotten-Baumann reaction. In this preparation Schotten-Baumann reaction is carried out by benzoylation of β-naphthol with benzoyl chloride in alkaline solution.

Reaction:

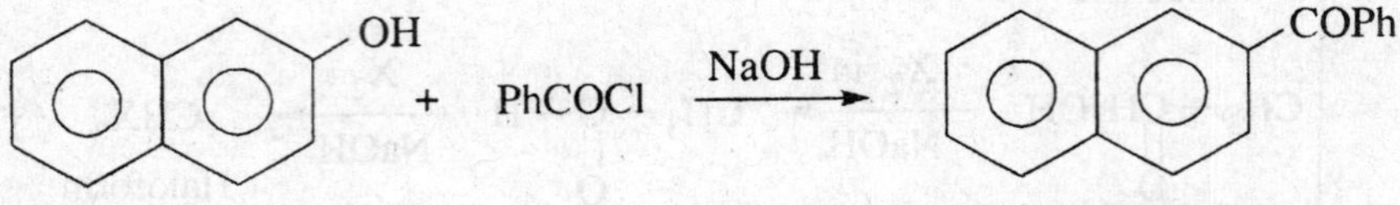

β-Naphthyl benzoate

Chemicals required:

β-Naphthol   10 g

Benzoyl chloride   8 ml

NaOH (5%) solution   50 ml

Procedure: 10 g of β-naphthol is dissolved in 50 ml of 5% NaOH solution in 500 ml conical flask fitted with a cork. To it 80 ml of benzoyl chloride is added and vigorously shaken by closing the mouth of the flask by the cork for more than 15 minutes until the smell of benzoyl chloride disappears. The solid separated is filtered at the pump, washed with cold water, crystallised from rectified spirit and dried. Yield and melting point are recorded.

Yield : 12 g

M.P. : 110 °C

1.11 Preparation of p-Nitro Aniline (by Hydrolysis Process from p-Nitro Acetanilide)

Principle: Since amino group is highly susceptible to oxidation by nitric acid, direct nitration of aniline is not possible. It is, therefore, convenient to prepare p-nitro aniline by the hydrolysis of p-nitro-acetanilide in acidic medium.

Reaction:

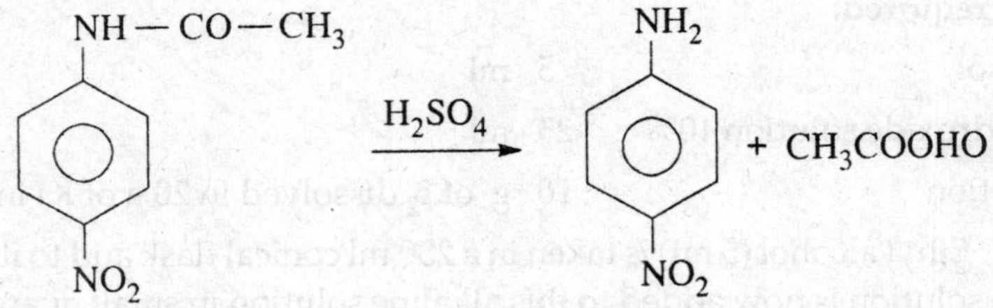

p-Nitroacetanilide   p-Nitroaniline

Chemicals required:

p-Nitro acetanilide   10 g

Sulphuric acid (70%)   50 ml

Sodium hydroxide solution (10%)

Procedure: In a 250 ml round bottom flask fitted with a reflux condenser 10 g of p-nitro-acetanilide and 50 ml of 70% H_2SO_4 are taken and the contents of the flask is refluxed for more than half an hour on a water bath. After completion of the reaction, reflux condenser is removed and the solution is cooled. This cold solution is now poured into crushed ice taken in an assorted size of beaker with stirring. To this solution dilute NaOH solution (10%) is added to make it alkaline, cooled and filtered at the pump. The solid product is crystallised from boiling water and dried. Yield and melting point are recorded.

Yield : 7 g

M.P. : 147 °C

1.12 Preparation of Methyl Orange Involving Diazotisation and Coupling

Principle: Methyl organe, an important dye is usually prepared by diazotisation of sulphanilic acid and coupling the diazotised sulphanilic acid with dimethyl aniline. The reactions involved are as below.

Reactions:

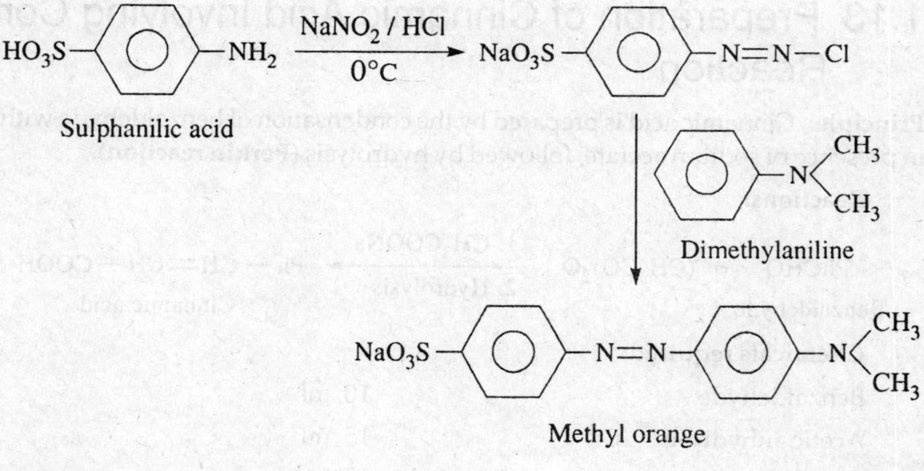

Sulphanilic acid

Dimethylaniline

Methyl orange

Chemicals required:

Dimethyl aniline	5 ml
Sulphanilic acid	10 g
Sodium carbonate	5 g
Sodium nitrite	5 g
Concentrated hydrochloric acid	5 ml
Glacial acetic acid	5 ml
Sodium hydroxide (20%)	100 ml
Sodium chloride	10 g

Procedure: 5 g of Na_2CO_3 solution in 100 ml of water is taken in a 500 ml beaker. To it 10 g of sulphanilic acid is added, warmed and cooled. To this cold solution, sodium nitrite solution (5 g dissolved in 100 ml water) is added keeping the beaker in a freezing mixture. Next 5 ml conc. HCl dissolved in 100 ml of water is slowly added with constant stirring keeping the temperature below 5 °C. To this cold diazotised sulphanilic acid solution, a solution of dimethyl aniline (5 ml) in 5 ml glacial acetic acid, 5 ml water is slowly added with vigorous stirring. After the completion of addition, the reaction mixture is allowed to stand for 20 minutes to complete the reaction. Now 100 ml NaOH solution (20%) is added in small portion till the reaction mixture appears orange in colour. Methyl orange now separates out as orange crystals. The mixture is heated at 90 °C to dissolve the crystals completely. When all the crystals have been dissolved, 10 g of powdered sodium chloride is added and heated so that all the sodium chloride added is completely dissolved. The reaction mixture is allowed to cool for half an hour at room temperature and then it is cooled by placing the beaker in ice-water. Methyl orange separates out. It is filtered at the pump, washed with ice-cold water several times, crystallised from water and dried by blotting paper. The yield is noted.

Yield : 12 g

Comment: Methyl orange obtained initially as crystals is very difficult to filter. That is why it is dissolved by heating and NaCl is added.

1.13 Preparation of Cinnamic Acid Involving Condensation Reaction

Principle: Cinnamic acid is prepared by the condensation of benzaldehyde with acetic anhydride in presence of sodium acetate, followed by hydrolysis (**Perkin reaction**).

Reactions:

$$PhCHO + (CH_3CO)_2O \xrightarrow[\text{2. Hydrolysis}]{\text{1. }CH_3COONa} Ph-CH=CH-COOH + CH_3COOH$$

Benzaldehyde   Cinnamic acid

Chemicals required:

Benzaldehyde	10 ml
Acetic anhydride	15 ml
Sodium acetate	5 g

Sodium hydroxide

Concentrated hydrochloric acid

Procedure: In 250 ml round bottom flask fitted with reflux condenser ,10 ml of benzaldehyde, 15 ml of acetic anhydride and 5 g of sodium acetate are taken and the mixture is refluxed on an oil bath at a temperature of 170-80 °C for 1 ½ hours. Foaming occurs initially due to evolution of CO_2. After completion of the reaction, the solution is cooled and 75 ml water is added to it. The diluted solution is made alkaline by adding 10% NaOH solution. The aqueous solution is acidified with concentrated HCl until there is no more evolution of CO_2. Cinnamic acid separates out, it is filtered at the pump, washed with water and crystallised from hot water. The sample is dried by blotting paper and its yield and melting point are recorded.

Yield : 8.5 g

M.P. : 133 °C

1.14 Preparation of Dibenzalacetone Involving Condensation Reaction

Principle: Dibenzalacetone is prepared by condensing benzaldehyde with acetone in presence of NaOH.

Reactions:

$$2PhCHO + CH_3COCH_3 \xrightarrow{\text{NaOH}} Ph-CH=CH-CO-CH=CH-Ph$$

    Benzaldehyde   Acetone   Dibenzalacetone

Chemicals required:

Benzaldehyde	10 ml
Acetone	5 ml
Ethyl alcohol	75 ml
10% NaOH solution	100 ml

Procedure: 10 ml benzaldehyde, 5 ml acetone, 100 ml ethyl alcohol and 100 ml of 10% NaOH are taken together in a 500 ml round bottom flask fitted with an air condenser and gently boiled under low flame for 10 minutes with occasional shaking. The solution is cooled by placing the flask in ice-water. The product separates out. It is filtered at the pump, washed with cold water several times to make it free from alkali and crystallised from rectified spirit. It is dried and its melting point and yield are noted.

Yield : 8 g

M.P. : 110 °C

1.15 Preparation of Naphthol Orange

Principle: Naphthol orange is prepared by diazotising sulphanilic acid followed by coupling with alkaline solution of β-naphthol.

Reactions:

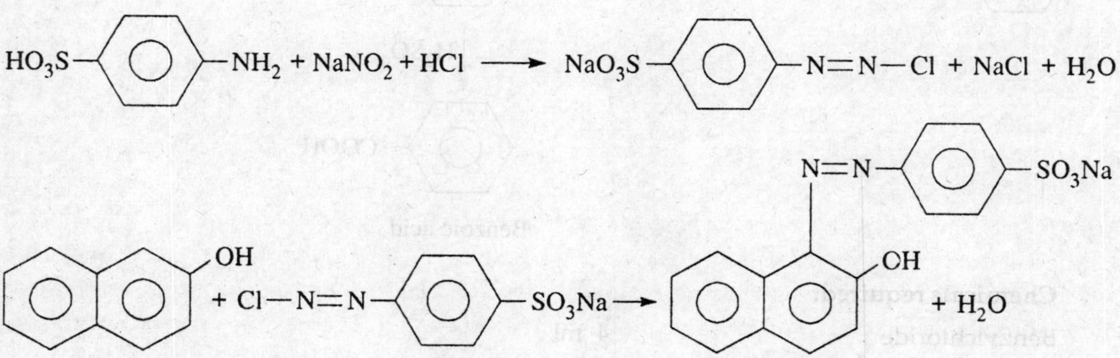

β-Naphthol
(Alkaline solution)

Naphthol orange

Chemicals required:

Sulphanilic acid	3.5 g
β-Naphthol	3 g
Concentrated HCl	5 ml
Sodium nitrite	2 g
Sodium hydroxide	2 g

Procedure: In a 250 ml beaker 3.5 g of sulphanilic acid and 5 ml conc. HCl dissolved in 50 ml water are taken and temperature kept at 0 °C by adding ice pieces to the solution. To it 2 g of sodium nitrite is slowly added. In another 250 ml beaker 3 g of β-naphthol, 2 g of sodium hydroxide dissolved 25 ml water are taken and an alkaline solution of β-naphthol is prepared. The beaker containing β-naphthol solution is kept in freezing mixture. Now the cold diazotised solution of sulphanilic acid prepared previously is added to β-naphthol solution slowly, little at a time with stirring. The reaction mixture is allowed to stand for 1½ hours and filtered. The solid is dried by pressing over blotting paper. The yield is noted.

Yield : 7 g

1.16 Preparation of Benzoic Acid by Oxidation Process

Principle: Benzoic acid is usually prepared by hydrolysis followed by oxidation of benzyl chloride by potassium permanganate solution.

Reactions:

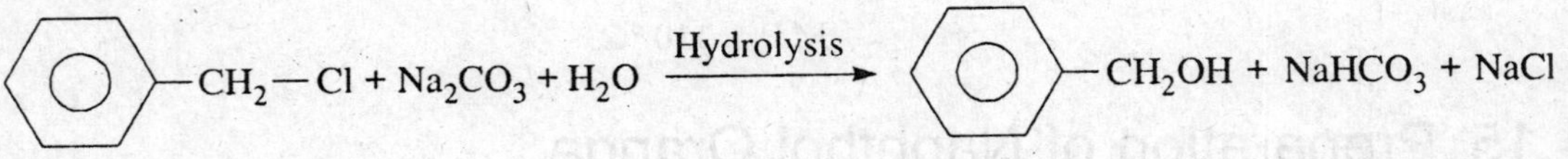

$$C_6H_5-CH_2-Cl + Na_2CO_3 + H_2O \xrightarrow{Hydrolysis} C_6H_5-CH_2OH + NaHCO_3 + NaCl$$

Benzyl chloride

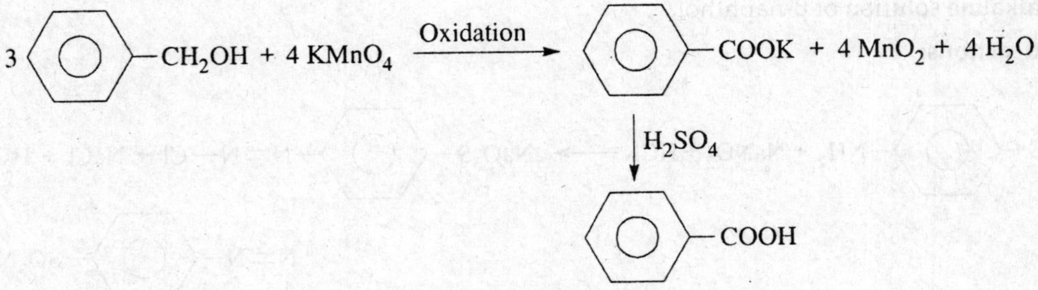

$$3\ C_6H_5-CH_2OH + 4\ KMnO_4 \xrightarrow{Oxidation} C_6H_5-COOK + 4\ MnO_2 + 4\ H_2O$$

$$\xrightarrow{H_2SO_4} C_6H_5-COOH$$

Benzoic acid

Chemicals required:

Benzylchloride	4 ml
Anhydrous sodium carbonate	5 g
KMnO₄ solution	7 g in 125 ml water

Procedure: In a 500 ml round bottom flask fitted with a reflux condenser, 5 g of anhydrous sodium carbonate and 7 g of $KMnO_4$ dissolved in 125 ml of water are taken. To it 5 ml of benzylchloride is added and the reaction mixture is refluxed for an hour. After completion of the reaction reflux condenser is removed and the brown manganese dioxide formed is filtered out and the filtrate is collected in a beaker. The beaker containing the filtrate is placed in freezing mixture and acidified with dilute sulphuric acid when benzoic acid is precipitated out. It is filtered, washed with cold water, crystallised from hot water and dried in air. The weight of the product is taken and its melting point is determined.

Yield : 4 g

M.P. : 122 °C

Comments

(i) Direct oxidation of toluene to benzoic acid is very slow. Hence benzylchloride is taken as starting material. During oxidation in the initial stage it is hydrolysed to benzyl alcohol which in the next step is oxidised to benzoic acid.

(ii) Benzylchloride is irritating to eyes. So care is to be taken.

1.17 Preparation of Benzil by Oxidative Method

Principle: Benzil is easily prepared by the oxidation of benzoin with concentrated nitric acid according to the reaction depicted below.

Reaction:

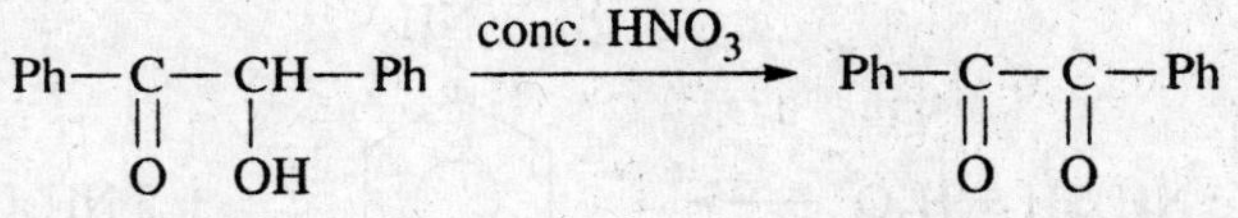

$$\underset{\text{Benzoin}}{Ph-\underset{\underset{O}{||}}{C}-\underset{\underset{OH}{|}}{C}H-Ph} \xrightarrow{\text{conc. } HNO_3} \underset{\text{Benzil}}{Ph-\underset{\underset{O}{||}}{C}-\underset{\underset{O}{||}}{C}-Ph}$$

Chemicals required:

Benzoin	6 g
Concentrated nitric acid	20 ml

Procedure: 6 g of benzoin and 20 ml concentrated nitric acid are taken in a 250 ml round bottom flask connected with a trap to absorb oxides of nitrogen as shown in the figure below:

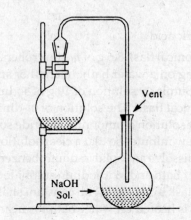

Vent

NaOH
Sol.

The round flask is heated on water bath for 15 minutes. The evolution of brown fumes due to oxides of nitrogen is very fast in the beginning but after a few minutes becomes slow. After the completion of the reaction the delivery tube for oxides of nitrogen is disconnected, and cooled in ice bath. Finally the cold solution is poured into 200 ml of water containing a few pieces of ice and stirred well with a glass rod. The solid benzil in yellow crystals separates out, it is filtered at the pump and washed with water first and next with little cold alcohol. Benzil is dried in air by spreading on a blotting paper. The yield and melting point are noted.

Yield : 5 g

M.P. : 130 °C

1.18 Preparation of *meta*-Nitroaniline by Reduction Method

Principle: *m*-Nitroaniline is generally prepared by the reduction of *meta*-dinitrobenzene. However, strong reducing agent like metals with acid reduce both the nitro groups to form m-phenylene diamine. But milder reducing agent such as ammonium hydrosulphide has unique character to reduce only one of the nitro groups to yield *m*-nitro aniline. Ammonium hydrosulphide is conveniently prepared by passing hydrogen sulphide into ammonium hydroxide solution. So in the process of preparation of *m*-nitroaniline a solution of ammonium chloride and sodium sulphide are used.

Reaction:

$$NH_4Cl + Na_2S + H_2O \longrightarrow NH_4SH + NaCl + NaOH$$

m-Dinitrobenzene   *m*-Nitroaniline

Chemicals required:

m-Dinitrobenzene	8.5 g
Ammonium chloride	10 g
Sodium sulphide	10 g
Ethyl alcohol	75 ml
Concentrated hydrochloric acid	50 ml

Procedure: In a 500 ml conical flask 8.5 g of *m*-dinitrobenzene is taken and is dissolved in 60 ml of ethyl alcohol by warming on a water bath. In another small conical flask 10 g of NH_4Cl is dissolved in 25 ml hot water. Similarly solution of 10 g of sodium sulphide in 250 ml hot water is prepared in another small conical flask. The solution of *m*-dinitrobenzene is warmed on a water bath at 50-60 °C and to this hot solution ammonium chloride solution is slowly added and heated again on the water bath for a few minutes so that a clear solution is obtained. A little more alcohol may be added, if needed, to redissolve any solid *m*-dinitrobenzene. The flask containing the reaction mixture is removed from water bath and to it sodium sulphide solution is added little at a time by holding the mouth of the hot flask by a towel with constant shaking. After completion of addition of sodium sulphide, the flask is heated on water bath for nearly 10 minutes. The flask is cooled under tap and 250 ml of water is added to it. The precipitate is filtered at the pump, washed several times with water.

Next the precipitate is taken in a 500 ml beaker and to it 50 ml of concentrated hydrochloric acid in 250 ml water are added, heated and filtered again to remove undissolved sulphur and unreacted *m*-dinitrobenzene. The filtrate is cooled in ice and *m*-nitroaniline is precipitated by the addition of 10% sodium hydroxide solution. Bright yellow crystals of *m*-nitroaniline is separated out by filtration, washed with cold water and crystallised from boiling water. The sample is dried in an oven at a temperature of 60 °C. Yield and melting point are recorded.

Yield : 6.5 g

M.P. : 114 °C

1.19 Preparation of Benzhydrol by Reduction Method

Principle: Benzhydrol is prepared by reduction of benzophenone with Zn-dust and alcoholic sodium hydroxide. The reaction takes place in the following manner.

Reactions:

$$Ph-\underset{\underset{O}{\|}}{C}-Ph \xrightarrow[\text{Zn / NaOH}]{2H^+} Ph-\underset{\underset{OH}{|}}{CH}-Ph$$

Benzophenone   Benzhydrol

Chemicals required:

Benzophenone	3 g
Ethyl alcohol	65 ml
Sodium hydroxide	6.5 g
Zinc-dust	6.5 g
Concentrated hydrochloric acid	25 ml

Procedure: In a 250 ml round bottom flask fitted with reflux condenser, 3 g of benzophenone, 65 ml of ethyl alcohol, 6.5 g of sodium hydroxide dissolved in minimum quantity of water and 6.5 g of Zn-dust are taken and mixed well by shaking. The mixture is then refluxed on a water bath for one and a half hour. The flask is cooled to 60 °C and filtered at the pump. The residue is washed 2-3 times with 5 ml of ethyl alcohol. The filtrate is poured into 250 ml of cold water taken in a 500 ml beaker and is acidified with 25 ml of concentrated hydrochloric acid. A viscous oil separates, which solidifies on cooling overnight. The solid is filtered at the pump and crystallised from 15 ml of hot ethyl alcohol and dried in air. Yield and melting point are recorded.

Yield : 4 g

M.P. : 68 °C

1.20 Preparation of Anthranilic Acid Involving Hydrolysis and Rearrangement

Principle: Phthalimide is usually taken as the starting material for the preparation of anthranilic acid. Phthalimide is treated with sodium hydroxide and bromine when anthranilic acid results. Reactions taking place may be described as below:

Reactions:

Phthalimide → Sodium salt of phthalamide → Anthranilic acid

Chemicals required:

Phthalimide	8	g
Sodium hydroxide	17.5	g
Bromine	3	ml
Concentrated hydrochloric acid	30	ml
Glacial acetic acid	20	ml

Procedure: In a 200 ml conical flask 10 g of NaOH is dissolved in 50 ml of water and is cooled to 0 °C in an ice bath. To this cold solution 3 ml of bromine is carefully added in single lot and shaken well until all the bromine dissolve. The flask is cooled to 0 °C.

In another conical flask of 250 ml capacity 7.5 g of NaOH is dissolved in 25 ml of water and cooled. To this cold solution 8 g of phthalimide is added in portion with shaking. To this solution previous solution of bromine in NaOH (sodium hypobromite) is added and the flask is shaken well when temperature may rise. The mixture is warmed on a water bath at 80 °C for 5 minutes and filtered. The filtrate is cooled in ice bath and 30 ml of concentrated hydrochloric acid is added to it slowly with constant stirring until the solution is just neutral to litmus. The mixture is tranferred to a one litre beaker and acidified with glacial acetic acid when anthranilic acid is precipitated. It is filtered and washed well several times with cold water. It is crystallised from water, dried in an oven at 100 °C. The yield and melting point are recorded.

Yield : 4.5 g

M.P. : 146°C

1.21 Preparation of Organic Compounds Involving More than One Step

1.21.1 Preparation of Benzilic Acid

Principle: Preparation of benzilic acid involves two steps. In the first step benzoin is oxidised to benzil and in the second step benzil, thus, obtained is converted to benzilic acid by a rearrangement reaction. Thus,

Step-I $Ph-\underset{O}{\underset{||}{C}}-\underset{OH}{\underset{|}{CH}}-Ph \xrightarrow[HNO_3]{[O]} Ph-\underset{O}{\underset{||}{C}}-\underset{O}{\underset{||}{C}}-Ph$

Benzil

Step-II Ph—C—C—Ph $\xrightarrow[\text{KOH}]{\text{Alcoholic}}$ $\underset{\underset{\text{OH}}{|}}{\overset{\overset{\text{Ph}}{\diagdown}}{\underset{\text{Ph}\diagup}{C}}}$—COOH

with the two C's bearing =O groups.

(Exist as salt in presence of KOH)

Step-I Preparation of Benzil: See Art. 1.17

Step-II Preparation of Benzilic acid

Procedure: About 3 g of benzil is taken in a 250 ml round bottom flask and to it a solution of 3 g of KOH in 10 ml of water is added. Then 10 ml of ethanol is also added to it and the reaction mixture is shaken thoroughly. This mixture is now refluxed on a water bath for 20 minutes. The reaction mixture is transferred to a beaker cooled in ice bath when benzilic acid as potassium salt separates out. The precipitate is dissolved in water (30 ml) and the solution is acidified with conc. HCl by constant stirring. A brown red precipitate is obtained. It is filtered, washed with cold water and is crystallised from benzene using activated charcoal. The yield is 3.5 g, and the melting point is 150 °C.

Comment: Benzoin may be prepared from benzaldehyde involving *Benzoin condensation*. 12 g of benzaldehyde is refluxed in a 200 ml round-bottomed flask with 25 g of KCN and 25 ml of ethyl alcohol on a water-bath for 45 minutes. The reaction mixture is cooled, filtred, washed with water and dried. Yield 10 g, M.P. 136 °C.

Ph—C—H + Ph—C—H $\xrightarrow{\text{KCN}}$ Ph—C—CH—Ph
with the first two bearing =O, and the product bearing =O and OH.

Benzaldehyde   Benzoin

1.21.2 Preparation of Anthranilic Acid from Phthalic Acid

Principle: Preparation of anthranilic acid from phthalic acid involves the following different steps.

Step-I Preparation of phthalic anhydride from phthalic acid.

Phthalic anhydride

Step-II Conversion of phthalic anhydride into phthalimide.

Phthalimide

Step-III Preparation of anthranilic acid from phthalimide.

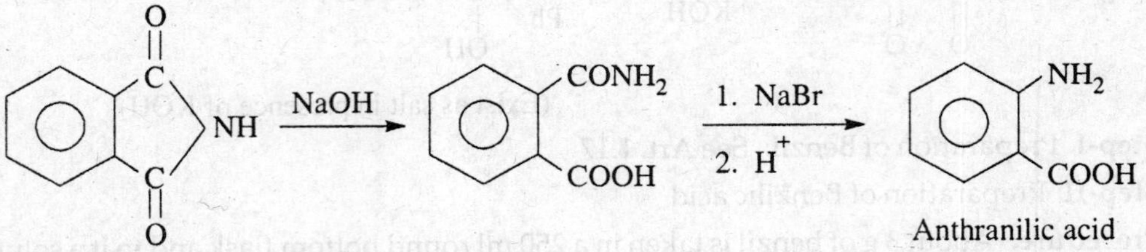

Anthranilic acid

Step-I Preparation of phthalic anhydride

Chemical required:

Phthalic acid: 5 g

Procedure: 20 g of phthalic acid is taken in a porcelain basin and a clean inverted funnel is placed over it. The glass tube of the funnel is lightly closed with cotton. The basin is heated strongly over a sand bath for 15-20 minutes. Then the basin is cooled when phthalic anhydride is deposited as sublimate. It is collected, yield 15 g, M.P. 195 °C.

Step-II Preparation of phthalimide from phthalic anhydride

Chemicals required:

Phthalic anhydride	10 g
Concentrated ammonia solution	10.5 ml

Procedure: 10.5 ml of concentrated ammonia is added to 10 g of phthalic anhydride taken in a small round-bottomed flask (100 ml) fitted with a wide air condenser. The flask is heated slowly and finally strongly with occasional shaking. The sublimate formed is pushed down with a glass rod. The molten mass is then poured into a porcelain basin, cooled and ground in a mortar. It is crystallised from alcohol and dried.

Yield : 9 g

M.P. : 223 °C

Step-III Preparation of anthranilic acid from phthalimide

As in 1.20

1.21.3 Preparation of *p*-Nitro Aniline from Aniline

Principle: Preparation of *p*-Nitroaniline from aniline consists of three steps as indicated below:

Step-I Preparation of acetanilide from aniline.

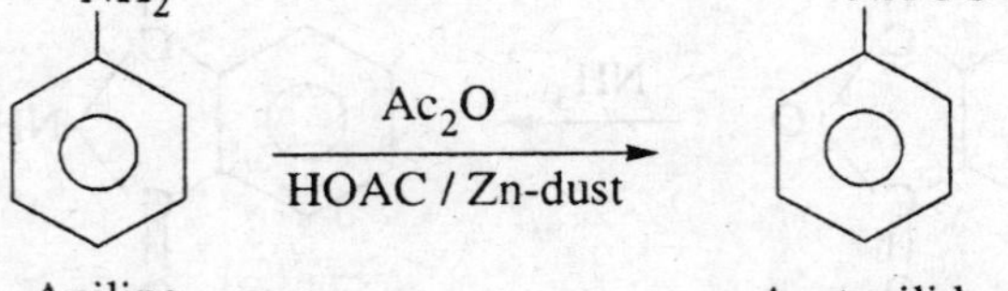

Aniline   Acetanilide

Step-II Preparation of p-Nitro acetanilide from acetanilide.

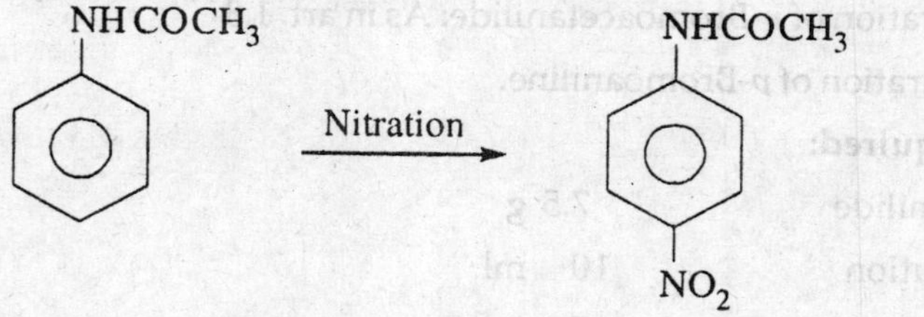

Step-III Formation of p-Nitro aniline from p-Nitro acetanilide

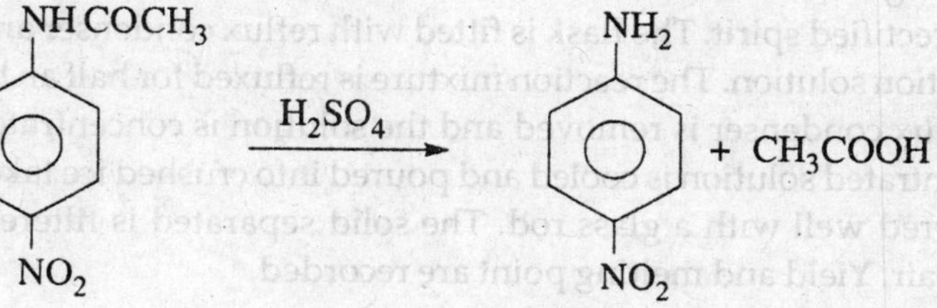

p-Nitroaniline

Procedure

Step-I Preparation of acetanilide: As in Art. 1.3

Step-II Preparation of p-Nitroacetanilide: As in Art. 1.1

Step-III Preparation of p-Nitroaniline: As in Art. 1.11.

1.21.4 Preparation of p-Bromo Aniline from Acetanilide

Principle: p-Bromoacetanilide may be prepared from acetanilide by the following sequence of steps.

Step-I Preparation of p-Bromoacetanilide.

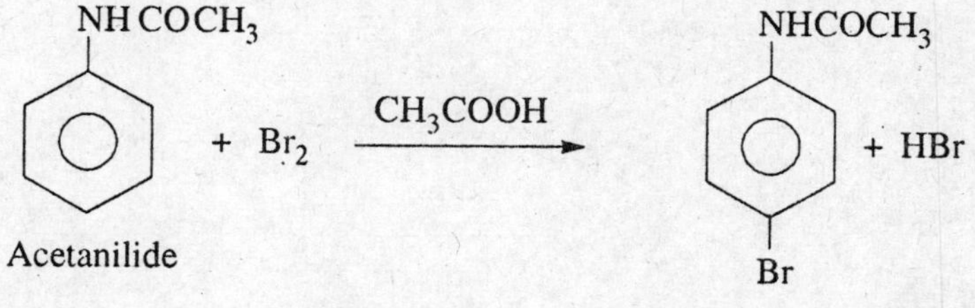

Acetanilide

Step-II Preparation of p-Bromoaniline

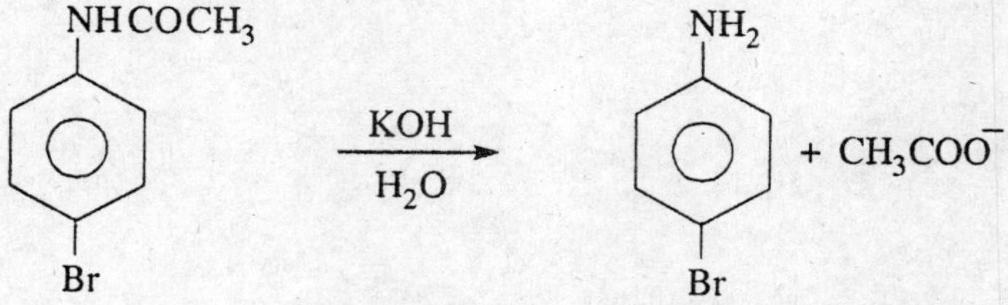

p-Bromoaniline

Procedure

Step-I Preparation of *p*-Bromoacetanilide: As in art. 1.8

Step-II Preparation of *p*-Bromoaniline.

Chemicals required:

p-Bromoacetanilide	7.5 g
60% KOH solution	10 ml
Rectified spirit	15 ml

Procedure: 7.5 g of *p*-Bromoacetanilide is taken in a 250 ml round-bottomed flask and is dissolved in 15 ml rectified spirit. The flask is fitted with reflux condenser and 60% KOH solution is added to the reaction solution. The reaction mixture is refluxed for half an hour, diluted with 50-60 ml of water, reflux condenser is removed and the solution is concentrated to about half of its volume. The concentrated solution is cooled and poured into crushed ice taken in a 500 ml beaker. The solution is stirred well with a glass rod. The solid separated is filtered, washed with cold water and dried in air. Yield and melting point are recorded.

Yield : 5 g

M.P. : 65 °C

1.22 Reporting of a Laboratory Preparation

Experiment No: Date:

1. Chemicals required

2. Reactions

3. Procedure

4. Yield

5. Melting point

Chapter 2

Questions and Answers for Viva Voce

1. Write down the mechanism of nitration.

   Ans.

   $$H-O-N{=}O + H^{+}(H_2SO_4) \longrightarrow \overset{\oplus}{N}{=}O + H_2O$$

2. What is iodoform? How is it prepared?

   Ans. Iodoform is Triiodomethane, CHI_3. It is prepared according to the method described in 1.9.

3. From what type of compound iodoform can be prepared?

   Ans. Compound containing ketomethyl group $(CH_3-\overset{\|}{\underset{O}{C}}-)$ like acetone $(CH_3-\overset{\|}{\underset{O}{C}}-CH_3)$

   or those which may be oxidised to keto-methyl compounds. Examples of such compounds are ethanol, isopropanol, etc.

4. Why aniline is acetylated before nitration?

   Ans. Amino group may be oxidised by nitric acid.

5. What happens when phenol is treated with bromine-water?

   Ans. 2, 4, 6-tribromophenol is formed.

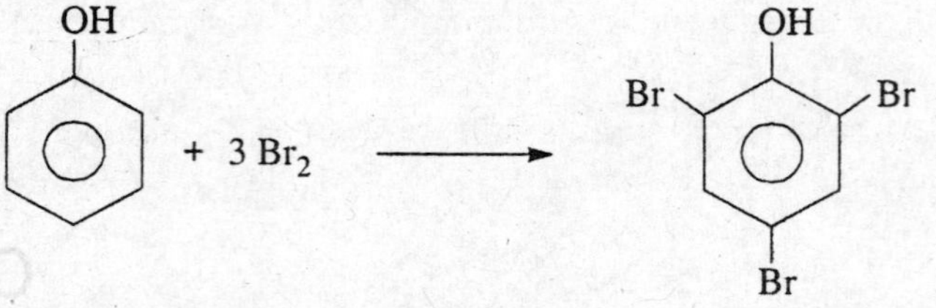

6. Why *p*-nitroacetanilide is the major product during nitration of acetanilide?

    Ans. $-NH-\underset{\underset{O}{\|}}{C}-CH_3$ group present in acetanilide is ortho-para orienting but due to

    steric hindrance ortho isomer is not formed as a major product.

7. Why diazotisation is carried out at low temperature?

    Ans. At high temperature diazocompounds are very unstable and readily decomposes.

8. Why para-nitroaniline cannot be prepared by direct nitration of aniline?

    Ans. Aniline is readily oxidised by air in presence of nitric acid.

9. What is an anilide? Name a very common anilide.

    Ans. Compound containing N-phenyl amide group is anilide. The most common member is acetanilide, $Ph-NH-\underset{\underset{O}{\|}}{C}-CH_3$

10. Why methyl orange formed initially is dissolved and reprecipitated by sodium chloride?

    Ans. The crystals of methyl orange first formed is so fine that they cannot be filtered. That is why it is dissolved by heating and reprecipitated by sodium chloride.

11. Suggest a route for synthesis of *p*-nitroacetanilide from aniline.

    Ans. Aniline $\xrightarrow{\text{Acetylation}}$ Acetanilide $\xrightarrow{\text{Nitration}}$ *p*-Nitroacetanilide

12. What happens when phthalimide is treated with bromine and sodium hydroxide?

    Ans. Anthranilic acid is finally formed according to the following reaction:

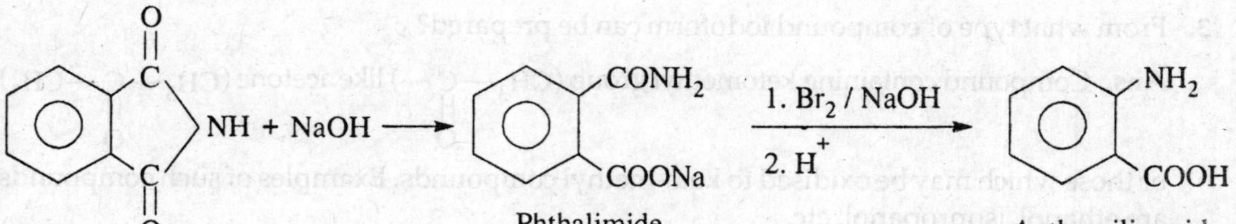

13. Why ammonium hydrosulphide is used as a reducing agent for the preparation of meta-nitroaniline from meta-dinitrobenzene?

    Ans. Strong reducing agent like metal and acid will reduce both the nitrogroup forming meta phenylene diamine. So to reduce only one nitro group milder reducing agent like NH_4HS is used.

14. Why is it necessary to use acetic acid but not mineral acid for the precipitation of anthranilic acid?

Ans. Mineral acids can form soluble salts through protonation of amino group.

15. Write the mechanism for the conversion of phthalamide to anthranilic acid.

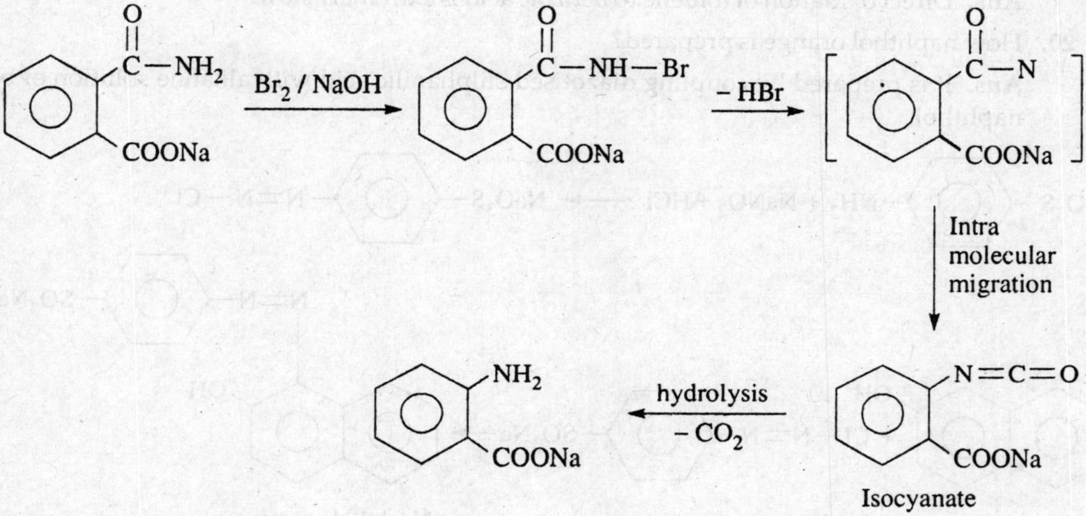

Isocyanate

16. What is acylation?

Ans. Introduction of any acyl group $(R-\underset{\underset{O}{\parallel}}{C}-)$ into atomic groups containing active hydrogen like OH, NH$_2$, $-$NH$-$R, etc.

$$R-OH + (CH_3CO)_2O \longrightarrow R-O-\underset{\underset{O}{\parallel}}{C}-CH_3$$

17. How does acylation and acetylation differ?

Ans. The term acylation is used in broad sense while acetylation is used in specific sense. Thus,

$$R-OH + R'-\underset{\underset{O}{\parallel}}{C}-Cl \xrightarrow{\text{Acylation}} R'-\underset{\underset{O}{\parallel}}{C}-O-R + HCl$$

Acyl derivative

$$R-OH + CH_3-\underset{\underset{O}{\parallel}}{C}-Cl \xrightarrow{\text{Acetylation}} CH_3-\underset{\underset{O}{\parallel}}{C}-O-R + HCl$$

Acetyl derivative

18. Suggest a probable route for the preparation of para-bromoacetanilide from aniline.

Ans. Aniline $\xrightarrow{\text{Acetylation}}$ Acetanilide $\xrightarrow{\text{Bromination}}$ p-bromoacetanilide

19. Why benzyl chloride but not toluene is taken for direct oxidation to benzoic acid?

Ans. Direct oxidation of toluene to benzoic acid is extremely slow.

20. How naphthol orange is prepared?

Ans. It is prepared by coupling diazotised sulphanilic acid with alkaline solution of b-naphthol.

$$HO_3S-\bigcirc-NH_2 + NaNO_2 + HCl \longrightarrow NaO_3S-\bigcirc-N=N-Cl$$

Naphthol orange

Organic Quantitative Analysis

Part III

Chapter 1

Quantitative Organic Analysis

1. Introduction

Quantitative analysis is an important part of analysis of chemical compounds. It provides a most significant evidence regarding the purity and identification of the compound under examination. It is, therefore, desirable to discuss some important and common experiments on quantitative organic analysis as described below.

1.1 Estimation of Saponification Value of an Ester

Theory: Saponification value of an ester is defined as the number of milligrams of potassium hydroxide required to hydrolyse one gram of an ester. This value is usually determined by titrametric method. The method involves the hydrolysis of an accurately weighed quantity of an ester with the measured excess of standard alcoholic potassium hydroxide solution and back titration of unconsumed potassium hydroxide by a standard acid. From the alkali consumed, saponification value may be estimated.

$$\text{RCOOR}' + \text{Alc. KOH} \longrightarrow \text{RCOOK} + \text{R}'\text{OH}$$
Ester

Reagents required:

1. 0.5 (N) alcoholic potassium hydroxide. It is prepared by dissolving 6 g of potassium hydroxide pellets in 250 ml of 95% ethanol in a measuring flask. It is standardised with standard 0.5 (N) HCl solution.
2. 0.5 (N) Hydrochloric acid solution.
3. 0.5 (N) Sodium carbonate solution.

Procedure: About 0.5 g of the ester is accurately weighed in a 250 ml round-bottomed flask fitted with a reflux condenser. To it 50 ml of alcoholic KOH solution is added by means of a pipette. The mixture is now refluxed for 30-40 minutes heating the flask by placing it on asbestos sintered wire gauze. Burner is removed and the solution is cooled. The condenser is washed with 25 ml of water, and 2 drops of phenolphthalein are added. The solution is now titrated with 0.5 (N) HCl solution.

A blank titration of 0.5 (N) alcoholic KOH with 0.5 (N) HCl is carried out.

Finally HCl solution is standardised by titration with a standard Na_2CO_3 solution.

Calculation: Weight of ester taken = w g

Let the strength of Na_2CO_3 is S'.

Let the strength of HCl is $S(0.5N)$.

50 ml KOH requires V_1 ml of 0.5 (N) HCl in the blank.

Final burette reading during estimation is V_2 ml.

So volume of 0.5N KOH required for hydrolysis in terms of HCl is (V_1-V_2) ml.

Thus, $(V_1-V_2) \times S \times 0.5$ (N) ml of HCl is required for hydrolysis of w g of ester.

Hence 1g of ester requires $\dfrac{(V_1-V_2) \times S \times 0.5(N)}{w}$ ml of HCl

or, $\dfrac{(V_1-V_2) \times S \times 0.5(N) \times 28}{w \times 1000}$ g of KOH (1 ml of 0.5 N KOH = 0.028 g of KOH)

$= \dfrac{(V_1-V_2) \times S \times 0.5(N)}{w} \times 28$ milligram of KOH.

This is the saponification value of ester.

1.2 Estimation of Phenol by Bromination

Theory: On bromination with excess of standard bromate-bromide solution in presence of HCl phenol forms 2, 4, 6-tribromophenol. Thus,

$$KBrO_3 + 5\,KBr + 6\,HCl \longrightarrow 3\,Br_2 + 6\,KCl + 3\,H_2O$$

The excess of bromine remained unconsumed is determined by the addition of potassium iodide and titration of the liberated iodine with standard thiosulphate solution.

$$Br_2 + 2\,KI \longrightarrow I_2 + 2\,KBr$$

$$I_2 + 2\,S_2O_3^{2-} \longrightarrow S_4O_6^{2-} + 2\,I^-$$

From equation, $1\ C_6H_5OH \equiv 3Br_2 \equiv 3I_2 \equiv 6\ S_2O_3^{2-}$

Reagents required:

1. KBrO₃-KBr solution (N/10)
2. Sodium thiosulphate solution (N/10)
3. KI solution (20%)
4. Starch indicator solution.

Procedure: Supplied phenol solution is diluted to 250 ml in a volumetric flask. 25 ml of the diluted soluiton is pipetted out into a 500 ml conical flask fitted with a stopper. To this solution 50 ml of bromate-bromide solution (accurately measured) is added followed by the addition of 5 ml of conc. HCl and the flask is stoppered immediately. The flask with its content is well shaken for about a minute and is allowed to stand for 20 minutes with occasional shaking. Next 10 ml of 20% KI solution is added to the flask, shaken well for 1-2 minutes and is allowed to stand for 10 minutes. Stopper is removed, neck of the flask and the stopper is well washed with little water and the liberated iodine is titrated with the standard (N/10) thiosulphate solution in presence of starch as indicator. Finally, thiosulphate is standardised with bromate-bromide solution under identical condition.

Calculations: Amount of phenol is calculated from the following formula.

$$\text{Amount of phenol supplied} = \frac{(V_1 - V_2) \times N \times 94 \times 10}{1000 \times 6}$$

where V_1 ml is the volume of thiosulphate required for 50 ml bromate-bromide solution in the blank. V_2 ml is the volume of thiosulphate required for the determination.

N is the strength of thiosulphate solution in normality and 94 is the molecular weight of phenol.

1.3 Estimation of Amines by Bromination

Theory: Bromination of aniline with excess of standard bromate-bromide solution in the presence of hydrochloric acid yields 2, 4, 6-tribromoaniline. Thus,

$$KBrO_3 + 5\,KBr + 6\,HCl \longrightarrow 3Br_2 + 6\,KCl + 3\,H_2O$$

Aniline   2, 4, 6-tribromoaniline

The excess of bromine is determined by the addition of potassium iodide solution and titration of liberated iodine with standard thiosulphate solution.

$$Br_2 + 2\,KI \longrightarrow I_2 + 2\,KBr$$

$$I_2 + 2Na_2S_2O_3 \longrightarrow Na_2S_4O_6 + 2NaI$$

From the above equation, 1 aniline ≡ 3Br₂ ≡ 3I₂ ≡ 6Na₂S₂O₃

Reagents required:

1. $KBrO_3$-KBr solution ($N/10$) : 6-8 g of $KBrO_3$ is accurately weighed and about 10 g of KBr (A.R.) is added to it and is dissolved in water and diluted to 250 ml in a volumetric flask.

2. Sodium thiosulphate solution ($N/10$)

3. Potassium iodide solution (20%)

4. Starch indicator solution.

Procedure: The supplied solution is diluted to 250 ml in a volumetric flask. 25 ml of the diluted solution is pipetted out into a 500 ml conical flask fitted with a stopper. To it 50 ml of bromate-bromide solution is added followed by addition of 5 ml of concentrated hydrochloric acid and the flask is stoppered immediately. The flask is well shaken for a minute to mix the reactants and is allowed to stand for 15 minutes with occasional shaking. 10 ml of 20% potassium iodide solution is added to it and the flask is allowed to stand for 10 minutes after shaking. Stopper is removed, the neck of the flask and the stopper is washed with a little water and the liberated iodine is titrated with standard ($N/10$) sodium thiosulphate solution using starch solution as indicator. Finally, the thiosulphate solution is standardised with bromate-bromide solution under identical condition.

Calculation: Amount of aniline is calculated from the following formula.

$$\text{Amount of aniline supplied} = \frac{(V_1 - V_2) \times N \times 93.10 \times 10}{1000 \times 6} \text{ g}$$

where V_1 ml is the volume of thiosulphate required for 50 ml of bromate-bromide solution in the blank.

V_2 ml is the volume of thiosulphate required for the determination.

N is the strength of thiosulphate solution in normality.

1.4 Estimation of Glucose Using Fehling's Solution

Theory: Glucose is a reducing sugar. This property is utilised in its estimation. Due to this reducing property, glucose can reduce Fehling's solution. So glucose is estimated by titrating with a standard Fehling's solution. The reaction that takes place may be depicted as below:

```
CHO                                      CHO
|                                        |
(CHOH)4   + 2Cu(OH)2    ———————►    (CHOH)4    +    Cu2O↓     +   2H2O
|                                        |
CH2OH      Fehling's solution           CH2OH            Red
                                                         precipitate
Glucose                                 Gluconic acid
```

It may be mentioned that Fehling's solution should be prepared fresh when required because it decomposes on keeping.

Reagents required:

1. Fehling's solution A

2. Fehling's solution B

3. Glucose (A.R. grade)

Preparation of Fehling's solution

Preparation of solution A: About 17.32 g of powdered crystalline cupric sulphate, $CuSO_4$, $5H_2O$ is weighed and dissolved in distilled water and the volume is made up to 250 ml in a volumetric flask.

Preparation of solution B: About 86.5 g of crystalline sodium potassium tartarate (*Rochelle salt*), $C_4H_4O_6$, Na, K, $4H_2O$ is weighed and dissolved in warm water in a beaker. 30 g of pure sodium hydroxide is dissolved in another beaker. These two solutions are mixed and cooled. It is then transferred to a volumetric flask and the volume is made up to 250 ml.

Preparation of standard glucose solution: Nearly 1.25 g of pure crystalline (A.R.) glucose is accurately weighed and dissolved in water in a 250 ml volumetric flask and the volume is made up to the mark.

Procedure: Standardisation of Fehling's solution: In a conical flask of 200 ml capacity 10 ml of Fehling's solution A and 10 ml of Fehling's solution B, i.e., total 20 ml solutions are taken. The solution is diluted by adding 20 ml of water and the liquid is kept gentle boiling over an asbestos-sintered wire-gauze. This boiling Fehling's solution is now titrated with the standard glucose solution in presence of 1-2 drops of methylene blue as indicator. It must be remembered that during titration the Fehling's solution must be kept boiling gently and at the beginning 1 ml of glucose solution be added at a time till the solution assumes a faint blue colour and then 1-2 drops at a time be added until the blue colour just disappears and a bright red precipitate settles down suddenly at a time. The volume of glucose solution required is noted. Similar experiments are repeated twice and burette readings are recorded. From these titre values average value is determined.

Similarly, another 20 ml of Fehling's solution is taken in a conical flask and is titrated with the unknown glucose sample solution.

Calculation: The percentage purity of the unknown glucose solution supplied is calculated from the following formula,

$$\% \text{ of glucose} = \frac{V_1 \times w}{V_2 \times w_1} \times 100$$

where w is the weight of known glucose taken

w_1 is the weight of unknown glucose taken

V_1 = volume of known glucose solution

V_2 = volume of unknown glucose solution.

1.5 Estimation of Sucrose (Cane-sugar) Using Fehling's Solution

Theory: Sucrose is a non-reducing sugar. So it cannot directly reduce Fehling's solution. Hence its estimation is usually performed by its hydrolysis by acid when one molecule of glucose and one molecule of fructose are formed.

$$C_{12}H_{22}O_{11} + H_2O \longrightarrow C_6H_{12}O_6 + C_6H_{12}O_6$$

$$\text{Sucrose} \qquad\qquad\qquad\qquad \text{Glucose} \qquad \text{Fructose}$$
$$\text{(Disaccharide)}$$

The hydrolysed cane sugar is known as invert sugar. The glucose formed is now titrated against a standard Fehling's solution using methylene blue solution as indicator.

Reagents required:

1. Standard glucose solution: It is prepared as in the case of glucose.
2. Standard Fehling's solution: It is prepared as in the case of glucose and is standardised with the standard solution following the procedure adapted in the case of glucose estimation.

Procedure: 25 ml of the supplied cane sugar solution is taken in a conical flask of 250 ml capacity and is diluted with 25 ml of water. To it 1-1.5 ml of concentrated HCl is added and warmed on a water bath for an hour keeping the temperature at 60-70 °C. Solution is cooled and is neutralised with Na_2CO_3 solution making it slightly alkaline. The cold solution is diluted to 100 ml. It is quantitatively transferred to a 250 ml volumetric flask. It is taken in the burette and is titrated against a standard Fehling's solution following exactly same procedure as in the case of glucose using methylene blue as indicator.

Calculations: From the equation given above it is seen that 342 g of cane sugar forms 180 g of glucose and 180 g of fructose, i.e., total 360 g of invert sugar.

Thus,

$$\text{Amount of sucrose} = \text{Amount of invert sugar} \times \frac{342}{360}$$

$$= \text{Amount of invert sugar} \times 0.95.$$

$$\text{Amount of invert sugar in the supplied solution} = \frac{w \times V_1}{V_2} \text{ g,}$$

where V_1 ml is the volume of standard glucose solution required to reduce 20 ml of Fehling's solution and V_2 ml is the volume of invert sugar consumed to reduce the same volume (20 ml) of the Fehling's solution. w is the weight of glucose taken for preparing standard solution.

Thus, the amount of cane sugar is $\frac{w \times V_1}{V_2} \times 0.95$ g in 25 ml of the supplied solution.

Hence content of cane sugar $= \frac{w \times V_1}{V_2} \times 0.95 \times 40$ g / litre.

1.6 Estimation of Amino Acid by Formol Titration

Theory: Amino acids cannot be estimated directly by titrating with a standard alkali because of the presence of two opposing groups—acidic carboxylic and basic amino groups and as they exist as "Zwitterion". For this reason the amino acids are first treated with formaldehyde when amino group is blocked making carboxylic group free which is then titrated with a standard alkali. But as the amino acids exist in Zwitterion they cannot directly react with formaldehyde. So at first they are converted to sodium salt by the treatment with NaOH which then reacts with formaldehyde. The reactions involved are as below:

$$NH_3^+ - CH_2 - COO^- + NaOH \longrightarrow NH_2 - CH_2 - COONa + H_2O$$

Glycine Amino acid
(Zwitterion)

$$NH_2 - CH_2 - COONa + \begin{matrix} H \\ H \end{matrix} \rangle C=O \longrightarrow CH_2=N-CH_2-COONa + H_2O$$

Reagents required:

1. Formaldehyde solution   40%
2. Sodium hydroxide solution (N/10).

Procedure: About 2-2.5 g of glycine is accurately weighed in a 250 ml volumetric flask, dissolved in distilled water and the volume is made up to the mark. About 50 ml of 40% formalin from the burette is taken in a conical flask and 2-4 drops of phenolphthalein are added to it. From another burette (N/10) NaOH solution is added with shaking till the solution is faintly pink.

In another conical flask 25 ml of glycine solution is taken through a pipette and 2 drops of phenolphthalein are added to it. The solution is made faintly alkaline by the addition of NaOH solution. To this solution 10 ml of neutralised formalin solution is added. The pink colour disappears and solution becomes acidic. This reaction mixture is titrated against (N/10) NaOH solution till the pink appears. The volume of alkali consumed is noted. Two more titrations are carried out and average titre value is determined.

Calculations: Let weight of glycine taken be w g, 25 ml of glycine solution (after addition of formaldehyde) requires V ml of (N/10) NaOH.

$\therefore$ 25 ml of glycine solution contains $V \times S \times 0.0075$ g of glycine, where S is the strength of (N/10) NaOH solution.

[1 ml of (N/10) NaOH solution $\equiv 0.0075$ g of glycine]

or, 250 ml of glycine (w g of sample glycine) contains $V \times S \times 0.0075 \times 10$ g

or, % purity of glycine supplied $= \dfrac{V \times S \times 0.0075 \times 10}{w} \times 100\%$.

Comments

(i) Since formalin may contain some formic acid, it should be neutralised before actual use.

(ii) Amino acids also contain some acidic component, so it must be neutralised prior to mixing with neutralised formalin.

1.7 Estimation of Acetic Acid in Vinegar by Sodium Hydroxide Solution

Theory: Vinegar is the commercial source of acetic acid. The quantity of acetic acid present in a sample of vinegar may be determined by titration with a standard sodium hydroxide solution. The reactions involved in this titration are as under:

$$CH_3COOH + NaOH \longrightarrow CH_3COONa + H_2O$$

Thus, from equation, $1\,CH_3COOH \equiv 1NaOH$

or, 1 ml (N) NaOH = 1 ml (N) CH_3COOH

or, 1 ml (N) NaOH = $\dfrac{60}{1000}$ g of CH_3COOH

60 is the equivalent weight of CH_3COOH.

Reagent required:

Sodium hydroxide solution 0.2 N.

Procedure: 25 ml of vinegar is pipetted out into a volumetric flask. It is diluted by distilled water and the volume is made uptp 250 ml. 25 ml of this dilute solution is pipetted out into a concical flask and 2 drops of phenolphthalein indicator are added. This solution is titrated against standard 0.2 N NaOH solution till the pink colour just appears. Burette reading is taken and two such titrations are carried out and an average burette reading is determined.

Calculations: Let the strength of (0.2N) NaOH is S. Volume of (0.2N) NaOH required for 25 ml of diluted vinegar is V ml.

Thus, 25 ml of diluted vinegar $\equiv V \times S \times$ (0.2N) ml of NaOH solution.

or, 25 ml of diluted vinegar contains $V \times S \times 0.012$ g of acetic acid

or, 250 ml of diluted vinegar (i.e., 25 ml of vinegar supplied) contains $V \times S \times 0.012 \times 10$ g of acetic acid.

Therefore, content of acetic acid in the supplied vinegar is $V \times S \times 0.012 \times 10 \times 4$ g per litre.

(1 ml of 0.2N NaOH = 0.012 g of acetic acid)

1.8 Estimation of Vitamin-C

Theory: Vitamin-C contains ascorbic acid. It is present in different fruit juices (lemon, orange, etc.). It is also marketed as vitamin-C tablet. The ascorbic acid content in different samples may be estimated by titrating a solution of the sample of vitamin-C against a solution of 2, 6-dichloro phenol indophenol dye. Reactions involved may be written as indicated below:

Dye
(Pink colour in acid solution)

Reagents required:

1. **Dye solution**: About 0.125 g of sodium salt of dye is dissolved in 240 ml of distilled water in a 250 ml volumetric flask and the volume is made up to the mark with phosphate buffer prepared by mixing 0.0165 g of K_2HPO_4 and 0.0202 g of KH_2PO_4 in 250 ml of water.

2. **Standard ascorbic acid solution**: About 10 mg of ascorbic acid (A.R.) is dissolved in distilled water in 100 ml volumetric flask.

Procedure: w g of vitamic-C sample is dissolved 100 ml of distilled water in a 100 ml volumetric flask. 5 ml of this sample solution is pipetted out in a small conical flask. To this 1 ml of glacial acetic acid is added followed by 1 ml of chloroform. This solution is now titrated against the dye solution taken in a burette till the pink colour appears. In the similar way titration is carried with 5 ml of standard ascorbic acid solution. A blank titration is carried out titrating only 5 ml of distilled water.

Calculation: Weight of vitamin-C sample taken be w g Weight of ascorbic acid taken for standardisation w_1 g.

Volume of dye solution required for

(i)   standard ascorbic acid (5 ml) solution V_1

(ii) sample (5 ml) solution V_2

(iii) blank V_3

Concentration of vitamin-C in the sample (w g) (in 5 ml)

Hence in 100 ml $= \dfrac{V_1 - V_3}{V_1 - V_2} \times w \times 20$.

1.9 Estimation of Urea by Hypobromite Method

Theory: Urea may be estimated by its reaction with alkaline hypobromite. When excess of hypobromite is allowed to react with urea, nitrogen is evolved which is measured. Thus,

$$\underset{\text{Urea}}{\overset{H_2N}{\underset{H_2N}{>}}C=O} + \underset{\text{Hypobromite}}{NaOBr} + 2NaOH \longrightarrow \underset{\text{Hydrazine}}{NH_2-NH_2} + NaBr + Na_2CO_3$$

$$NH_2-NH_2 + 2NaOBr \longrightarrow N_2\uparrow + 2H_2O + 2NaBr$$

It may be mentioned in this connection that this reaction is not quantitative and it gives the result which is seven percent below the theoretical value. This method is usually employed for clinical purpose where rough estimation of urea in urine is sufficient.

Apparatus required: The design of the apparatus is simple as shown in the figure below.

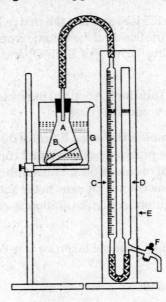

The reaction is carried out in a 100 ml or 150 ml conical flask A, closed by a rubber stopper. B is a small sample tube, C is a graduated gas burette and D is a levelling tube. Both C and D tubes are strongly held to a wooden board E. F is a stopcock to enable easy levelling of the liquid in C and D to be made by adding water through the open end. G is a big beaker containing water at the room temperature. All connections are made with heavy walled pressure tube and should be gas-tight.

Reagents required:

(i) Sodium hypobromite solution: It is prepared by dissolving 50 g of sodium hydroxide in 250 ml of water and is cooled in ice bath at a temperature of 0.5 °C. To this slowly 12.5 ml of A.R. bromine is added with stirring.

(ii) Urea.

Procedure: 60 ml of sodium hypobromite solution is taken in the conical flask. About 100 mg of urea is accurately weighed in the sample tube B and it is carefully placed in the conical flask with the help of a pair of forceps. The conical flask A is properly stoppered and the conical flask containing the sample tube is dipped in the water bath G. The water levels in C and D tubes are adjusted in such a way that both the levels become the same. When thermal equilibrium is attained (usually requires 30 minutes), level in the gas burette is adjusted to the same level with levelling tube, and burette reading is taken. Now the conical flask is fitted in such a way that urea and hypobromite can thoroughly mix each other. Nitrogen gas now evolves. Water is run off to maintain the same level in the tubes C and D. After evolution of nitrogen is ceased, the reaction tube C is allowed to cool to room temperature of the bath. Levels in the gas burette and levelling tube are equalised. Reading of the gas burette, temperature of water in G and barometric presure are noted.

Calculations: 1 g of pure urea yields 373 ml of nitrogen at N.T.P. or in other words, 1 ml of

$$\text{nitrogen} \equiv \frac{1}{373} = 0.00268 \text{ g of urea.}$$

1.10 Determination of Carbonyl Compounds

Theory: Carbonyl compounds, both aldehydes and ketones, react with hydroxylamine hydrochloride in the following way:

$$>C=O + H_2N-OH.HCl \rightleftharpoons >C=N-OH + H_2O + HCl$$

Aldehyde
or
ketone

The equilibrium of this reversible reaction may be shifted to the right- hand direction in presence of pyridine and of excess of hydroxylamine hydrochloride and the reaction is practically quantitative. Pyridine combines with HCl to form pyridine hydrochloride. Thus,

$$>C=O + H_2N-OH.HCl + \underset{\text{Pyridine}}{\bigcirc_N} = >C=N-OH + H_2O + \bigcirc_N HCl$$

Pyridine hydrochloride is acidic in nature and can be titrated with a standard sodium hydroxide solution in presence of bromophenol blue as indicator.

Reagents required:

(i) *Hydroxylamine hydrochloride solution (0.5N)*: It is prepared by dissolving 35 g of pure hydroxylamine hydrochloride in 160 ml of distilled water and is diluted to one litre with 95% ethanol.

(ii) *Pyridine-indicator solution*: 0.25 of bromophenol blue (4%) solution in alcohol is mixed with 20 ml of pure pyridine and is diluted to one litre with 95% ethanol.

(iii) *Methanolic sodium hydroxide solution* (o.5N): 20 g of sodium hydroxide (A.R.) pellets is dissolved in 100 ml of distilled water and is diluted to one litre with absolute methanol.

Procedure: In a 250 ml conical flask fitted with glass stopper, 30 ml of hydroxylamine hydrochloride solution and 100 ml of pyridine-indicator solution are taken, and to it 10 milli-equivalent of carbonyl compound is added. The flask is stoppered and the reaction mixture is allowed to stand for half an hour. Next the liberated hydrochloric acid is titrated with 0.5 N methanolic sodium hydroxide solution till the colour of the solution becomes identical with the colour developed in the *blank titration* of mixture of 30 ml of hydroxylamine hydrochloride and 100 ml of pyridine-indicator solution under identical condition. The volume of methanolic hydroxide required for determination of carbonyl compound is noted.

Calculation: Percentage of purity of carbonyl compound is calculated from the following formula.

$$\% \text{ carbonyl compound} = \frac{V \times N \times M \times 100}{W \times 1000},$$

where   V = Volume of methanolic sodium hydroxide solution required for sample,

N = Normality of methanolic sodium hydroxide solution.

M = Molecular weight of carbonyl compound.

W = Weight in g of the sample.

1.11 Determination of Acetone

Theory: Acetone reacts with iodine in presence of sodium hydroxide solution to form iodoform. Thus,

$$\underset{\substack{\text{Acetone}}}{\overset{\displaystyle CH_3}{\underset{\displaystyle CH_3}{>}}C=O} + 3I_2 + NaOH = \underset{\text{Iodoform}}{CHI_3} + CH_3COONa + NaI + 3H_2O$$

A dilute solution of acetone is added to a known volume of 1 N sodium hydroxide solution followed by an excess of standard 0.1 N iodine solution. After acidification, unreacted iodine is determined by titration with sodium thiosulphate solution.

1 litre of 0.1 NI_2 = 1 litre of 0.N $Na_2S_2O_3$

$$= \frac{CH_3COCH_3}{6 \times 10} = 0.9680 \text{ g of acetone.} = 0.9680 \text{ g of acetone}$$

Since 1 acetone = $3I_2$ = 6 iodine,

so 1 N acetone = 6 × 10 iodine

or, one iodine = $\dfrac{1}{6 \times 10}$ acetone.

This procedure is known as *Messinger's method*.

Reagents required:

1. NaOH solution (N)
2. I_2 solution (0.1 N)
3. H_2SO_4 solution (N)
4. $Na_2S_2O_3$ solution (0.1 N)
5. Starch indicator.

Procedure: A measured volume of aqueous solution containing about 0.01-0.25 g of acetone is taken in a 500 ml conical flask. It is diluted to 200 ml and to it 25 ml of 1N sodium hydroxide solution is added and allowed to stand for 10 minutes after vigorous shaking. From a burette 50 ml of 0.1 N iodine solution is added to the solution with shaking. The mixture is allowed to stand for 15 minutes. Next 25 ml of 1 N H_2SO_4 solution is added and is titrated immediately with standard 0.1 N $Na_2S_2O_3$ solution in presence of starch as indicator.

A blank titration is carried out omitting acetone.

Calculation: Precentage of acetone is calculated from the following relation:

1 ml of 0.1 N $Na_2S_2O_3$ = 0.009680 g of acetone.

Chapter 2

Reporting of Organic Quantitative Analysis

Experiment No: Date:

Estimation of Aniline

Weight of $KBrO_3$ taken: 0.6875
    in 250 ml distilled water

Strength of $KBrO_3$ solution $= \dfrac{0.6875}{0.6875} = 1(N/10)$

Standardisation of thiosulphate solution.

Volume of $KBrO_3$ solution taken	Burette reading	Average
25 ml	V_1	V ml
25 ml	V_2	
25 ml	V_3	

Strength of thiosulphate solution $= 25 \times 1(N/10) = V \times S$ or $S = \left(\dfrac{25}{V}\right) N/10$.

Volume of thiosulphate required during determination
(For 25 ml of diluted aniline solution)

Volume of $KBrO_3$ solution	Burette reading	Average
50 ml	x_1	
50 ml	x_2	V_1 ml
50 ml	x_3	

Calculations: 50 ml $KBrO_3$ solution (in the blank) $\equiv$ 2V ml of thiosulphate

$\therefore$ volume of $KBrO_3$ solution consumed in terms of thiosulphate solution $= (2V - V_1)$ ml.

$\therefore$ Amount of aniline in 25 ml $\equiv \dfrac{(2V - V_1) \times S \times 93.10}{1000 \times 6}$ g

or amount of aniline in the supplied solution is $\dfrac{(2V - V_1) \times S \times 93.10 \times 10}{1000 \times 6}$ g,

since the supplied solution has been diluted to 250 ml.

Chapter 3

Questions and Answers for Viva Voce

1. Explain why *p*-nitroaniline cannot be prepared by direct nitration of aniline.

   Ans. Aniline is highly susceptible to oxidation by HNO_3. So —NH_2 group must be protected before nitration.

2. What do you mean by invert sugar?

   Ans. Sucrose on hydrolysis forms equimolecular mixture of D (+) glucose, $[\alpha]_D = 52.76$ and D(-) fructose, $[\alpha]_D = 92.40$. Because of high negative rotation of fructose the net rotation is negative. But sucrose itself has specific rotation of + 66.50. Since there is change from positive to negative rotation, hydrolysed sucrose is known as invert sugar.

3. Why sucrose cannot be directly estimated by Fehling's solution?

   Ans. Sucrose does not contain any reducible group and so it cannot be titrated by Fehling's solution.

4. What happens when glucose is treated with Fehling's solution.

   Ans. Cupric ion in Fehling's solution is reduced to cuprous ion and glucose is oxidised to gluconic acid, i.e.,

   $$\underset{\substack{(R = \text{remaining portion} \\ \text{of glucose})}}{\overset{\text{CHO}}{\underset{\text{R}}{|}}} + 2Cu^{++} \xrightarrow{2OH} \overset{\text{COOH}}{\underset{\text{R}}{|}} + \underset{\text{Red}}{2Cu_2O\downarrow} + H_2O$$

5. How will you explain that one molecule of aniline is quantitatively equivalent to six molecules of sodium thiosulphate.

   Ans. See Art. 1.3.

6. Discuss the theoretical basis of estimation of phenol by bromination method.

   Ans. See Art. 1.2.

7. What do you mean by saponification value of an ester?

   Ans. It is the number of milligrams of potassium hydroxide required to hydrolyse one gram of an ester.

8. Explain why amino acids cannot be estimated directly by titrating with an alkali?

   Ans. This is because in amino acid there are two opposing groups carboxylic and amino groups as a result they exist as *"Zwitterion"*.

$$K_2N-\underset{\underset{R}{|}}{CH}-COOH \rightleftharpoons H_3\overset{+}{N}-\underset{\underset{R}{|}}{CH}-COO^-$$

Zwitterion

9. How amino acids are estimated?

   Ans. Amino acids are treated with formaldehyde when amino group is blocked and carboxylic group becomes free which is then titrated with an alkali.

10. How the content of acetic acid in vinegar be estimated?

    Ans. The content of acetic acid in venegar may be estimated by titration with an alkali.

11. Discuss the theoretical basis of estimation of vitamin C.

    Ans. See the text.

12. If a compound gives negative Fehling's test does it mean the compound is not a sugar.

    Ans. No. Non-redicing sugars do not respound to Fehling's test.

Separation of Components of Organic Mixture and Isolation of Organic Compounds from Natural Source

Part IV

Chapter 1

Separation of Organic Mixture

In organic chemistry laboratory, different types of techniques are frequently applied for the separation and purification of compounds. The different techniques that are in use in the laboratory may broadly be classified into two categories as mentioned below:

1. Physical Methods.
2. Chemical Methods.

1.1 Physical Methods

Various types of physical techniques like chromatography, electrophoresis are now widely used in chemical laboratories. Of the variety of physical techniques commonly in use in the laboratory, chromatography becomes the most important and popular because of the simplicity and ease of its operation. Its operational technique is so easy and simple that even the students of undergraduate courses feel very comfort in handling this technique.

1.1.1 Chromatography

It is one of the most valuable and relatively a modern technique. It was first invented by *M.Tswett*, a Botanist in 1906 for the separation of coloured substances. That is why its name *chromatography* (Greek *chroma* means colour) has been assigned to it. Since its invention, this technique has undergone an explosive modification as a result of which a variety of chromatographic techniques are in use today for separation and purification purpose of different types of chemicals.

The basic principle of this technique is the preferential distribution of the components of the mixture in two phases—one is stationary and the other is mobile. The stationary phase may be either solid or liquid. When it is solid, the separation of components occurs through selective adsorption but in the case of liquid stationary phase the separation is achieved by partition. The mobile phase may be liquid or gas. Different types of chromatography developed so far are:

(a) Column chromatography (b) Thin layer chromatography (c) Paper chromatography and (d) Gas chromatography.

1.1.1.1 Column Chromatography

The basic principle of this chromatographic technique is adsorption which is a surface phenommenon and so the degree of separation depends upon the surface area of the adsorbent.

It is known that the properties of the molecule on the surface of a solid are different from its inherent properties. The layer on the surface is of higher energy. When the solution of any compound is placed on an adsorbent, active surface attracts the molecule and tends to absorb it. The forces of attraction that may operate may be electrostatic, dipole-dipole, van der Waals or combination of these forces. The separation of components of the mixture occurs due to transport of the molecules through the system and interchange between adsorbent and the liquid phase.

When a solution of a mixture of components is placed in a columr. containing adsorbent, different components are adsorbed differently. During running of the column by solvents desorption takes place and components which are comparatively held loosely travel faster down the column than those held firmly. This process of desorption is known as *elution* of the column.

The adsorbent used should be chemically inert, colourless and should be insoluble in the solvents used. Variety of adsorbents are in use. Some of the most commonly used adsorbents are alumina, silica gel, charcoal, etc. The columns generally used are made of glass tubes of about 2-5 cm in diameter and 20-30 cm in length. Columns of big diameter and long length may be used depending upon the quantity of materials to be separated. Before the start of the actual experiment, adsorbent is placed in the column firmly.

The polarity is the most important criteria for the solvents to be used. Normally column is run by solvents of increasing polarity. The fractions eluted from the column are collected serially and solvent is evaported when solid sample is obtained in pure form.

Procedure

(a) **Preparation of chromatographic column:** A long narrow glass tube of standard size is taken. It is washed and dried. The bottom of the glass tube is plugged with cotton and approximately 100-125 g of adsorbent is taken into it through the top of the tube so that $1/5$ to $1/3$ rd of the tube is left empty. The packing of the tube is made uniform and free from any air bubble by applying suction. This glass tube with uniformly packed adsorbent is clamped vertically and is ready for introducing solution of the mixture.

(b) **Preparation of solution of the mixture:** About 0.6 to 0.8 g of the mixture is taken in a small beaker or in a small conical flask and is dissolved in a minimum quantity of suitable solvent such as alcohol, benzene, etc. by warming, if necessary, and cooled.

(c) **Introduction of the solution to the column:** The solution, thus, prepared is transferred to the column without any disturbance to the column and as soon as the solution is adsorbed, the column is covered with a solvent of least polarity. Finally the column is run with the solvents of increasing polarity. Different zones or bands are formed in the column as shown in the following figure.

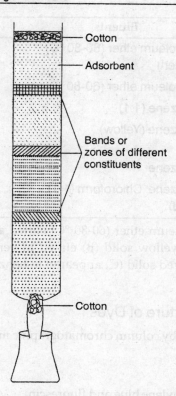

Cotton

Adsorbent

Bands or
zones of different
constituents

Cotton

The eluents are collected in a 100 ml conical flask according to the following programme as shown in the table.

Fractions 100 ml each	Eluents	Residue
1-3	Petroleum ether (60-80 °C)	Solid, m.p. ... (A)
3-4	Do	Practically nil
5	Petroleum ether (60-80 °C): Benzene mixture (1:1)	Nil
6-8	Benzene	Solid, m, p. ... (B)
9	Do	Nil

The solid residues (A) and (B) obtained are identified by usual procedure.

1.1.1.1.1 Separation of the Pigments Present in Leaves

Procedure: A few leaves are cut into pieces and ground in a mortar with a pestle in presence of a few drops of alcohol. More alcohol is then added and grinding is continued for 5-10 minutes. The solution is filtered. The clear solution is concentrated by heating on a water bath. The concentrated extract is cooled. The cold solution is now transferred to a chromatographic column prepared according to procedure in 1.1.1.1. The column is eluted successively with the solvents of increasing polarity. Eluents are collected in 100 ml conical flask according to the plan recorded in the table below.

Fractions	Eluents	Residue
1-2	Petroleum ether (60-80 °C) (Green)	Solid (A) (Green)
3	Petroleum ether (60-80 °C): Benzene (1:1)	Nil
4-5	Benzene (Yellow)	Solid (B) (Yellow)
6	Benzene	Nil
7-8	Benzene: Chloroform (1:1) (Red)	Solid (C) (Red)

Solid (A) obtained in petroleum ether (60-80 °C) eluted as green coloured solid has been identified as chlorophyll while yellow solid (B) eluted in benzene has been characterised as xanthophyll. The identity of the red solid (C) appeared in benzene-chloroform (1:1) eluents has been established as carotene.

1.1.1.1.2 Separation of Mixture of Dyes

Mixture of dyes can be separated by column chromatographic method by adapting the procedure discussed below.

Chemicals required:

1. Mixture of dyes–Methylene blue and fluorescin.
2. Common solvents
3. Ethyl alcohol
4. Alumina as adsorbent.

Procedure: A solution of the mixture (0.1 g) of the above two dyes are prepared in minimum quantity of ethanol. This concentrated solution is transferred to a chromatographic column of 2.5 ×30 cm size prepared according to the procedure in 1.1.1.1, when two bands—(1) blue and the other yellow, are formed. The column is eluted successively with the solvents of increasing polarity. Eluents are collected in 50 ml conical flask according to the plan tabulated below.

Fractions	Eluents	Residue
1-2	Petroleum ether (60-80 °C)	Nil
3	Benzene	Nil
4-5	Benzene-chloroform (1:1)	Nil
6	Chloroform	Nil
7	Chloroform: Ethanol (1:1)	Residue (trace)
8	Ethanol (Blue)	Solid (A) (Blue)
9	Ethanol	Nil
10	Ethanol (Yellow)	Solid (B) (Yellow)

The solid (A) obtained in ethanol eluent as green coloured solid has been identified as methylene blue while the solid (B) obtained in the latter fraction of ethanol eluents has been characterised as fluorescin.

1.1.1.2 Paper Chromatography

It is a kind of partition chromatography in which the substances are distributed between two liquids—one is the stationary liquid usually water, held in the fibres of the paper known as *stationary phase* and the other is the moving liquid or developing solvent and is normally called as *moving phase*. The components of the mixture to be separated migrate at different rates and appear as spots on the paper.

Initially this technique was applied in the separation of mixture of organic substances such as dyes and amino acids only. But now this method is also widely used to separate cations and anions of inorganic substances.

In the paper chromatographic method a drop of test solution is applied on a filter paper (Whatmann No. 1) and the spot is dried. The filter paper is hanged in a close chamber by a hook as shown in the figure below.

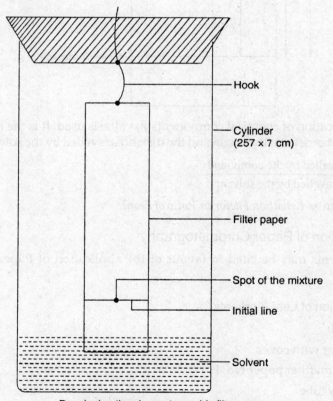

Developing the chromatographic filter paper

The edge of the filter paper is dipped just into the solvent so that the initial line on which a drop of the sample has been placed does not dip more than 1 cm into the solvent called *developing solvent*. As soon as the filter paper is dipped into the solvent system, the liquid begins to move through capillary action and ultimately reaches the spot of the sample containing mixture of the components, the different substances present in the spot of the mixture are moved by the solvent at different speeds. When the solvent moves with different substances to an appreciable height, normally 15 cm, the filter paper is taken out and the solvent front is marked by a pencil. This is known as the *solvent front*. The filter paper is dried. It is called as the *Chromatogram*. The different spots are developed by suitable reagents known as *developers*. This is normally done by spraying a very dilute solution (1-2%) of a developer. Spraying is done by a sprayer. The number of spots in the filter paper indicates the number of components in the mixture.

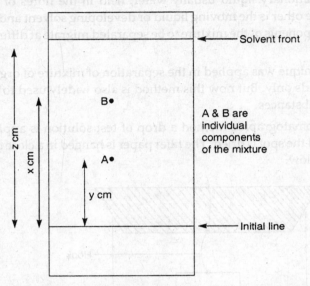

For the identification of chemical components R_f value is used. It is the ratio of the distance travelled by the substance from the origin and the distance travelled by the solvent from the origin,

i.e., $R_f = \dfrac{\text{distance travelled by the compound}}{\text{distance travelled by the solvent}}$.

This R_f is known as *Retention Factor* or *Ratio of Front*.

1.1.1.2.1 Application of Paper Chromatography

Following experiments may be cited in favour of the application of Paper Chromatographic technique.

1.1.1.2.1.1 Separation of Leaf Pigments

Apparatus required:

1. A glass jar with cover
2. Whatmann filter paper No. 1
3. Capillary tube.

Chemicals required:

1. Acetone
2. Alcohol.

Materials: Spinach leaves.

Procedure

(a) **Preparation of extract:** A few spinach leaves are dried in sun and cut into small pieces. These pieces are ground in a mortar with a pestle in presence of a few drops of alcohol. Further amount of alcohol are added and grinding is continued for 15 minutes. The solution is filtered, taken in a test tube and concentrated by heating on a water bath. It is cooled and is used for spotting.

(b) **Experiment:** A line is drawn 4 cm above from one end on a strip of Whatmann No. 1 filter paper of 20 × 3 cm size. A spot of leaf extract prepared is placed on the line of the filter paper with the help of a capillary tube. The spot is dried and another spot of the extract is placed on the same place so that the spot is rich in the extract. The filter paper strip is hung in a glass jar containing aqueous acetone solution (1:1) as developing solvent. The filter paper is placed in such a way that the spot and the pencil line must be at least 2 cm above the solvent. The jar is covered with glass-plate and is kept undisturbed till the solvent has risen about 15 cm from the pencil line. Now the filter paper is taken out, solvent front marked and dried. Three distinct coloured spots are observed on the filter paper. The green spot is due to chlorophyll, orange spot indicates xanthophyll while third red spot reveals the presence of carotene. The distances of the initial line and solvent front and also between the initial line and the middle point of the spots are measured and R_f values are calculated.

Results

Colour of the spot	Distance between the initial line and solvent front	Distance between the initial line and centre of the spot	R_f value
Green (chlorophyll)	a	x	x/a
Yellow (xanthopyll)	b	y	y/b
Red (carotene)	c	z	z/c

1.1.1.2.1.2 Separation of Mixture of Amino Acids

Apparatus required: Same as in Art. 1.1.1.2.1.1.

Chemicals required:

1. Developing solvent: *n*-Butanol: Glacial acetic acid: water (4:5:1)
2. Developing reagent: Ninhydrin (1% solution)

Materials: Glycine, Proline, Phenyl alanine.

Procedure

(a) **Preparation of solution of mixture of Amino acids:** Solution of amino acids is prepared by dissolving 120 mg of each of glycine, proline and phenyl alanine in 20 ml of distilled water.

(b) **Experiment:** A line is drawn 4 cm above from one end on a strip of Whatmann No. 1 filter paper of 20 × 3 cm size. A spot of the solution is placed on the line of the filter paper with the help of a capillary tube. The spot is dried and another spot is placed in the same spot. The filter paper strip is hung in a glass jar containing developing solvent (n-Butanol: glacial acetic acid: water (4:5:1). The filter paper is placed properly 2 cm above the solvent. The jar is covered with a cover and is kept undisturbed till the solvent has risen about 15 cm from the pencil line. The filter paper is taken out, solvent front is marked and dried. The dried filter paper is sprayed with ninhydrin solution. Three coloured spots are observed at three different positions. The positions of the spots are marked and R_f values are determined. From R_f values amino acids are identified.

Results

Spot	Distance between the initial line and solvent front	Distance between the intial line and centre of the spot	R_f values
1	a	x	x/a
2	b	y	y/b
3	c	z	z/c

1.1.1.2.1.3 Separation of Sugars in a Mixture

Apparatus required: Same as in Art. 1.1.1.2.1.1.

Chemicals required:

    1. Developing solvent: Ethyl acetate: Ethanol (2:1)

    2. Developing reagent: Anisaldehyde—sulphuric acid solution

Materials: Mixture of sugars (at least three)

Procedure

  (a) **Preparation of solution:** Nearly 350 mg of the mixture of sugars is taken in a small conical flask and dissolved in distilled water.

  (b) **Experiment:** As in Art. 1.1.1.2.1.1. a spot is placed on the filter paper, hung in glass jar containing ethyl acetate: ethanol (2:1) as developing solvent. After the completion of the procedure as was done in Art. 1.1.1.2.1.1. the filter paper is sprayed with anisaldehyde-sulphuric acid solution and heated for 10 minutes at 100 °C. Different coloured spots at different positions on the filter paper are obtained. The positions of the spots are marked and R_f values are determined. From R_f values sugars are identified.

Results

Spot	Distance between the initial line and solvent front	Distance between the intial line and centre of the spot	R_f values
1	a	x	x/a
2	b	y	y/b
3	c	z	z/c

1.1.1.3 Thin Layer Chromatography (TLC)

Thin layer chromatography involves the same principle as column chromatography. It is known as *thin flim, open column* or *chromatoplate* chromatography. This technique was first introduced by

Izmailov and Shraiber in 1938. It has been found to be more advantageous than column and paper chromatographies. The *main advantages* of thin layer chromatography may be enlisted below.

(a) It requires simple equipments.

(b) In TLC, development time is much shorter than other two chromatographies. It requires only one hour.

(c) The method may be employed for partition and ion exchange chromatography.

(d) The spot or zone may be quantitatively separated.

(e) The separation effects in this chromatography is much better than paper chromatography.

(f) Spot may be easily detected.

(g) The great merit of inert stationary phase as is used in TLC affords a good means of detection.

In this chromatography, a thin layer of chromatographic plate is prepared by spreading a uniform layer of slurry of the adsorbent on glass plates and is allowed to dry for at least 30 minutes. Sometimes layers are activated by heating. The slurry is prepared by mixing 25 g of silica gel with 50 ml of water taken in a stoppered conical flask with occasional shaking till it becomes free from air bubble. Besides silica gel, alumina, kieselguhr and cellulose may be used as adsorbents. The solvents may be pure solvent or may be mixture of solvents. A drop of the solution of the mixture is put on one end of the glass plate by a capillary tube and is kept vertically in a glass jar containing the developing solvent. The developing solvent should be below the level of the spot as shown in the following figure.

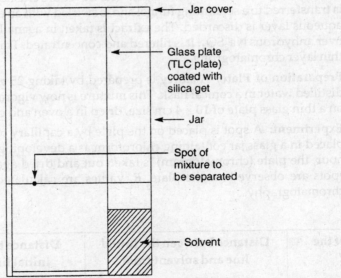

Jar cover

Glass plate (TLC plate) coated with silica gel

Jar

Spot of mixture to be separated

Solvent

Due to capillary action the solvent rises up carrying with it the constituents of the solution adsorbed at the plate at different distances depending upon the degree of adsorption. The weakly adsorbed component rises to more height. The spots of the mixture are developed by using suitable spraying agents (developers). However, for development of the spots, the plate (chromatogram) may be placed in an iodine chamber. Iodine is considered as an universal developer. The R_f value for each component is calculated as in the case of paper chromatography.

1.1.1.3.1 Application of Thin Layer Chromatography

Some commonly illustrated examples of this chromatographic technique are discussed below.

1.1.1.3.1.1 Separation of Leaf Pigments (Spinach)

Apparatus required:

1. A glass Jar with cover
2. TLC plate (10 × 4 cm)
3. Capillary tube
4. Oven
5. Mortar with pestle,
6. 5 separating funnel.

Chemicals required:

1. Silica gel
2. Chloroform
3. Ethanol
4. Petroleum ether (60-80 °C)

Materials required: A few pieces of leaves.

Procedure

(a) **Preparation of the solution:** A few pieces of leaves are cut into pieces and are dried on the sun rays. In mortar 15 ml of petroleum ether (60-80 °C) and ethanol in the ratio 2:1 and dry cut pieces of leaves are taken. The leaves are crushed with a pestle. The extract is transferred to a separating funnel and is swirled with an equal volume of water. The aqueous layer is discarded. The extract is taken in a small conical flask and is dried over anhydrous Na_2SO_4. It is filtered and concentrated. This solution is now ready for thin layer chromatogrphy.

(b) **Preparation of Plate:** A slurry is prepared by taking 25 g of silica gel and 50 ml of distilled water in a conical flask. This mixture is now vigorously shaken and is spread on a thin glass plate of 10 × 4 cm size, dried in a oven and cooled.

(c) **Experiment:** A spot is placed on the plate by a capillary tube and is dried. It is now placed in a glass jar containing chloroform as a developing solvent. After nearly one hour, the plate (chromatogram) is taken out and dried again. Three major coloured spots are observed on the plate. R_f values are calculated as in the case of paper chromatography.

Result

Colour of the spot	Distance between the initial line and solvent front	Distance between the initial line and the centre of the spot	R_f value
Green (Chlorophyll)	a	x	x/a
Yellow (Xanthophylls)	b	y	y/b
Red (Carotenes)	c	z	z/c

1.1.1.3.1.2 Separation of Mixture of Amino Acids

Apparatus required: Same as in Art. 1.1.1.3.1.1

Chemicals required

1. Developing solvent: n-Butanol:glacial acetic acid:water (4:5:2)
2. Depeloping reagent: Ninhydrin (1%)
3. Materials: Mixture of three amino acids.

Procedure

(a) **Preparation of solution of amino acids:** 350 mg of amino acid mixture is dissolved in 20 ml of water.

(b) **Preparation of TLC plate:** As in Art. 1.1.1.3.1.1.(b).

(c) **Experiment:** A small spot of the solution of mixture of amino acids is placed on the plate by a capillary tube and is dried. It is now placed on a glass jar containing n-butanol:glacial acetic acid:water (4:5:2) as developing solvent. It is kept undisturbed for an hour and is taken out. It is dried again and is sprayed with 1% ninhydrin solution. Three coloured spots are observed at three different positions on the plate. The positions of spots are marked and R_f values are calculated.

Results

Spot	Distance between the initial line solvent front	Distance between the initial line and centre of the spot	R_f value
1	a	x	x/a
2	b	y	y/b
3	c	z	z/c

1.1.1.3.1.3 Separation of Mixture of Dyes

Example 1

Apparatus required: Same as in Art. 1.1.1.3.1.1.

Chemicals required:

1. Developing solvents: n-Butanol:ethanol:water (90:10:10)
2. Mixture of two basic dyes (melachite green and methyl violet)
3. Silica Gel G.

Preparation of solution: 100 mg of each of the above dyes are dissolved in 25 ml ethanol and mixed together.

Preparation of TLC plate: As in Art. 1.1.1.3.1.1.

Experiment: Thin layer chromatographic experiment is carried out in the usual way and after completion of experiment two different coloured spots are obtained at ditterent positions and their R_f values are determined in the usual way. Melachite green produces green spot with R_f 0.35 while methyi violet develops red spot having R_f 0.45.

For separation of constituents of acid dyes similar procedure is applied but different developing solvent system is to be used. Thus, triphenyl methane dyes may be separated using the same adsorbent, i.e., silica gel G but using n-butanol:ethanol:water:acetic acid (60:10:20:0.05) or pure ethanol or *n*-butanol:acetic acid:water (40:10:50) as solvent system. Different spots are obtained at different positions of the plate.

Example 2

Apparatus required: As in Art. 1.1.1.3.1.1.

Chemicals required

1. Chloroform ⎤ Developing solvent
2. Methanol ⎦
3. Ethanol
4. Silica gel G
5. Methylene blue
6. Fluorescin.

Preparation of solution: 50 mg of each dye is dissolved in 50 ml of ethanol, and 10 ml of each solution is mixed together.

Preparation of TLC plate: As in Art. 1.1.1.3.1.1.

Experiment: The experiment is carried out in the usual way using chloroform:methanol (9:1) as developing solvent and after completion of the expriment two different coloured spots are obtained at different positions of the plate and their R_f values are determined as usual. Methylene blue produces a blue spot with R_f 0.15 and fluorescien develops a yellow spot on the plate having R_f 0.50.

1.2 Chemical Methods

The chemical methods of separation of constituents of a mixture of organic compounds primarily depend on the chemical and physical properties of the substances involved. It may be mentioned in this connection that it is practically impossible to suggest any particular set of procedures without any modification because of the variety of combinations that may be encountered. In separating the constituents of a mixture, advantage should be taken of any fact that may be emerged in the preliminary examination of the mixture. Preliminary examination of the mixture is, therefore, an essential and fundamental step prior to adapt a suitable procedure for the separation.

Generally, the procedures for the separation of constituents of any mixture may be classified into three major categories.

1.2.1 Separation Based on the Differences in the Chemical Properties of the Constituents

When the components of the mixture appreciably differ in their chemical properties, the separation may be easily performed. Thus, if a mixture contains a neutral component like toluene and a basic component, i.e., aniline, they may be separated by extraction with dilute hydrochloric acid. Aniline forms a salt, aniline hydrochloride, and will pass on to the aqueous layer and may be recovered by neutralisation with an alkali. Similarly mixture of toluene and phenol may be separated by the treatment with dilute sodium hydroxide. Again, the components of a mixture containing phenol and carboxylic acid may be separated by the treatment with a dilute solution of sodium bicarbonate when weakly acidic components like phenols and enols are not converted to their salts by this reagent and may be removed by extraction with ether or any other solvent, the acids pass into solution as their salts and may be recovered after acidification.

1.2.2 Separation Based on the Difference in the Volatilities of the Components

When the components are soluble in water, this procedure may be employed. After dissolving in water, it is subjected to steam distillation when steam volatile components may be separated out through steam.

1.2.3 Separation Based on the Difference in Physical Properties of the Components

Sometimes differences in physical properties of the components of the mixture may be utilised for their separation. Thus, a mixture of volatile liquids may be separated by fractional distillation.

1.2.4 Preliminary Examinations of the Mixture

As mentioned before, preliminary investigation of the mixture is an essential step for adapting a particular scheme for the separation of the components. So it is considered partinent to discuss some preliminary tests to be performed before going into the actual separation of the constituents of the mixture. A portion of the sample of the mixture is taken in a test tube, vigorously shaken with water, filtered and with the filtrate following tests are performed.

1(a) A portion of the filtrate of the sample is taken in a test tube and evaporated to dryness.	**1(a)** A solid remains in the test tube or No solid residue.	**1(a)** Water soluble component is present or No water soluble component is present.
(b) Filtrate is treated with blue litmus paper.	**(b)** Blue litmus paper turns red or Neutral to litmus paper.	**(b)** Water soluble component is acidic in nature or Water soluble portion is neutral.
(c) A portion of the filtrate is treated with $NaHCO_3$ solution.	**(c)** Effervescence occurs or No effervescence.	**(c)** Water soluble portion is acidic in nature or Water soluble portion is neutral.
2(a) A portion of the sample is taken in a test tube and is treated with $NaHCO_3$ solution, shaken well and allowed to stand for a minute. (*This test is to be performed when no residue in 1(a) is obtained*).	**2(a)** Effervescence occurs or No effervescence.	**2(a)** Carboxylic acid component is present or No carboxylic acid component is present.
(b) Since the mixture contains a carboxylic component, a portion of the sample is taken in a test tube and is completely neutralised with $NaHCO_3$ solution, filtered and the filtrate is acidified.	**(b)** A precipitate appears.	**(b)** A sparingly soluble carboxylic acid component is present.

1.2.5 Remarks on the Separation Scheme

From above preliminary examinations, following conclusions may be drawn regarding the separation scheme.

1. When the sample contains a water soluble component (acidic or neutral), this component should be separated by the treatment with water.

2. If the sample contains one sparingly soluble carboxylic acid, this acidic constituent is to be separated from other component by $NaHCO_3$ solution treatment.

3. When the preliminary examinations do not indicate the presence of any water soluble component (acidic or neutral) or any sparingly soluble carboxylic component, then one of the components may be basic in character which may be separated by dilute hydrochloric acid followed by the treatment of the filtrate with dilute sodium hydroxide solution.

1.2.6 Procedures of Separation of Different Types of Components

1.2.6.1 Procedure of Separation for Water Soluble Acidic Component

A major portion of the sample is taken in a 250 ml conical flask and is treated with 50 ml of distilled water, vigorously shaken, warmed gently and filtered. The filtrate is collected in a 500 ml beaker. The residue on the filter paper is washed with dilute solution of $NaHCO_3$ 2-3 times to remove any acidic component that may adhere to the insoluble portion and $NaHCO_3$ washing is rejected. The residue is dried by blotting paper. Both the residue and filtrate collected, are separately worked out for the identification of the individual component as indicated below.

Treatment of the Filtrate: The filtrate collected in the beaker is evaporated to dryness and the residue obtained is dried and solid residue is subjected to qualitative analysis according to plan discussed in Part-I for its identification.

Treatment of the Residue: The residue obtained is subjected to qualitative analysis for its identification.

1.2.6.2 Procedure of Separation for Water Soluble Neutral Component

A major portion of the mixture is taken in a 250 ml conical flask and is treated with 50 ml of distilled water, vigorously shaken, warmed gently and filtered. The filtrate is collected in a beaker and the residue is washed 2-3 times with water to remove the last traces of water soluble portion. Washings and filtrate are mixed together. Both the filtrate and residue are separately treated for identification of individual components as in the case of water soluble acid constituents, i.e., the filtrate is evaporated to dryness and solid obtained is dried. The solid and water insoluble solid residue are subjected separately to qualitative analysis for their identification.

1.2.6.3 Procedure of Separation for Sparingly Soluble Acid Using Sodium Bicarbonate Solution

A substantial portion of the sample is taken in a 250 ml conical flask and is treated with a dilute $NaHCO_3$ solution till neutralisation with occasional shaking. It is now filtered and the residue is washed with $NaHCO_3$ solution to remove any trace of carboxylic acid component that may be present with the insoluble component. The filtrate and washings are collected together. The residue(A) and filtrate (A) are worked up separately for further analysis.

Treatment of the filtrate(A): The filtrate in the beaker is placed in cold water and is acidified with dilute HCl when solid precipitate appears. It is allowed to stand for at least 15 minutes, filtered, washed 2-3 times with water to remove any acid, dried, and dry residue is subjected to qualitative analysis for its identification.

Treatment of the residue(A): Residue(A) obtained previously during separation is subjected to qualitative analysis for its identification in the usual way.

1.2.6.4 Procedure of Separation for Basic Component Involving NaOH Treatment

A major portion of the sample is taken in a 250 ml conical flask and is treated with dilute HCl, vigorously shaken and filtered. The residue is repeatedly washed with dilute HCl to remove any basic component that may be present. The washings and the filtrate are collected together. The residue (A) and filtrate (A) are separately taken up for further analysis.

1.2.6.4.1 Treatment of the Filtrate (A)

The filtrate (A) taken in a beaker is placed in cold water and is made alkaline with 20% NaOH solution when solid precipitate appears. It is allowed to stand for at least 15 minutes, filtered and the residue is washed repeatedly with water to remove any NaCl that may be present, dried and the dry residue is subjected to qualitative analysis for its identification.

1.2.6.4.2 Treatment of the Residue (A)

The residue (A) obtained during the separation is subjected to qualitative analysis as usual for its identification.

1.2.6.5 Examples of Separation of Mixture

The above procedures may be illustrated by taking the separation of the following mixtures:

1.2.6.5.1 Benzil and Benzoic Acid

Both the compnents are insoluble in water but are soluble in organic solvents such as ether. The mixture is acidic to litmus. Hence the mixture is vigorously shaken with dilute $NaHCO_3$ solution. Benzil remains insoluble in aqueous medium. The solution is filtered when benzil is separated and benzoic acid is precipitated by acidifying the filtrate with dilute HCl (10%).

1.2.6.5.2 p-Nitroaniline and Succinic Acid

Succinic acid is soluble in water but the other component, p-nitroaniline is insoluble in water. So the mixture can be separated by dissolving the mixture in water. The solution is filtered when p-nitroaniline is separated out as precipitate. Succinic acid is obtained by evaporating the filtrate.

1.2.6.5.3 Aniline and m-Dinitrobenzene

Both the substances are insoluble in water but soluble in ether. The mixture is basic to litmus. The mixture is acidified with dilute HCl when aniline goes into solution as aniline hydrochloride but m-dinitrobenzene remains unaffected. m-Dinitrobenzene is obtained by extraction with ether and from aqueous solution aniline is recovered by basifying the solution with dilute NaOH (10%).

1.2.6.5.4 Some Other Examples

Mixture	Probable solvent to be used for separation
Urea and iodoform	Ether
Benzophenone and benzoic acid	Dilute NaHCO$_3$ solution
Benzoic acid and anthracene	Dilute NaHCO$_3$ solution
p-Toluidine and benzophenone	Dilute HCl
α-Naphthol and Naphthalene	Dilute NaOH

Chapter 2

Reporting of Results of Analysis of Mixture

Sample No.:   Date:

1. Preliminary examination of the mixture.
2. Conclusion reagarding the mixture.
3. Separation of the mixture.
4. Identification of the component (A).
5. Identification of the component (B).
6. Final conclusion. From the experiments carried out above, it is concluded that the supplied sample contains .... (A) and .... (B).

Chapter 3

Isolation of Organic Compounds from Natural Sources

Organic compounds primarily owe their origin from natural sources specially the plants. So isolation of organic compounds from plants constitutes an important aspect of organic chemistry. Many organic compounds from natural sources were isolated in the early nineteenth century, the study of their reactions constituted the beginning of organic chemistry and indeed during the whole of that century only these natural products were the main source of organic chemicals and afforded the major problems of organic chemistry. Pigments for dying and painting, perfumes and folk medicines are all organic compounds and have been isolated from plants. Many organic compounds isolated from plants have been found to possess curative properties in the treatment of various diseases and find frequent applications in modern medicine.

Besides medicinal efficacies, organic compounds isolated from nature have provided immense fund of problems, the solution of which in many instances, have afforded the stimulation for the theories that is now fundamental to organic chemistry. Further, the structures of natural products have provided challenging source of problems to synthetic organic chemistry.

Once again, many chemicals from natural source have been found to possess pesticidal properties and in recent years, in many instances, plant products are being used in protecting the loss of crop-production from the attack of insects and parasites. So it is felt partinent to discuss some processes of isolation of natural products. Recently isolation techniques have been so modernised and simplified that they can be easily adapted. Some of the most common and general methods of isolation of natural products are discussed in sequel.

3.1 General Methods for the Isolation of Natural Products

In general four methods have been developed for the isolation of natural products, viz., (i) mechanical expression, (ii) steam distillation, (iii) solvent extraction and (iv) adsorption in purified fats. A short resume of these methods are furnished below.

3.1.1 Mechanical Expression

This method is usually applied when the source material is solid in character. In this method the solid plant material is crushed and the liquid that is obtained is passed through a screen to separate solid particles. The liquid, thus, obtained is now centrifuged. This technique is employed for the isolation of mustard oil, ground nut oil, citrus, lemon and grass oils.

3.1.2 Steam Distillation

This is the most widely used method for the isolation of essential oils because it can be employed both for soluble and insoluble oils in water. This method involves the soaking of powdered or finely cut plant materials and then the soaked material is subjected to steam distillation. The steam distillate contains mostly essential oils along with water. As essential oils are lighter than water they can be easily separated. However, this method is to be used with care because some essential oils are decomposed during distillation and some esters are hydrolysed. A typical extraction process may be shown by the following diagram.

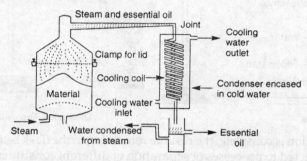

Some important essential oil isolated by this method are the oils of eucalyptus, sandal wood, khus-khus, etc.

3.1.3 Extraction with Volatile Solvents

This is the most important and common method usually employed for the isolation of natural products. The general procedure as followed in most of the cases is as described below.

The dried and powdered plant material is extracted with petroleum ether to remove the fatty materials in a soxhlet apparatus as shown in the figure (Soxlet Apparatus, page 284).

The bottom portion of the apparatus is plugged with cotton to check the passing of powdered plant material. The apparatus is fitted with a round-bottomed flask of assorted capacity containing solvent with which the plant materials are to be extracted. The top of the soxhlet apparatus is fitted with a water condenser. The round-bottomed flask with all its assemblies is placed on a water bath and heated gently at a temperature of 80-85 °C. The extraction is first carried out with petroleum ether (60-80 °C). Petroleum ether passes through the outer tube of the soxhlet apparatus and is condensed by water condenser fitted on the top of soxhlet apparatus. The solvent (petroleum ether) is collected in the central portion where plant material have been taken. When the level of petroleum ether reaches the level of siphon tube, it is siphoned back to the round-bottomed flask. This process is continued for several hours (50-56 hours). It is now cooled, the assembly is disconnected and the extract obtained in the round-bottomed flask is distilled using distillation assembly as shown in the figure (Distillation Apparatus, page 284).

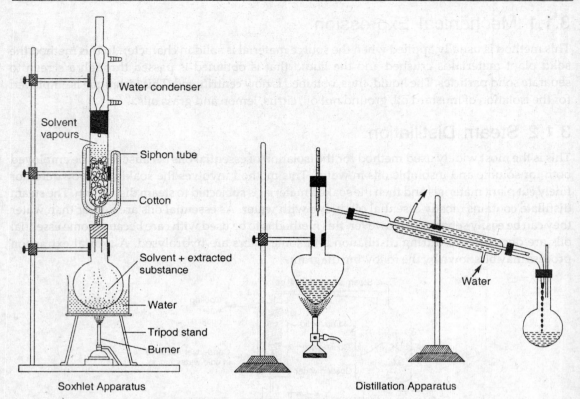

Soxhlet Apparatus   Distillation Apparatus

When the distillation is complete, the residue remaining in the flask is transferred to a conical flask, cooled and subjected to processes of separation of different constituents present. The marc (plant materials remaining in the soxhlet) is successively extracted with other solvents such as benzene, chloroform, ethylacetate, and the same procedure as before is followed to get the extracts of plant materials for further processing. Finally, the marc left out is taken in an aspirator or any stoppered Jar fitted with an outlet tap is soaked in rectified spirit and is allowed to stand for several days. Lastly alcohol is filtered out, distilled and the residue obtained is kept for further processing in the usual way.

3.1.4 Adsorption in Purified Fats (Enfleurage)

This process of isolation is not very common and is primarily applied for extraction of essential oils from flowers. In this process purified fat is taken in a glass plates and is warmed to about 50 °C. This warmed fat is now covered with flower materials and is allowed to stand for several days until the fat is saturated with essential oils. The flowery materials are then removed and the fat is digested with ethyl alcohol and cooled. The extract containing ethyl alcohol and essential oils is distilled under reduced preseure to remove the solvent.

Very recently, the activated coconut charcoal is used in place of fat owing to the greater stability and more surface as compared to fat.

3.2 Isolation of Natural Products as a Classroom Experiment

Natural products can also be isolated in a small scale as a classroom experiment by adapting modified procedures. Isolation of a few of such phytochemicals are discussed below.

3.2.1 Isolation of Nicotine from Tobacco

Tobacco plants belong to botanical family *Solanceac*. The commonly and widely used species from which tobacco is prepared is *Nicotiana tabacium*. The main constituent of this plant is an alkaloidal component–Nicotine. This nicotine, as we know, is deadly poison and causes various respiratory and circulatory diseases. It is isolated by the following procedure:

Procedure: About 50 g of tobacco is is taken in a 250 ml conical flask and to it 75 ml of concentrated NaOH solution is added. The mixture is warmed on a very low flame with constant shaking till a strong smell of tobacco begins to evolve. The flask with its content is cooled and is transferred to a separating funnel. About 100 ml ether is added, shaken gently and is allowed to stand for half an hour. Ether layer is collected in a beaker and is evaporated on keeping the beaker on hot water. The residue left is the desired nicotine. It is a colourless, volatile, oily liquid boiling at 245 °C. It has the following structure.

3.2.2 Isolation of **Piperine** from Pepper

Piperine is an alkaloidal **constituent** of black pepper. It belongs to piperidine skeleton family. it is isoalated by adapting the following procedure:

Procedure: 50 g of black pepper is dried under sunrays and crushed into powdery mass. It is taken in a one litre round-bottomed flask fitted with reflux condenser. About 500 ml of rectified spirit is taken into the flask and the mixture is refluxed on a water bath for 3-4 hours. After reflux the flask is cooled and filtered. The filtrate is concentrated to 50 ml by distillation. To this concentrate 50 ml of 2N ethanolic KOH solution is added with stirring and filtered. The filtrate is warmed on a water bath and 25 ml of water is added when a turbidity followed by yellow needles appear. It is allowed to stand for 2-3 hours and filtered again to get the crude piperine. It is crystallised from acetone when very fine needles of piperine is obtained, M.P. 128-130 °C, yield 0.25g. Piperine has been assigned the following structure.

3.2.3 Isolation of Casein and Lactose from Milk

Milk, one of the most important liquid food, contains proteins, fats, vitamins, minerals, carbohydrates and water. The major constituent of proteins present in milk is casein while carbohydrates present in milk is primarily a disaccharidic component–lactose. Both these components are isolated by the following process:

Procedure: About 200 ml of milk is taken in a 1 litre beaker and is diluted with 200 ml of water. The diluted milk is warmed to 40 °C on a water bath and to this hot solution 10% acetic acid is added dropwise until all the protein precipitates out. The beaker is allowed to stand for 5-10 minutes and the precipitate is filtered. The residue contains casein. It is washed successively with small amount of water, alcohol and ether, and washings are collected along with the filtrate for the isolation of lactose.

A. Working up of the residue (Casein): The washed residue is dissolved in 5% NaOH solution and is filtered. The filtrate is acidified with 10% acetic acid when precipitate of casein appears. It is washed with water and ethanol and finally dried. Casein is the phospho-protein. It is amorphous and hygroscopic white solid and is insoluble in organic solvents.

B. Treatment of the filtrate and washings (Lactose): The acidic filtrate left after the removal of casein is neutralised with 5% NaOH solution and boiled to precipitate out water soluble proteins (albumin). It is filtered and the filtrate is evaporated to a small volume and filtered again. Small amount of activated charcoal and ethanol are added. The mixture is boiled on water bath and filtered once again. The filtrate is again evaporated on a water bath. Ethanol is added to the syrupy liquid thus obtained and is allowed to stand for 15-20 minutes when lactose crystallises out. It is filtered, dried in a desiccator and weighed to get the yield.

As stated, lactose is a disaccharide with the following structure having melting point 250-254 °C.

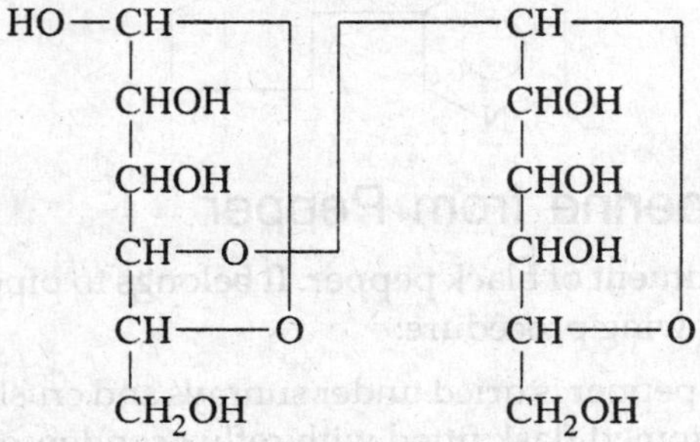

$$
\begin{array}{ll}
\text{HO—CH——} & \text{CH—} \\
\quad\text{CHOH} & \quad\text{CHOH} \\
\quad\text{CHOH} & \quad\text{CHOH} \\
\quad\text{CH—O—} & \quad\text{CHOH} \\
\quad\text{CH——O} & \quad\text{CH——O} \\
\quad\text{CH}_2\text{OH} & \quad\text{CH}_2\text{OH}
\end{array}
$$

3.2.4 Isolation of Caffeine from Tea Leaves

Caffeine is an alkaloid belonging to xanthine family and is one of the major constituent of tea leaves. It is isolated by the following process.

Procedure: Tea leaves are cut into small pieces and dried under sunrays. The dry leaves are crushed into powder. 50 g of powdered dry tea leaves are taken in a one litre beaker and 500 ml of water is added. It is boiled for half an hour, cooled and filtered. The filtrate is collected in a one litre beaker and to it 100 ml of 10% lead-acetate solution is added with stirring. After complete addition of lead acetate the mixture is kept undisturbed for 3-4 days to precipitate tannins completely. Next the content of the beaker is filtered through glass wool and the filtrate is concentrated to about 75 ml by heating on a sand bath. The concentrated solution is cooled and is extracted several times with chloroform by means of a separating funnel. All the chloroform extracts are collected together and chloroform is distilled off. The residue is cooled and to it 75 ml of petroleum ether (60-80 °C) is added and the mixture is stirred by a mechanical stirrer for 10-15 minutes. The mixture is allowed to stand for 5-10 minutes when crude caffeine is precipitated. It is filtered. It melts at 238 °C. It has the following structure.

$$
\begin{array}{c}
\quad\quad\quad\quad\text{O} \\
\quad\quad\quad\quad\|\\
\text{H}_3\text{C—N}\quad\quad\quad\quad\text{N—CH}_3 \\
\\
\text{O}\quad\quad\text{N}\quad\quad\text{N} \\
\quad\quad\quad|\\
\quad\quad\quad\text{CH}_3
\end{array}
$$

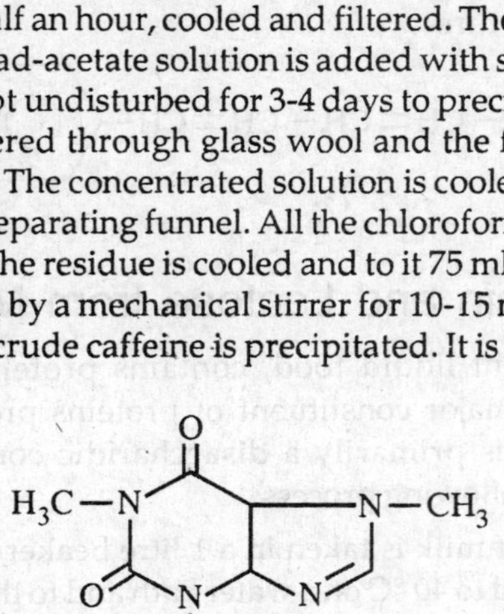

Chapter 4

Questions and Answers for Viva Voce

1. What is chromatography?

    Ans. It is one of the best physical methods for separation of the constituents of a mixture as well as an important method for purification of the chemical compound.

2. How many types of chromatography are in use?

    Ans. Different types of chromatography developed so far are (i) column chromatography (ii) paper chromatography (iii) thin-layer chromatography and (iv) gas chromatography.

3. What is the principle of paper chromatography?

    Ans. It is a kind of partition chromatography in which the substances are distributed between two liquids-one is statinary liquid usually water held in the fibre of the paper known as stationary phase and the other is the moving liquid or developing solvent and is normally known as moving phase. The components of the mixture to be separated migrate at different rates and appear as spots on the paper.

4. What is meant by R_f?

    Ans. R_f stands for retention factor or ratio of fronts. It is measured as the ratio of the distances travelled by the compound and the solvent.

5. How will you separate (a) Leaf pigments (b) amino acids and (c) sugars by paper chromatography?

    Ans. See Art. 1.1.1.2.1.1., .1.1.1.2.1.2. and 1.1.1.2.1.3.

6. How many types of components be separated and identified by thin-layer chromatography?

    Ans. TLC may be employed for the separation of cationic, anionic, purely covalent compounds and some organic derivatives.

7. How thin-layer chromatography is carried out?

    Ans. See Art. 1.1.1.3.

8. What are the major advantages of thin-layer chromatography?

   Ans. See Art. 1.1.1.3.

9. What developing solvent is to be used for separation of leaf pigments in TLC.

   Ans. Chloroform.

10. What is developing solvent usually used for separating amino acid by thin layer chromatography?

    Ans. *n*-Butanol-acetic acid-water (4:5:2).

11. What is the developing reagent normally used to identify amino acids in TLC?

    Ans. 1% Ninhydrin solution.

12. What is the basic principle of column chromatography?

    Ans. The basic principle of column chromatography is adsorption which is a surface phenomenon and so the degree of separation depends upon the surface area of the adsorbent.

13. What do you mean by—(i) Zone formation (ii) Elution (iii) Eluent.

    Ans. See Art. 1.1.1.1.

14. How the procedures for the separation of constituents by chemical methods have been classified?

    Ans. Procedures have been chlassified on the basis of properties of the components.

15. What are the different types of procedures available for separation of mixture by chemical methods?

    Ans. (i) Based on chemical properties (ii) based on volatilities in aqueous solution and (iii) based on physical properties.

16. How the mixture containing toluene and aniline can be separated?

    Ans. By treatment with dilute HCl.

17. What is the essential step for the separation of mixture by chemical method?

    Ans. Preliminary test of the mixture.

18. Why the preliminary tests of the mixture is considered as an essential step?

    Ans. It guides for planning the scheme for separation.

19. When the mixture contains a water insoluble acidic component what procedure is to be followed?

    Ans. Separation is to be carried out with sodium bicarbonate solution.

20. If the sample contains a basic component what procedure is to be adapted?

    Ans. Treatment with dilute HCl, filtration and the treatment of filtrate with dilute sodium hydroxide solution.

SECTION III

PHYSICAL CHEMISTRY
PRACTICAL

Introduction

It is known that *chemistry* is the science which deals with the transformation of matter, i.e., properties of matter while its branch of *Physical Chemistry* may be looked upon as the science which concerns itself with the laws governing these transformation and the effect of various physical factors such as temperature, pressure, concentration, light and electricity on these transformations. It is also the purpose of physical chemistry to organise and systematise theories underlying the various processes involved in chemistry. Consequently experiments in physical chemistry laboratory are designed to provide knowledge regarding the properties of matter. Some of such experiments as included in the syllabus of general and honours courses in chemistry of most of the Indian universities are discussed in sequel.

Chapter 1

Experiments on Physical Chemistry

1.1 Determination of pH of a Buffer Solution by Colour Matching of Indicator

Theory: The resistance of a solution to change in H^+ ion concentration upon the addition of small quantity of acid or base is termed as *Buffer action* and the solutions which possess such properties are known as *Buffer solutions*, or simply *Buffers*.

Buffer solutions usually consist of mixtures of solutions of weak acid or base and its salt. The pH of a buffer solution can be easily determined by colour matching of indicator. The method involves the addition of definite volume of a suitable indicator solution to buffrer solutions having known pH when buffer solutions with different known pH will have different shades of colour. Now to the experimental buffer solution same volume of the same indicator solution is added. The colour produced is then compared with the colour produced in buffer solutions of known pH. When a complete matching is obtained the experimental solution will have the same pH as of that buffer solution with which matching has been done.

Reagents required:

1. Acetic acid (0.2N)

2. Sodium acetate solution (0.2N)

3. Bromo cresol green indicator.

Procedure

(a) **Preparation of buffer solutions of known pH:** A series of buffer solutions of known pH are prepared by mixing different volumes of 0.2N acetic acid and 0.2N sodium acetate solution as shown in the table below. It may be mentioned that 0.2N sodium acetate solution is prepared by dissolving accurately weighed quantity of sodium acetate (A.R.) in a definite volume of water or by mixing equal volume of 0.4N acetic acid and 0.4N NaOH solutions.

Buffer solutions of known pH

No. of Test tube	Volume of acetic acid (0.2N)	Volume of sodium acetate (0.2N)	pH
1	9 ml	1 ml	3.72
2	8 ml	2 ml	4.05
3	7 ml	3 ml	4.27
4	6 ml	4 ml	4.45
5	5 ml	5 ml	4.63
6	4 ml	6 ml	4.80
7	3 ml	7 ml	4.99
8	2 ml	8 ml	5.23
9	1 ml	9 ml	5.57

(b) **Determination of pH of the unknown buffer solution**: Nine test tubes of equal width are taken and in each test tube 10 ml of buffer solution with different pH are taken. Test tubes are marked 1, 2, 3, 4,..., 9, where number indicates pH level, i.e. the pH of the solution in test tube number 1 is 3.72, that in test tube number 2 is 4.05 and so on. To each test tube equal volume (5 drops) of bromo cresol green or any suitable indicator is added. In another test tube 10 ml of buffer solution of unknown pH is taken and same volume (5 drops) of same indicator is added. The colour developed in this test tube is compared with the colour of the buffer solutions of other test tubes. The pH of the buffer solution which shows the best matching in colour is taken as the pH of the unknown (supplied) solution. Similar experiment is repeated two to three times to get the concordant result.

Conclusion: The colour of unknown buffer solution shows the best match with the colour of the buffer solution in test tube number ... which has pH ... . Hence the pH of the unknown buffer solutions is ... .

Comments

(i) This method gives an approximate value of pH.

(ii) If needed, 0.2N sodium acetate solution may be prepared as mentioned earlier by mixing exactly equal volumes of 0.4N solutions of acetic acid and NaOH. These two solutions (acetic acid and sodium hydroxide) are prepared in the usual ways.

1.2 Determination of Distribution Coefficient of an Organic Acid between Water and an Organic Solvent

Theory: When a particular solute soluble in two immiscible solvents is allowed to distribute between these two solvents, the ratio of the concentration of that particular solute in these two immiscible solvents remains constant. Thus if C_1 is the concentration in one solvent and C_2 in other solvent, their C_1/C_2 ratio is a constant quantity. However, this formula may be changed depending upon the nature of the solute in two solvents. If both exist as monomer in both the solvents, then C_1/C_2 ratio is a constant, but if it exists as n-mer in solvent 1, then the factor is $\dfrac{\sqrt[n]{C_1}}{C_2}$ constant but not C_1/C_2. These constants are known as *partition coefficient*.

Let us consider the distribution of an organic acid, benzoic acid, in two immiscible solvents—water and benzene. It has been observed that when benzoic acid is allowed to distribute between benzene and water, it (benzoic acid) remains as a monomer in water and as a dimer in benzene. It is thus, reasonable that in this case $\dfrac{\sqrt{C_1}}{C_2}$ will be a constant quantity, where C_1 is the concentration of benzoic acid in benzene and C_2 is that of the same in water.

Chemicals required:

1. Benzoic acid (A.R.)
2. Benzene
3. NaOH solution ($N/10$)
4. Phenolphthalein indicator.

Procedure: In three stoppered bottles of 250 ml capacity the following mixtures are prepared.

Bottle No.	Volume of benzene 'ml	Volume of water ml	Weight of benzoic acid taken (g)
1	40	60	1.00
2	40	60	1.50
3	40	60	2.00

The bottles are well stoppered and are shaken for about 45 minutes in a mechanical shaker. After completion of the shaking, the mixtures are allowed to stand for about half an hour so that the two layers separate out completely. Benzene being lighter than water, it exists in upper layer while water remains in the lower layer.

From each bottle, 5 ml of benzene layer is pipetted out into a 100 ml conical flask and is titrated with ($N/10$) NaOH solution in presence of phenolphthalein as indicator. Similar experiment is repeated twice.

In the similar way, 20 ml of water layer is pipetted out from each bottle and is titrated against ($N/10$) NaOh solution using phenolphthalein indicator. Similar experiment is repeated twice to get concordant burette readings. Room temperature is noted.

Result: Room temperature ... °C.

Bottle No.	Titration of Benzene layer		Titration of water layer		Concentration of benzoic acid		$\dfrac{C_B}{C_W}$	$\dfrac{\sqrt{C_B}}{C_W}$
	Volume layer taken	Volume of NaOH required	Volume of layer taken	Volume of NaOH required	Benzene layer	Water layer		
1	5 ml	V_1 ml	20 ml	x_1 ml	a	d		
2	5 ml	V_2 ml	20 ml	x_2 ml	b	e		
3	5 ml	V_3 ml	20 ml	x_3 ml	c	f		

Calculations: Let the strength of NaOH is S(N/10). Concentrations of benzoic acid in benzene and water in each bottle are calculated utilising the formula, $S_1V_1 = S_2V_2$. From these concentrations,

ratios C_B/C_W and $\dfrac{\sqrt{C_B}}{C_W}$ are calculated in each case, where C_B and C_W indicate concentrations of benzoic acid in benzene and water layers.

From the above results it is evident that $\dfrac{\sqrt{C_B}}{C_W}$ is practically constant. So it can be concluded that benzoic acid exists as dimer in benzene layer which is in equilibrium with monomers in the water layer.

Comments

(i) Shaking of the solution must be for sufficient time for uniform mixing.

(ii) During pipetting out care should be taken so that one layer must not be contaminated with other layer.

(iii) Temperature should be noted carefully.

1.3 Determination of Partition Coefficient of Iodine between Water and an Organic Solvent

Theory: It is known that when a solute is allowed to distribute between two immiscible solvents, the distribution occurs in such a way that the ratio of concentration of the solute in two solvents is a constant at a constant temperature, if following conditions are fulfilled.

(i) The solute dissolves in both the solvents.

(ii) No chemical reaction occurs and

(iii) the solute does not undergo any association or dissociation.

This constant is known as *Partition Coefficient* of the solute.

Partition coefficient of iodine between water and an organic solvent may be determined following titrimetric method as discussed below.

Reagents required:

1. Iodine
2. Sodium thiosulphate
3. Potassium dichromate
4. Starch indicator
5. Benzene.

Procedure: A $(N/10)$ $Na_2S_2O_3$ solution is prepared and is standardised with a standard $(N/10)$ $K_2Cr_2O_7$ solution. In a dry stoppered bottle 100 ml of pure benzene is taken and a saturated solution of iodine is prepared by shaking with solid iodine (A.R.) in a mechanical shaker for 30 minutes. Three stoppered reagent bottles are taken and labelled as 1, 2, 3. In each of these bottles saturated iodine solution just prepared, pure benzene and distilled water are taken as tabulated below.

Bottle No.	Volume of I_2 solution taken	Volume of pure benzene taken	Volume of distilled water taken
1	25 ml	5 ml	50 ml
2	20 ml	10 ml	50 ml
3	15 ml	15 ml	50 ml

Each bottle after taking the above liquids are well stoppered (if necessary, rubber sheet and cotton may be used) and shaken for about an hour in a mechanical shaker and then is allowed to stand for 20 minutes so that water and benzene layers are well separated.

From each bottle 5 ml of benzene is pipetted out into a 100 ml conical flask and is titrated with $(N/10)$ $Na_2S_2O_3$ solution in presence of starch solution as indicator. Similar experiment is repeated twice to get concordant burette readings.

In the similar fashion 20 ml of water is pipetted out from each of the bottle and titrated against $(N/10)$ $Na_2S_2O_3$ solution in the presence of starch solution in the usual way. Similar experiment is repeated two to three times. Finally room temperatue is recorded.

Results: Room temperature : ...

Strength of $K_2Cr_2O_7$ solution = $S(N/10)$

Strength of $Na_2S_2O_3$ solution = $S_1(N/10)$

Bottle No.	Volume of each layer taken		Volume of $Na_2S_2O_3$ solution required for		Concentration of I_2 in molarity		$K(C_1/C_2)$
	Benzene layer	Aqueous layer	Benzene layer	Aqueous layer	In Benzene layer C_1	In Aqueous layer C_2	
1	5 ml	20 ml	V_1 ml	x_1 ml			
2	5 ml	20 ml	V_2 ml	x_2 ml			
3	5 ml	20 ml	V_3 ml	x_3 ml			

In each layer for each bottle concentration of iodine is calculated utilising $S_1 V_1 = S_2 V_2$ formula and from these concentrations C_1/C_2 ratios are calculated for each bottle and average value is taken.

Conclusion: From the above results, it is thus evident that the partition coefficient of iodine between benzene and water is .... at °C temperature.

Comments

(i) During pipetting out of the iodine solution for titrations, care should be taken so that one layer must not be contaminated with other.

(ii) Temperature should be carefully noted.

(iii) Shaking of the solution must be for sufficient time for uniform mixing.

(iv) In place of benzene, other organic solvent such as chloroform, carbon tetrachloride, etc. may be used.

1.4 Determination of the Equilibrium Constant of the Reaction, $KI + I_2 \rightleftharpoons KI_3$ by Partition Method

Theory: When I_2 is allowed to distribute in KI solution a complex, KI_3, is formed and an equilibrium is established. Thus,

$$KI + I_2 \rightleftharpoons KI_3 \tag{I}$$

The equilibrium constant of the above reaction may be written according to law of mass action as

$$K = \frac{[KI_3]}{[KI][I_2]}, \tag{II}$$

where $[KI_3]$, $[KI]$ and $[I_2]$ refer to the concentrations of substances in equilibrium. Thus, from the equation (II) it is evident that knowing the concentrations of KI_3, KI and I_2, the equilibrium constant, K, at a constant temperature can be determined.

It may, however, be remembered that after equilibrium is reached, concentration of free iodine cannot be directly determined by titration with standard sodium thiosulphate solution because the gradual removal of iodine during titration will cause the shifting of the equilibrium (I) towards left and more KI_3 will dissociate into KI and I_2. For this reason, to estimate the concentration of free iodine at equilibrium a saturated solution of iodine in water-immiscible solvents such as benzene, chloroform, carbon tetrachloride, etc. are used. In this situation iodine is distributed between water-immiscible solvent and KI solution, and free iodine remains in the free-state in the organic layer, but will react as usual with KI in aqueous layer to form the equilibrium (I).

The concentration of free iodine in organic layer can be estimated by direct titration with sodium thiosulphate solution and so the concentration of free iodine in aqueous layer can be calculated from the following formula.

$$\frac{\text{Concentration of free iodine in organic layer}}{\text{Concentration of free iodine in aqueous layer}} = K_d,$$

where K_d is the partition coefficient of iodine in between water and the organic solvent. Therefore,

$$\text{concentration of free iodine in aqueous layer} = \frac{\text{Concentration of free iodine in organic layer}}{K_d}.$$

Again, titration of the aqueous layer by sodium thiosulphate solution gives the total concentration of iodine. If the concentration of free iodine is subtracted from the total concentration of iodine, equilibrium concentration (concentration in the equilibrium state) of iodine will be obtained. The concentrations of KI_3 and KI in the equilibrium can now be determined by calculations as below.

Let us assume that the initial concentration of KI solution is c moles/litre.

Concentration of free iodine in organic layer = c_1 moles/litre.

Concentratioon of free iodine in aqueous layer = c_1/K_d moles/litre.   (III)

Total concentration of free iodine in aqueous layer as determined by direct titration = c_2 moles/litre.

Now equilibrium concentration of KI_3 = total concentration of iodine in aqueous layer – concentration of free iodine in aqueous layer = $(c_2 - c_1/K_d)$ moles/litre.   (IV)

Again as 1 mole of KI_3 is formed from 1 mole of KI, the concentration of KI at equilibrium is equal to initial concentration of KI – equilibrium concentration of KI_3,

i.e., $c - [c_2 - c_1/K_d]$ moles/litre.   (V)

Now knowing the concentrations (IV), (III) and (V), the equilibrium constant of the reaction K can be computed as

$$K = \frac{(IV)}{(III) \times (V)}.$$

Reagents required:

1. KI
2. I_2
3. Organic solvent ($CHCl_3$, CCl_4 or C_6H_6)
4. $Na_2S_2O_3$
5. Starch indicator
6. $K_2Cr_2O_7$.

Procedure: A standard (N/10) $K_2Cr_2O_7$ is prepared by accurately weighing $K_2Cr_2O_7$ and is used for standardisation of (N/10) thiosulphate solution.

(N/10) KI solution is prepared by accurately weighing pure KI. From this solution nearly (N/100) KI solution is prepared by the method of dilution.

In a dry stoppered bottle (500 ml) a saturated solution of iodine in CCl_4 or benzene is prepared by shaking in a mechanical shaker for half an hour.

Two stoppered bottle (500 ml capacity) are taken and they are labelled as 1 and 2. Two bottles are filled up with liquids having following compositions.

Bottle No.	Volume of saturated solution of I_2 in CCl_4 (ml)	Volume of CCl_4 (ml)	Volume of KI solution
1	15 ml	5 ml	100 ml of (N/10)
2	10 ml	10 ml	100 ml of (N/100)

The bottles are well stoppered (if needed, rubber sheet and cotton may be used) and vigorously shaken by a mechanical shaker for an hour. Next the bottles are allowed to stand for at least 20 minutes so that aqueous and organic layers are completely separated.

Now 10 ml of iodine solution from CCl_4 layer from the bottle no. 1 is pipitted out into a 250 ml conical flask, to it little water and KI solution are added and titrated with standard $Na_2S_2O_3$ solution. In this way concentrations of I_2 in other bottles are determined.

Results: Room temperature .... °C

No. of observation	Original strength of KI in g-mole /litre	Volume of saturated I_2 in CCl_4 layer	Concentration of I_2 in CCl_4 layer in g-mole /litre	Concentration of free iodine in g-mole /litre	Concentration of total I_2 in aqueous layer in g-mole /litre	Equilibrium concentration of KI_3 in aqueous layer in g-mole /litre	Equilibrium concentration of KI in g-mole /litre
1							
2							
3							

From the above, equilibrium constants are calculated for each bottle according to equation (II), and mean value is taken.

1.5 Determination of Rate Constant of a First Order Reaction (Acid Hydrolysis of an Ester) by Titrimetric Method

Theory: Hydrolysis of methyl acetate in acid medium takes place as

$$CH_3COOCH_3 + H_2O \xrightarrow{\text{Acid}} CH_3COOH + CH_3OH \qquad (1)$$

It is a first order reaction and the rate of hydrolysis may be expressed as

$$\frac{dx}{dt} = K_1[CH_3COOCH_3][H_2O]. \qquad (2)$$

But since water is present in large excess its change in concentration is very negligible. So $[H_2O]$ remains practically constant. Thus, the rate equation (2) may be written as

$$\frac{dx}{dt} = K[CH_3COOH]$$

$$\text{where } K = K_1[H_2O] = \text{constant.} \qquad (3)$$

The constant, K, is the rate constant for the hydrolysis of methyl ester. Now if a is the initial concentration of ester in g-mole/litre and x is the concentration of ester in g-mole/litre after time 't', then the rate equation (3) may be written as

$$\frac{dx}{dt} = K(a-x) \quad \text{or,} \quad \frac{dx}{ax} = Kdt.$$

Integrating we get

$$-\ln(a-x) = Kt + I,\qquad(4)$$

where I is the integration constant.

when $t = 0$, x is also 0, the equation (4) becomes

$$-\ln a = I.$$

Thus, the above equation (4) may be rewritten as

$$-\ln(a-x) = Kt - \ln a$$

$$\text{or,} \quad -\ln(a-x) + \ln a = Kt$$

$$\text{or,} \quad \ln\frac{a}{a-x} = Kt$$

$$\text{or,} \quad 2.303 \log\frac{a}{a-x} = Kt\qquad(5)$$

$$\text{or,} \quad K = \frac{2.303}{t} \log\frac{a}{a-x}.\qquad(6)$$

As the reaction (1) proceeds, methyl acetate is gradually converted to equivalent amount of acetic acid, hence the progress of the reaction can be studied by titrating the equivalent acid produced by a standard alkali. If V_0, V_t and V_∞ be the volumes of alkali required to neutralise a definite quantity of the reaction mixture at the beginning, after time t and at the end of the reaction respectively, then $a \propto (V_\infty - V_0)$ and $(a - x) \propto (V_\infty - V_t)$ and so the equation (5) may be expressed as

$$\log\frac{(V_\infty - V_0)}{(V_\infty - V_t)} = \frac{K}{2.303} \times t$$

If $\log\dfrac{V_\infty - V_0}{V_\infty - V_t}$ is plotted against t, the time, a straight line is obtained which passes through the origin. The slope of the straight line is $\dfrac{K}{2.303}$ from which the rate constant K can be calculated.

Reagents required:
  1. Methyl acetate
  2. $(N/2)$ HCl
  3. $(N/20)$ NaOH solution.

Procedure: About 200 ml of $(N/2)$ HCl is prepared by diluting 8.5 ml of concentrated HCl to 200 ml. 250 ml of $(N/20)$ NaOH solution is prepared by dissolving 0.5 g of NaOH in 250 ml of water.

In a 100 ml conical flask 25 ml of $(N/2)$ HCl is taken and the flask is placed in the thermostat. In another small bottle freshly distilled methyl acetate is taken and also placed in the thermostat.

When both $(N/2)$ HCl and methyl acetate have attained the temperature of the bath, 2 ml of methyl acetate is pipetted out by a graduated pipette and is added to the $(N/2)$ HCl (kept in thermostat).

The mixture is shaken well and immediately 2 ml of the reaction mixture is withdrawn by a pipette and is added to 100 ml ice cold water in a 250 ml conical flask to arrest the reaction. The time of half discharge of the mixture from the pipette is noted and the mixture is immediately titrated with (N/20) NaOH solution using phenolphthalein as indicator. The titre value corresponds to V_0. This process of withdrawing 2 ml of reaction mixture and putting it into the ice-cold water and titrating the mixture against the same (N/20) NaOH solution is repeated at 5, 10, 15, 20, 25 and 30 minutes noting each time the time of half discharge from the pipette. These titre values correspond to V_t at different times t.

To find out the reading at infinite time (V_∞), the flask containing the reaction mixture is properly stoppered and kept in a water bath maintained at about the temperature of 70 °C for nearly an hour. Now 2 ml of this solution is pipetted out into a conical flask and is titrated against the same (N/20) NaOH solution in presence of phenolphthalein indicator. The graph of $\log \dfrac{V_\infty - V_0}{V_\infty - V_t}$ versus t, the time is plotted as in the figure and from the slope of the straight line thus obtained, the rate constant is determined.

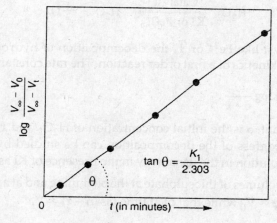

Results: Temperature of the thermostat .... °C.

Volume of reaction mixture withdrawn for each titration = 2 ml.

Time in minutes	Volume of (N/20) NaOH solution required (V_t ml)	$\dfrac{V_\infty - V_0}{V_\infty - V_t}$	$\log \dfrac{V_\infty - V_0}{V_\infty - V_t}$
0	V_0		
5			
10			
15			
20			
25			
30			
∞	V_∞		

Conclusion: From the slope of the straight line as in the figure, the value of rate constant K becomes ......

Comments

(i) The value of rate constant is dependant upon temperature, so temperature of the theremostat must be kept constant during the experiment.

(ii) Titrations must be completed as quickly as possible.

(iii) Distilled water used must be free from carbon dioxide.

1.6 Determination of Rate Constant of Decomposition of Hydrogen Peroxide by Acidified Potassium Iodide

Theory: Decomposition of hydrogen peroxide occurs as

$$H_2O_2 \xrightarrow[\text{KI or FeCl}_3]{\text{Catalyst}} H_2O + \tfrac{1}{2}O_2$$

In presence of catalyst like Fe^{3+} or $\bar{I}$, the deocmposition of hydrogen peroxide proceeds smoothly and follows the kinetics of a first order reaction. The rate constant of this decomposition may be written as $\dfrac{Kt}{2.303} = \log \dfrac{a}{a-x}$

where K is the rate constant, a is the initial concentration of H_2O_2 and x is the concentration of H_2O_2 after time t. The progress of the decomposition can be studied by titrating the peroxide present by thiosulphate solution in the usual way in the presence of KI as catalyst.

In V_0 and V_t are the volumes of thiosulphate at the beginning and at any time t, then the initial concentration of H_2O_2 is $a \propto V_0$ while that of at time t is $(a - x) \propto V_t$.

$$\therefore \quad \frac{a}{a-x} = \frac{V_0}{V_t}.$$

Hence $\log \dfrac{V_0}{V_t} = \dfrac{K.t}{2.303}.$

When $\log \dfrac{V_0}{V_t}$ is plotted against the time t a straight line passing through the origin is obtained.

The slope of the straight line is $\dfrac{K}{2.303}$ from which the rate constant K can be calculated.

Reagents required:

1. H_2O_2 (2 volumes)

2. KI (10%)

3. $Na_2S_2O_3$ (N/10)

4. Starch indicator

5. 5% H_2SO_4

6. Ammonium molybdate solution.

Procedure: About 250 ml of 2 volumes hydrogen peroxide is prepared. Following solutions are also prepared (i) 100 ml of 10% KI solution (ii) 250 ml 5% H_2SO_4 and 500 ml $(N/10)$ $Na_2S_2O_3$ solution.

In each of the five different 250 ml conical flasks 10 ml of 10% KI, 25 ml of 5% H_2SO_4 and 1 ml ammonium molybdate solutions are taken and a few pices of ice are added to each flask.

In a 250 ml concial flask 100 ml of 2 volume H_2O_2 is taken and is placed in a thermostat. Bottle of KI solution is also placed in the thermostat. When the solutions have attained the temperature of the bath, 5 ml of 10% KI solution is added to hydrogen peroxide, shaken and the time is noted. This is the starting time.

10 ml of the reaction mixture is pipetted out into each of the five conical flasks containing KI, H_2SO_4 and molybdate solutions at a regular intervals of 5 minutes. Iodine is liberated which is titrated by $(N/10)$ $Na_2S_2O_3$ solution in presence of starch as indicator. The titre value corresponds to V_t at different times.

The graph of $\log \dfrac{V_0}{V_t}$ against the time 't' is plotted when a straight line is obtained and from the slope of the straight line, the rate constant is calculated.

Results: Temperature of the thermostat .... °C.

Volume of reaction mixture withdrawn for each titration = 10 ml.

Time in minutes	Volume of $(N/10)$ $Na_2S_2O_3$ required $(V_t$ ml$)$	$\dfrac{V_0}{V_t}$	$\log \dfrac{V_0}{V_t}$
0	V_0		
5			
10			
15			
20			

1.7 Solubility and Solubility Product of a Sparingly Soluble Salt

General discussion: In the case of solutions of solids in liquids, the liquid is invariably known as *solvent* and the solid dissolving in it is referred to as *solute*.

If in a given amount of solvent, maintained at a particular temperature, a solute is added in increasing amounts, a stage is reached when some amount of solute remains undissolved even after vigorous stirring. The solution thus obtained is known as *saturated solution of the solute*.

The amount of solute dissolved in one litre of solvent so as to give a saturated solution at that temperature and pressure is known as *solubility*.

In a saturated solution there exists an equilibrium between the dissolved and undissolved solute.

$$\text{Solute (Solid in solution)} \rightleftharpoons \text{Solute dissolved in solution}$$
$$\text{(BA)} \qquad\qquad\qquad\qquad\qquad \text{(BA)}$$

Again, when solute is dissolved in solvent, it is ionised.

Thus, Solute dissolved in solution (BA) $\rightleftharpoons$ B^+ + $\bar{A}$
$\qquad$ (BA)

Therefore, according to law of mass action,

$$K = \frac{[B^+] \times [A^-]}{[BA]},$$

where K is equilibrium constant and $[BA]$, $[B^+]$ and $[A^-]$ are the respective molar concentrations.

$\therefore K \times [BA] = [B^+] \times [A^-] = K_a$ (constant)

This constant is known as solubity product and is usually denoted as K_{sp} i.e., product of ionic concentration in saturated solution.

Again, since the solution is very dilute, in saturated solution, the salt is assumed to be completely dissociated and the concentrations of the ions are

$$[B^+] = c, [A^-] = c = S \text{ (solubility of solute)},$$

where c is the molar concentration of the salt in the solution which is nothing but solubility of the salt in the solvent at that particular temperature. Thus, the solubility product of the salt BA is

$$[B^+] \times [A^-] = c \times c = S \times S = S^2.$$

In general, the solubility of a salt of the type $A_p B_q$ in pure water is $S^p \times S^q = S^{p+q}$.

This is the relation between the solubility and and solubility product. From this relation it may be concluded that an estimation of solubility enables us to determine the solubility product. It may be mentioned that solubility of a solute in a given solvent varies appreciably with temperature. In general, higher the temperature greater is the solubility.

1.7.1 Determination of Solubility of a Sparingly Soluble Salt (Silver Acetate) by Titrimetric Method

Theory: When solid silver acetate is dissolved in water it dissociates as

$$CH_3COOAg \rightleftharpoons Ag^+ + CH_3COO^-$$
$$\text{Silver acetate}$$
$$\text{(solid)}$$

If S is the solubility of silver acetate at given temperature, then

$$S = C_{Ag^+} = C_{CH_3COO^-}$$

where C_{Ag^+} and $C_{CH_3COO^-}$ are the molar concentrations of Ag^+ and CH_3COO^- in a saturated solution. The solubility of silver acetate is determined by titrating Ag^+ against standard solution of ammonium thiocyanate solution.

Reagents required:

1. Silver acetate (A.R.)
2. HNO_3 (6N)
3. Ammonium thiocyanate solution ($N/20$)
4. $AgNO_3$ solution ($N/10$)
5. Ferric ammonium sulphate (saturated solution).

Procedure

(a) **Standardisation of ammonium thiocyanate solution by standard silver nitrate solution:** Approximately 0.4245 g of $AgNO_3$ (A.R.) is accurately weighed and dissolved in 250 ml of distilled water in a volumetric flask to get a ($N/100$) $AgNO_3$ solution. In another conical flask of 500 ml capacity 2.2 g of ammonium thiocyanate is dissolved in 500 ml of distilled water.

25 ml of $AgNO_3$ ($N/100$) solution is pipetted out into a 250 ml conical flask. To it 5 ml of (6N)HNO_3 and 1 ml of saturated solution of ferric ammonium sulphate solution (indicator) are added. This solution-mixture is now titrated with ammonium thiocyanate solution taken in a burette slowly with constant shaking until a faint brown colour persists. Similar experiment is repeated thrice to get concordant burette readings. From the average titre value, strength of thiocyanate solution is calculated using $S_1V_1 = S_2V_2$ formula.

(b) **Determination of solubility of silver acetate:** In a 250 ml beaker about 150 ml of water is taken and to it some amount of silver acetate is added and stirred well. When the solid completely dissolves some more amount of silver acetate is added and stirred well. This process of addition of silver acetate is continued until some amount of silver acetate remains undissolved even after vigorous stirring.

A 25 ml pipette is taken and at its tip some cotton is attached to prevent the entry of the solid matter. With this pipette 50 ml of supernatant liquid is pipetted out into 500 ml conical falsk and to it 5 ml of (6N)HNO_3 and 1 ml of ferric ammonium sulphate are added. This solution is then titrated with standard ammonium thiocyanate as in the case of its standardisation discribed in (a). Similar experiment is repeated thrice. Temperatures of the solution of silver acetate just at the beginning and at the end are noted.

Results

Temperature at the beginning = ... °C

Temperature at the end = ... °C

Average temperature ... °C

Strength of ammonium thiocyanate solution = S ($N/100$).

No. of observation	Volume of silver acetate solution taken	Volume of ammonium of thiocyanate required	Concentration of Ag^+	Solubility of Ag acetate
1	25 ml	V_1	S_1	S_1
2	25 ml	V_2	S_2	S_2
3	25 ml	V_3	S_3	S_3

Conclusion: The average solubility of silver acetate in water is S = ... g/litre.

1.7.2 Determination of Solubility of a Given Substance in Water at Different Temperatures and Construction of Solubility Curves

Theory: It is known that solubility of a solute in a given solvent varies with temperature. Generally speaking, higher the temperature, greater is the solubility. However, only in a few cases such as calcium sulphate, calcium hydroxide, etc. solubility decreases with the rise in temperature. The solubilities of substances at different temperatures may be expressed by graphs of temperature against solubility. Such graphs are known as *solubility curves*. The study of variation of solubility with temperatures and construction of solubility curve may be elaborated taking potassium nitrate as an example. For this purpose, a *definite amount of water* is taken and is raised to a definite temperature. At this temperature a *definite amount of potassium* nitrate is added with constant stirring maintaining the same temperature. At this temperature a definite amount of solution is pipetted out with dry pipette into a previously weighed porcelain dish. Water is evaporated to dryness and the dish is weighed again. From this amount of potassium nitrate dissolved at that temperature may be calculated.

Reagents required:

KNO$_3$

Apparatus required:

1. Porcelain dish
2. Thermometers
3. Water bath.

Procedure: In a 500 ml beaker 200 ml of water, 50 g of potassium nitrate are taken. The beaker with all its content is placed on a water bath, and a thermometer is dipped into the beaker. The temperature is raised to 75 °C and this temperature is maintained constant with continuous stirring for 5 minutes. With a dry pipette 25 ml of the saturated solution is withdrawn and is transferred to a preweighed porcelain dish and its weight is taken. The solution is evaporated to dryness on a water bath, cooled in a desiccator and the weight of the porcelain is taken again. Similar experiment is repeated once again to get the concordant result.

Now the temperature is allowed to fall at 50 °C and the solubility is determined as before. Similar experiments at 40 °C and 30 °C are repeated to find out the solubilities of potassium nitrate at those temperatures. A graph is drawn by plotting solubility against temperature.

Results

No. of observation	Temperature (in °C)	Weight of porcelain dish (g)	Weight of porcelain dish and solution (g)	Weight of porcelain dish and residue (g)	Weight of residue (g)	Weight of water (g)
1	60	x_1	y_1	z_1	$(z_1 - x_1)$	$(y_1 - z_1)$
2	50	x_2	y_2	z_2	$(z_2 - x_2)$	$(y_2 - z_2)$
3	40	x_3	y_3	z_3	$(z_3 - x_3)$	$(y_3 - z_3)$
4	30	x_4	y_4	z_4	$(z_4 - x_4)$	$(y_4 - z_4)$

Calculation: Solubility of KNO_3

at 40 °C $\quad \dfrac{(z_1 - x_1)}{(y_1 - z_1)} \times 100 = a_1$

at 30 °C $\quad \dfrac{(z_2 - x_2)}{(y_2 - z_2)} \times 100 = a_2$

at 20 °C $\quad \dfrac{(z_3 - x_3)}{(y_3 - z_3)} \times 100 = a_3$

at 10 °C $\quad \dfrac{(z_3 - x_3)}{(y_3 - z_3)} \times 100 = a_4$

The solubility values a_1, a_2, a_3 and are plotted respectively against 40 °C, 30 °C, 20 °C and 10 °C and the following curve is obtained.

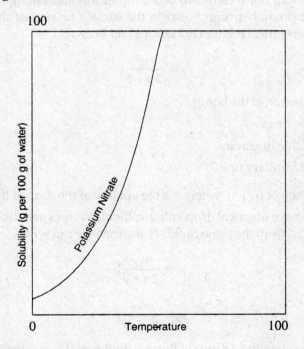

Result: The solubility of KNO_3 at .... °C is ....

1.8 Determination of Surface Tension of a Given Liquid by Drop Weight Method

General discussion: Surface tension is an important property of liquids. A partiucular molecule present in the bulk of the liquid is attracted equally in all directions by other molecules surrounding that particular molecule and so cancel the effect of one another. But when the particular molecule is present at the surface the downward attractive forces are greater than the upward forces because in downward direction there are more molecules of the liquid than in the air above the surface. This unbalanced attractive force acting downward tends to draw the surface molecules into the body of the liquid. As a result surface is reduced to a minimum. The liquid thus behaves, as if it is under a strain or tension. It is this contracting force which is termed as *surface tension*. Hence, *surface tension* may be defined as *the forces in* dynes *acting along the surface of a liquid at right angles to one* centimetre *length of the surface*. Its unit is dynes/cm. It is the surface tension which accounts for the tendency of the drops of a liquid to become spherical because *in a sphere the surface area is minimum* for a *given volume*. The surface tension also explains many common phenomena such as the rise of a liquid in a capillary tube, rise of oil in wick of a lamp, upward movement of water in soils, etc.

A variety of methods are available for the measurement of surface tension among which *Drop Weight Method* is most convenient and is commonly used.

Drop Weight Method

Theory: In drop weight method the relative surface tension is measured. This method is based on the principle that the weight (m) of a drop of a liquid falling from a vertically held capillary tube is approximately proportional to the surface tension of the liquid and may be expressed by the semi-empirical relation of Harkins and Brown.

$$\gamma = \frac{mg}{2\pi r \psi} \tag{1}$$

where γ is the surface tension of the liquid,

m, the weight of the drop

g, the acceleration due to gravity

r, the radius of the capillary tip

and ψ is the function of $(r/v^{\frac{1}{3}})$, where v is the volume of the drop of the liquid.

When two liquids have identical drop volume, their ψ values are also the same. If two such liquids are allowed to fall from the same capillary tip, then we can write,

$$\gamma_1 = \frac{m_1 g}{2\pi r \psi} \tag{2}$$

$$\gamma_2 = \frac{m_2 g}{2\pi r \psi} \tag{3}$$

where m_1 and m_2 are the weights of drops of the two liquids and γ_1, γ_2 are their respective surface tensions. Thus, we can write,

$$\frac{\gamma_1}{\gamma_2} = \frac{m_1}{m_2} \tag{4}$$

Thus, measuring m_1 and m_2, surface tension of one liquid may be determined if that of other is known.

Again, $m_1 = V_1 \rho_1$ and $m_2 = V_2 \rho_2$, where V_1 and V_2 are the volumes occupied by the drops and ρ_1 and ρ_2 are the respective densities of the two liquids. Thus, equation (4) may be written as

$$\frac{\gamma_1}{\gamma_2} = \frac{V_1 \rho_1}{V_2 \rho_2}.$$

If one of the liquids be water, then its density and and surface tension are known. So from the determination of density of unknown liquid and measuring V_1 and V_2, the surface tesion of the unknown liquid may be calculated.

Procedure: The liquid is taken in a clean *Stalagnometer*. It is a pipette-like tube one end of which is a uniform capillary tube. It is graduated for measuring the fraction of the drop. The design of a typical *stalagnometer* is shown below.

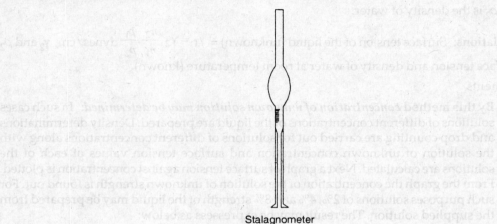

Stalagnometer

Water is sucked into this stalagnometer just up to the top mark of the tube and is allowed to fall slowly in such a rate that one drop falls in every four seconds. The number of drops are accurately counted until the water level moves from the upper mark to the lower mark. The volume of water between upper and lower marks in the tube is also noted. From this, the volume of one drop is calculated.

Now the stalagnometer tube is dried by passing out hot air through it and the similar experiment is carried out with the unknown solution. Volume of one drop of unknown liquid is calculated. Next the density of unknown liquid is determined with the help of a specific gravity bottle or a pyknometer.

Results: Room temperature during the experiment ..... °C

A. Determination of n_2/n_1

No. of observation	No. of drops of water falling for volume v (n_2)	No. of drops of unknown liquid falling for volume v (n_1)	Volume of one drop of liquid volume of one drop of water $v/n_1 / vn_2 = n_2/n_1$	Mean n_2/n_1
1				
2				
3				
4				
5				

B. Determination of Density

Weight of empty Sp.Gr. Bottole/ Pyknometer (w_1 g)	Weight of Sp. Gr. Bottole/ Pyknometer with water (w_2 g)	Weight of Sp. Gr. Bottole/Pyknometer with the liquid (w_3 g)	Density of the liquid $\dfrac{w_3 - w_1}{w_2 - w_1} \times \rho_2$ g/ml

N.B. ρ_2 is the density of water.

Calculations: Surface tension of the liquid (unknown) = $\gamma_1 = \gamma_2 \cdot \dfrac{n_2}{n_1} \cdot \dfrac{\rho_1}{\rho_2}$ dynes/cm, γ_2 and ρ_2 are the surface tension and density of water at room temperature (known).

Comments

(i) **By this method** *concentration of unknown solution may be determined*: In such cases solutions of different concentrations of the liquid are prepared. Density determinations and drop counting are carried out for solutions of different concentrations along with the solution of unknown concentration and surface tension values of each of the solutions are calculated. Next a graph of surface tension against concentration is plotted. From the graph the concentration of the solution of unknown strength is found out. For such purposes solutions of 2%, 4% and 8% strength of the liquid may be prepared from the supplied solution. The result may be expressess as below:

Results

Temperature of the room .... °C

Concentration of solution	Number of drops	Density g/ml	Surface tension
0% (water)			
2%			
4%			
8%			
unknown			

(ii) Temperature should be maintained constant because surface tension varies with temperature.

(iii) Stalagnometer must be perfectly cleaned and held exactly vertical during the experiment.

1.9 Determination of Viscosity Coefficient of a Given Liquid/ Solution with Ostwald's Viscometer

General discussion: Viscosity implies resistance to flow. It is well known that all liquids do not flow equally readily. Some liquids flow slowly as for example, glycerine, castor oil, honey, etc. Such liquids are said to have high viscosity while some other liquids like water, alcohol, ether, etc. are said to have low viscosity.

The significance of viscosity may be elucidated by considering the flow of a liquid through a narrow capillary glass tube. The liquid column in the glass tube is assumed to be composed of a large number of concentric cylindrical layers as shown in the figure. These layers slides over one another and moves downward due to the difference in pressure. The layer, immediately in contact with the walls of the glass tube, is almost stationary. Each succeeding layer of the liquid moves with gradually increasing velocity which becomes maximum as the centre of the tube is approached. *The resistance that one part of the liquid flowing with a particular velocity offers to another part of the liquid flowing with a different velocity, is known as viscosity.* Or in other words, *viscosity may be looked upon as the force of friction between two layers of a liquid moving past one another with different velocities.*

Concentric
cylindrical layers

Let us consider a cylindrical layer of area A square cm moves over another similar layer at a distance d cm with velocity difference v cm per second. Thus the tangential force of friction (f) required to maintain constant difference of velocity is given by

$$f = \frac{\eta.A.v}{d},$$

where η is a constant at a given temperature depending upon the nature of the liquid and is known as *coefficient of viscosity*.

When A is 1 square cm and v and d are also 1 cm each, then $f = \eta$. Thus, *the coefficient of viscosity of a liquid may be defined as the force in dynes per square centimetre required to maintain a difference of velocity of 1 cm per second between two parallel layers of the liquid held at a distance of 1 cm from one another.* The unit of coefficient of viscosity is called poise.

1.9.1 Determination of Coefficient of Viscosity

Theory: There are a number of methods for the determination of coefficient of viscosity of which the most commonly employed method is due to Ostwald. This method is based on Poisculle equation

$$\eta = \frac{\pi.r^4.t.p}{8.v.l}, \tag{1}$$

where v is the volume in ml of the liquid flowing in t seconds through a narrow tube of radius r cm and length l cm under a hydrostatic pressure of p dynes per square centimetre and η is the coefficient of viscosity in poise (i.e., dynes per square centimetre).

In ostwald's viscometer, the relative viscosity of a liquid is measured. So if t_1 and t_2 represent the times required for the same volume of two different liquids to flow through the same capillary tube, we have for two liquids,

$$\eta_1 = \frac{\pi.r^4 t_1 p_1}{8.v.l} \tag{2}$$

$$\eta_2 = \frac{\pi.r^4 t_2 p_2}{8.v.l}. \tag{3}$$

Hence $\dfrac{\eta_1}{\eta_2} = \dfrac{t_1 p_1}{t_2 p_2}$.   (4)

Since the hydrostatic pressure is proportional to density, so

$$\frac{\eta_1}{\eta_2} = \frac{t_1 d_1}{t_2 d_2},$$ (5)

where d_1, d_2 are densities of two liquids. Now if η_2, d_1, d_2, t_1 and t_2 are known, η_1 can be calculated from the equation (5).

Procedure: Ostwald's viscometer as shown in the figure is thoroughly cleaned with chromic acid mixture and dried. A known volume of water is pipetted into the bulb B. It is then sucked into

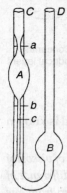

the bulb A with the help of a rubber tube attached at the end C till it rises to the mark a. Water is now allowed to flow down the tube. The stopwatch is started when it falls at the mark b and when the water level falls at the mark c the stopwatch is stopped. The time taken by water to flow through the capillary bc is noted. Similar experiment is repeated several times.

The viscometer is dried by passing hot air and the same volume of the liquid/solution under examination is taken into the bulb B and the process is repeated as before. The time of flow of liquid is noted.

Next the density of the liquid is determined either by a specific gravity bottle or with the help of a pyknometer in the usual way.

Results: Room temperature = ... °C

A. Determination of time of flow

No. of observation	Time taken by water to flow from one mark to other in the viscometer (t_2 seconds)	Time taken by the liquid to flow from one mark to other in the viscometer (t_1 seconds)	Mean t_2 in seconds	Mean t_1 in seconds
1				
2				
3				
4				
5				

B. Determination of density of the liquid

Weight of the empty sp. gr. bottle : w_1 g	Weight of the sp. gr. bottle with water : w_2 g	Weight of sp. gr. bottle with liquid : w_3 g	Density of water at room temp : d_2 g/ml	Density of the liquid at room temperature : d_1 $= \left(\dfrac{w_3 - w_1}{w_2 - w_1}\right) \times d_2$ g/ml

Calculations

$$\frac{\eta_1}{\eta_2} = \frac{t_1 d_1}{t_2 d_2}$$

$$\text{or,} \quad \eta_1 = \frac{t_1 d_1}{t_2 d_2} \times \eta_2 \text{ poise}$$

Comments

(i) Temperature should be maintained constant.

(ii) Volume of water and the liquid taken in the viscometer must be equal.

(iii) Viscosmeter must be thoroughly clean so that it is completely grease-free.

(iv) The viscometer should be held perfectly vertical.

(v) For volatile liquids pyknometer should be used for the determination of specific gravity.

(vi) As mentioned before, viscosity depends upon concentration. It is, therefore, obvious that the above method may be applied for studying the variation of viscosity with concentration as discussed below.

1.9.2 Variation of Viscosity with Concentration of the Solution

Theory: Since viscosity depends upon the concentration of the solution of the liquid under consideration, by determining the viscosity of the solution of unknown concentration, its concentration may be found out by the graphical method. For this purpose, viscosities of different concentrations of solution are determined and the viscosities are plotted against concentrations and from the graph concentration of unknown solution may be found out.

Procedure: A number of solutions of different concentrations 5%, 10% and 20% are prepared. For each solution the flow time is measured by Ostwald's viscometer as in the case of previous experiment. Time of flow of the solution of unknown concentration is also measured. Densities of different solutions including the solution of unknown concentration are determined in the usual way. Viscosities of different solutions are calculated and plotted against their concentrations. From the graph concentration of the unknown solution is found out.

Results

Room temperature .... °C

Solution	Time taken by the liquid (t_1 second)	Time taken by water (t_2 second)	Density of the liquid (d_1 g/ml)	Density (d_2 g/ml)	η_1 (poise)
water					
20 %					
10 %					
5 %					
unknown					
solution					

Conclusion: From the graph obtained by plotting viscosity against concentration, the concentration of the solution supplied is .... % at .... °C.

1.10 Conductometric Titrations

General discussion: Conductometric titrations are based on the measurement of conductance of the solution of electrolytes. The conductance is related to the flow of electric current through ions of the electrolyte and the process of conduction is guided by Ohm's Law of resistance which states that the resistance (R) offered by a solution on its placing between electrodes is inversely proportional to the potential difference (E), i.e.,

$$R = \frac{E}{I}, \tag{1}$$

where I is the strength of current. The potential difference is measured in volts which is defined as the difference of potential that is necessary to make a current of 1 ampere flow through a resistance of 1 ohm. In electro chemistry, the term conductance (C) is referred to the case with which the current flows through a conductor, i.e., electrolyte. It is, therefore, reciprocal of resistance, i.e.,

$$C = \frac{1}{R}. \tag{2}$$

It is expressed in the units called reciprocal ohm or mho.

The conductance of a solution depends upon the number and mobility of ions present and hence on concentration. The measurement of electrical conductance of a solution in fact amounts to the determination of electrical resistance of the solution because as mentioned before (2) conductance is just the reciprocal of the resistance. The Wheatstone bridge method is generally employed.

In such bridge four resistances are connected as shown in the figure below:

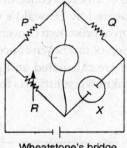

Wheatstone's bridge

When there is flow of current, the four resistances are related as

$$\frac{P}{Q} = \frac{R}{X}, \tag{3}$$

where P and Q are two fixed (i.e., known) resistances, X is the resistance of the conductor (electrolyte) whose resistance is being measured and R is variable. If $P = Q$, then $R = X$ (4)

and so from the value of R, resistance of the solution of electrolyte can be easily determined and hence conductance of the solution can be known.

The conductance measurements are frequently employed for the determination of the end points of acid-base and other titrations.

1.10.1 Conductometric Titration of a Strong Acid with a Strong Base

Theory: In the conductometric titration of a strong acid with a strong base, the acid is taken in a beaker containing conductivity cell and base in the burette. The conductance of the acid (say, HCl) is due to the presence of hydrogen and chloride ions. As alkali (say, NaOH) is added gradually, the hydrogen ions are replaced by sodium ions of lower mobility as represented below:

$$\overset{+}{H} + \overset{-}{Cl} + [\overset{+}{Na} + \overset{-}{OH}] \longrightarrow \overset{+}{Na} + \overset{-}{Cl} + H_2O \text{ (un ionised)}$$

Thus, on continued addition of sodium hydroxide, the conductance will go on decreasing till the acid has been completely neutralised. Any further addition of alkali will result in introducing faster moving hydroxyl ions and so the conductance, after reaching a certain minimum value, will begin to increase. If the conductance is plotted against volume of alkali two straight lines having opposite slopes will be obtained. The point of intersection of these two lines is the end point and gives the volume of alkali required for neutralisation. It may be mentioned in this connection that the strength of NaOH should be at least 4-5 times more than that of HCl so that the effect of volume change on conductance be negligible.

Reagents required:

1. HCl $(N/10)$ solution
2. NaOH (N) solution
3. Oxalic acid $(N/10)$.

Apparatus required:

1. Conductivity bridge
2. Burette
3. Pipette
4. Conductivity cell
5. Beaker.

Procedure: The strength of NaOH (N) is determined by titrating with oxalic acid.

(N) NaOH solution is taken in a clean burette and 10 ml of supplied HCl solution is pipetted out in a 100 ml beaker and to it about 100 ml of water is added. The conductivity cell is placed in the beaker in such a way that the electrodes are completely immeresed in acid solution. The conductivity cell is connected to the conductivity bridge. Now NaOH solution from the burette is added 0.5 ml at a time and conductance is measured after well stirring the mixture.

The process is repeated until the end point and again addition of NaOH 0.5 at a time is continued after the end point, and after each addition of NaOH solution conductance is measured. Finally a graph is drawn by plotting the conductance against the burette reading.

Results

Room temperature .... °C

Standardisation of NaOH solution by oxalic acid.

Measurement of Conductance

Volume of HCl taken (ml)	Volume of NaOH added (ml)	Observed resistance (ohm)	Observed conductance ($\frac{1}{R}$) (ohm^{-1})
10	0		
	0.5		
	1.0		
	1.5		
	2.0		
	2.5		
	3.0		

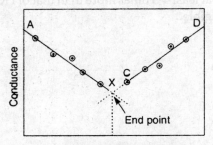

End point

Volume of Alkali added
Titration of a strong acid against a strong base

From the graph, the point of intersection of the straight lines is at V ml of NaOH. Thus V ml of NaOH is required to neutralise 10 ml of HCl. Hence.

$$V \times S = 10 \times S_1$$

or, $$S_1 = \frac{V \times S}{10}(N),$$

where S is the strength of NaOH and S_1 is that of HCl supplied.

1.10.2 Conductometric Titration of an Weak Acid with a Strong Base

Theory: In the conductometric titration of an weak acid with a strong base, the conductance of the acid (say, acetic acid) will be low on account of its poor dissociation. On adding a strong base (say, sodium hydroxide) highly ionised sodium acetate is formed and the conductance begins to increase.

$$CH_3COOH + [\overset{+}{Na} + \overset{-}{OH}] \longrightarrow CH_3\overset{-}{COO} + \overset{+}{Na} + H_2O \text{ (unionised)}$$

When the acid is completely neutralised, further addition of base introduces excess of fast moving hydroxyl ions. Hence the conductance begins to increase even more sharply than before. If conductance is plotted against volume of base, added two lines will be obtained and the point of intersection of the two lines will give the end point.

Reagents required:

1. CH_3COOH $(N/10)$ solution
2. NaOH (N) solution
3. Oxalic acid $(N/10)$ solution.

Apparatus required:

1. Conductivity bridge
2. Conductivity cell
3. Beaker
4. Burette
5. Pipette.

Procecure: NaOH (N) solution is standardised by titrating against oxalic acid solution.

10 ml of supplied acetic acid solution is taken in a 100 ml beaker and 100 ml of water is added to it. To this solution conductivity cells are dipped. The conductivity cell is connected to the conductivity bridge. From burette, NaOH solution is added 0.5 ml at a time and conductance is measured. Addition of NaOH solution is continued until the break in the curve is obtained, i.e., the rapid increase in conductance values occurs. Finally a graph of conductance versus volume of base is drawn.

Results

Room temperature .... °C

Standardisation of NaOH with oxalic acid.

Measurement of Conductance

Volume of CH$_3$COOH taken (ml)	Volume of NaOH added (ml)	Observed resistance (ohm)	Observed conductance (ohm^{-1})
10	0		
	0.5		
	1.0		
	1.5		
	2.0		
	2.5		

Graph and calculations: A graph of conductance against volume of base is drawn. From the graph it is seen that the point of intersection of two lines is at V ml. Thus V ml of base is required to neutralise 10 ml of CH_3COOH.

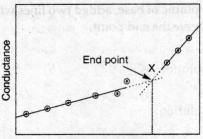

Titration of a weak acid against a strong base

Thus $V \times S = 10 \times S_1$

or, $S_1 = \dfrac{V \times S}{10}$,

where S and S_1 are the strengths of NaOH and CH_3COOH.

1.10.3 Conductometric Titration of a Strong Acid with a Weak Base

Theory: In the above type of conductometric titration the conductance at the beginning will fall due to the replacement of fast moving H^+ ions of the strong acid (say, HCl) by the slow moving NH_4^+ ions of weak base (say, NH_4OH).

$$H^+ + \overline{Cl} + [NH_4OH] \longrightarrow NH_4^+ + \overline{Cl} + H_2O \text{ (unionised)}$$

After neutralisation of the acid, further addition of weakly ionised ammonium hydroxide solution will not cause any change in the conductance. The nature of the graph of conductance versus volume of base will be as shown below. The procedure is similar as in other cases.

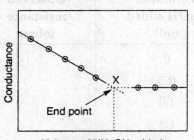

Titration of a strong acid against a weak base

1.11 Verification of Lambert-Beer's Law and to Determine the Concentration of a Given Solution

Theory: It has been observed that when a beam of electromagnetic radiation is passed through a solution of an absorbing substance contained in a transparent cell the intensity of electromagnetic radiation is reduced. Lambert and Beer independently investigated the nature of change of intensity of electromagnetic radiation and proposed two different laws.

(i) **Lambert's law:** According to Lambert's law, rate of decrease in intensity of radiation with space (path length) is proportional to the intensity of the incident radiation (light). This may be mathematically expressed as

$$\frac{-\mathrm{d}I}{\mathrm{d}x} \propto I, \tag{1}$$

where I is the intensity of incident light, x is the path length through which light beam passes. Minus sign implies decrease in intensity.

(ii) **Beer's law:** Beer stated that the rate of decrease in intensity of electromagnetic radiation with space (path length) is proportional to the concentration of the solution through which the *radiation passes*. This may be expressed mathematically as

$$\frac{-\mathrm{d}I}{\mathrm{d}x} \propto c, \tag{2}$$

where c is the molar concentration.

Combining the two laws (1) and (2), we get

$$\frac{-\mathrm{d}I}{\mathrm{d}x} \propto I.c. \tag{3}$$

The expression (3) is known as Lambert-Beer's Law.

$$\text{or,} \quad \frac{-\mathrm{d}I}{\mathrm{d}x} = k.I.c.$$

$$\text{or,} \quad \frac{-\mathrm{d}I}{I} = k.c.dx., \text{ where } k \text{ is proportionality constant.}$$

Integrating, we get

$$-\int_{I_0}^{I} \frac{\mathrm{d}I}{I} = k.c. \int_{x=0}^{x=x}$$

$$\text{or,} \quad \log \frac{I_0}{I} = k.c.x.$$

The proportionality constant k is generally denoted by ε and is known as molar absorption coefficient, which is constant at any given wavelength and is independent of concentration of the solution.

Thus, $\log \dfrac{I_0}{I} = \varepsilon.c.x.$ \hfill (4)

It may be mentioned that the space x is the size of cell in which the solution of absorbing substance is taken. It is usually taken one cubic centimetre, i.e., $x = 1$.

Hence, $\log \dfrac{I_0}{I} = \varepsilon.c.$ \hfill (5)

The term $\log \dfrac{I_0}{I}$ is called absorbance and is generally indicated by A. Thus,

$$A = \varepsilon.c. \tag{6}$$

For the determination of concentration of the solution of absorbing substance wavelength of maximum absorption (usually denoted by λ_{max} where λ is the wavelength) for the compound is selected. Then the absorbances (A) of the solution of the substance are measured for different concentrations. Next the absorbances are plotted against concentration of the substance over a range of concentrations. If Lambert-Beer's law holds good a straight line should be obtained. This plot is used as a calibration curve for determining the unknown concentrations of a substance. The solution of unknown strength is taken in the uv-cell and its absorbance is measured. Corresponding to this absorbance the concentration of unknown solution can be calculated.

Apparatus required: Colorimeter as shown in the figure.

Reagents required:

1. Absorbing substance $KMnO_4$ or $K_2Cr_2O_7$ solutions of the order M/50
2. Dilute H_2SO_4 (1N).

Procedure: A solution of known concentration is prepared and from this solution, by the method of dilution other solutions of different strength are prepared. Generally, M/50 and less concentrated solutions are prepared. In the case of $KMnO_4$ aqueous solution is used but in the case of $K_2Cr_2O_7$ dilute H_2SO_4 (1N) solution is used. For each solution of known strength absorbance is measured. Finally absorbance for solution of unknown strength is also measured. A plot of conductance against absorbance is drawn when a straight line is obtained. From this graph, concentration of unknown solution is measured. It may be mentioned that suitable filter (monochromator) is to be used in the colorimeter to adjust the required wavelength. Filter of 475 nm for $K_2Cr_2O_7$ and 530 nm for $KMnO_4$ solutions are to be used.

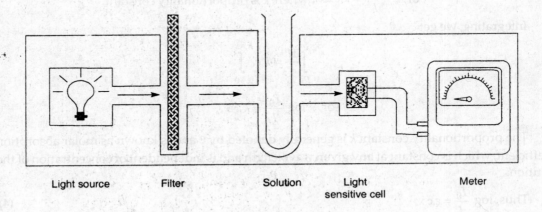

| Light source | Filter | Solution | Light sensitive cell | Meter |

Colorimeter

Preparation of solutions of different strengths: Solutions of different strengths are prepared by mixing different volumes of solution of absorbing substence (N/50) and solvent according to the table given below:

Volume of KMnO₄ or K₂Cr₂O₇ solution (M/50) (ml)	Volume of solvent (water for KMnO₄ and (1N) H₂SO₄ for K₂Cr₂O₇ ml	Serial number of solutions
1	9	1
2	8	2
3	7	3
4	6	4
5	5	5
6	4	6
7	3	7
8	2	8
9	1	9

Results

(i) Wavelength (filter) .... nm

Observation Solution No.	Absorbances
1	
2	
3	
.	
.	
unknown solution	

A graph is drawn by plotting absorbance against concentration. The linearity of the graph proves the validity of Lambert-Beer's law. From the graph, the concentration of unknown solution is found to .... *a* molar.

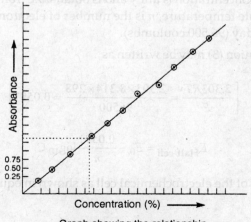

Graph showing the relationship between absorbance and concentration

1.12 Potentiometric Titration

General discussion: Potentiometric titration involves the measurement of E.M.F. of a reaction mixture and, in fact, this type of titrations constitutes one of the most important example of application of E.M.F. measurement. Potentiometric titrations is usually defined as a titration in which the end-point of a reaction is detected by measuring the potential of a reaction mixture. It has been observed that the potential of a reversible electrode varies with the concentration of the ion with respect to which it is reversible. In order to measure the potential of such reversible electrode, a suitable electrochemical cell is constructed by connecting the reversible electrode which is normally designated as *indicator electrode* with a reference electrode through external connection. As a result, a spontaneous chemical reaction occurs with the flow of electrons from cathode (−) to anode (+). The E.M.F. of the electrochemical cell, thus, constructed is given by the following equation.

$$E_{Cell} = E_{Reference} + E_{Indicator} + E_{Junction} \tag{1}$$

The E.M.F. of the cell is measured by connecting the two electrodes (reference and indicator) to a potentiaometer.

It may be mentioned that the liquid junction potential is generally eliminated by using *Salt bridge* as a connector of the above two electrodes. Under this condition the E.M.F. of the cell stands as under.

$$E_{Cell} = E_{Reference} + E_{Indicator} \tag{2}$$

Again, the reference electrode is such that its potential is indiependent of the composition of the solution and so is assumed to remain constant. Its value can be obtained from literature. Thus under these circumstances, only the indicator electrode can furnish the necessary information regarding the substances capable of exchanging electrons. Again, the potential of the half-cell (in this case indicator electrode) is given by *Nernst equation*.

$$\underset{\text{(Electrode)}}{E_{\text{Half-cell}}} = E_0 - \frac{2.303RT}{nF} \log_{10} C, \tag{3}$$

where E is the potential of the half-cell, E_0 is the standard potential of the electrode, i.e., the potential of the electrode when the concentration is unity and is obtainable from literature; R, the universal gas constant; T, the absolute temperature; n is the number of electrons invclved in the electrode reaction and F is one Faraday (96 500 coulombs).

At 25 °C, Nernst equation (3) may be written as

$$\left[\frac{2.303RT}{F} = \frac{2.303 \times 8.314 \times 298}{96500} = 0.0591 \right]$$

$$E_{\text{Half-cell}} = E_0 - \frac{0.0591}{n} \log_{10} C. \tag{4}$$

Therefore, the E.M.F. of the electrochemical cell as shown in equation (2) may be written as under:

$$E_{Cell} = E_{Reference} + E_0 - \frac{0.0591}{n} \log_{10} C$$

$$\text{or,} \quad \frac{0.0591}{n} \log_{10} C = E_{Ref} + E_0 - E_{cell}$$

$$\text{or,} \quad \log_{10} C = \frac{(E_{Ref} + E_0 - E_{cell}) \times n}{0.0591}. \tag{5}$$

Thus from the equation (5) it is evident that the concentration at the end-point of the reaction can be easily determined by measuring the E.M.F. of the electrochemical cell constructed and knowing the potentials of reference and standard electrodes from the literature.

Types of Potentiometric Titrations: Potentiometric titrations have several advantages over indicator methods. Some of these are as given below:

1. Apparatus required is generally inexpensive, reliable and readily available.

2. It is easy to interpret.

3. This method is applicable to dilute solution.

4. Several components may be titrated in the same solution without any interference.

5. This type of titrations can be used for coloured solution.

1.12.1 Potentiometric Titration of a Standard Solution of KCl against AgNO₃ Solution

Principle: It is a precipitation type of potentiometric titration. This is because the concentration of the reactant ($AgNO_3$) gradually decreases during the titration with the standard KCl solution due to the formation of a precipitate of AgCl.

$$\overset{+}{Ag} + \overset{-}{NO_3} + (\overset{+}{K} + \overset{-}{Cl}) \longrightarrow AgCl\downarrow + \overset{+}{K} + \overset{-}{NO_3}$$

In this titration a known volume of $AgNO_3$ solution is taken in a beaker and to it a silver electrode is dipped to act as indicator electrode. The potential of this electrode is measured by connecting it with saturated calomel reference electrode through a salt bridge. The electrochemical cell thus constructed is

$$Hg|Hg_2\overline{Cl}_2(S)|KCl|\overset{+}{Ag}|Ag(S)$$

In this electrochemical cell the silver becomes the positive terminal and saturated colomel acts as the negative terminal. The E.M.F. of the cell is given by

$$E_{cell} = E_{Ag^+/Ag} - E_{calomel}$$

$$E_{cell} = E^0_{Ag^+/Ag} + 0.0591 \log_{10}\overset{+}{Ag} - E_{calomel} \text{ at } 25\,°C$$

$$= 0.799 + 0.0591 \log_{10}\overset{+}{Ag} - 0.246 \text{ at } 25\,°C$$

where standard electrode potential $E^0_{Ag^+/Ag} = 0.799$ V and $E_{calomel}$ is $+0.246$V.

Thus as the concentration of Ag^+ decreases by the addition of chloride ion, the E.M.F. decreases. But there will be a sharp change in E.M.F. at the equivalence point (end-point). If a plot of E.M.F. against the volume of KCl added is drawn, the end-point corresponds to the point of inflexion (i.e., the point where the slope is maximum).

Apparatus Required:
  (i)   Pipette and burette
  (ii) Beaker
  (iii) Salt-bridge
  (iv) Saturated calomel electrode
  (v)   Potentiometer.

Chemicals Required:
  (i) $(N/50)$ AgNO$_3$ solution
  (ii) $(N/50)$ KCl solution
  (iii) 2(N) HNO$_3$

Procedure: 15 ml of AgNO$_3$ solution is taken in a beaker and a clean silver electrode is dipped into this solution. This serves as indicator electrode. This electrode is connected to a saturated calomel electrode through a salt bridge. Potentiometer is connected with the cell—the positive terminal to indicator electrode and negative terminal to calomel electrode.

Initial E.M.F. is noted and then addition of KCl is started from the burette. E.M.F. of the cell is noted after each addition of 2 drops of KCl and such addition of KCl is continued beyond the sharp change in E.M.F.

A graph of E.M.F. against the volume of KCl required is plotted. The end-point corresponds to the point of inflexion, i.e., the point where the slope of the curve is maximum. The volume of KCl required at the equivalence point is noted and the concentration of AgNO$_3$ is calculated from the formula,

$$V_1S_1 = V_2S_2.$$

Results: At Room Temperature:

Volume of AgNO$_3$ taken	Volume of KCl added	Strength of KCl	Observed E. M. F.
15 ml	0.00 ml	$S_1(^N/_{50})$	
	0.05 ml	''	
	0.10 ml	''	
	0.15 ml	''	
	0.20 ml	''	

Graph and Calculation

A graph of E.M.F. against the volume of KCl required is drawn as shown in the figure below.

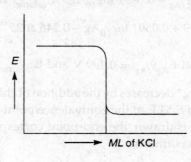

From the graph the point of inflexion is noted. This equavalent point (point of inflexion) gives the volume of KCl required to completely precipitate silver as silver chloride from 15 ml of $AgNO_3$. Let the strength of KCl be $S_1(N/50)$ and S_2 be the strength of $AgNO_3$ solution taken. Thus,

$15 \times S_2 = S_1 \times V_1$, where V_1 is the volume of KCl at equivalent point or,

$$S_2 = \frac{S_1 V_1}{15}.$$

1.12.2 Potentiometric Titration of Ferrous Iron in Mohr's Salt against a Standard Solution of $K_2Cr_2O_7$ or $KMnO_4$

Principle: It is a redox titration in which ferrous iron is oxidised to ferric iron by the oxidant $K_2Cr_2O_7$ or $KMnO_4$. In this titration the indicator electrode is a platinum electrode dipped into a standard solution of Mohr's salt. To complete the cell, this electrode is connected with a sturated calomel electrode through KCl salt-bridge. The electrochemical cell thus formed is

$$\overset{(-)}{P+}|Hg|Hg_2Cl_2(S)|KCl(aq) \text{ (saturated)}\| Fe^{2+}(aq) \overset{(+)}{,} Fe^{3+}(aq)|_{Pt}$$

The platinum electrode is connected to the positive terminal and calomel electrode is attached to the negative terminal of the potentiometer.

A known volume of acidified Mohr's salt solution is taken in a beaker and to it platinum wire is inserted. From the burette, standard solution of $KMnO_4$ or $K_2Cr_2O_7$ is added to this Mohr's salt solution. At any instant during the titration the solution contains a mixture of Fe^{2+} and Fe^{3+} ions with a platinum-wire in it and this forms a reversible electrode (indicator electrode). The progressive addition of $K_2Cr_2O_7$ or $KMnO_4$ will cause a change in E.M.F. of the cell because the ratio Fe^{3+}/Fe^{2+} increases. If the E.M.F. of the cell is plotted against the titre added, the curve that is obtained shows its greatest slope when the equivalence point is reached. Thus from the slope, equivalence point ean be determined. The overall reaction taking place when $K_2Cr_2O_7$ is used as oxidant is as below:

$$6Fe^{2+} + 14H^+ + Cr_2O_7^{2-} + 14H^+ = 2Cr^{3+} + 6Fe^{3+} + 7H_2O$$

The E.M.F. of the cell is given by the following equation.

$$E_{cell} = E_{Fe^{3+}/Fe^{2+}} - E_{calomel}$$

$$E_{cell} = E^0_{Fe^{3+}/Fe2+} + 0.591 \log_{10} Fe^{3+}/Fe2+ - E_{calomel}$$

At the mid-point of the titrations, $[Fe^{2+}] = [Fe^{3+}]$, so the above euqation stands as

$$E_{cell} = E^0_{Fe^{3+}/Fe2+} - E_{calomel} \tag{A}$$

Thus from the volume of titrant required at the equivalence point and knowing the potentials of reference calomel electrode and standard electrode, concentration of ferrous iron in the solution can estimated. Again, from the value of E.M.F. at the mid-point of titration standard redox potential of Fe^{3+}/Fe^{2+} system can be evaluated putting value of potential of reference electrode in equation (A).

Apparatus Required:

(i) Potentiometer
(ii) Platinum electrode
(iii) Calomel electrode
(iv) Beaker, burette and pipette
(v) Salt-bridge.

Chemicals Required:

  (i) (N/10) Mohr's salt solution

  (ii) (2N) H_2SO_4

  (iii) (N/2) $K_2Cr_2O_7$/(N/2) $KMnO_4$

Procedure: 20 ml of (N/10) Mohr's salt solution is taken in a beaker. A clean platinum electrode is inserted into it. This beaker is connected with a saturated calomel electrode through a salt-bridge. The two electrodes are connected to the two terminals of the potentiometer. From a burette, $K_2Cr_2O_7$ or $KMnO_4$ solution is added to the solution of Mohr's salt, 4 drops at a time. The solution is stirred well and the E.M.F. is noted. Finally the graph of E.M.F. versus volume of oxidant ($K_2Cr_2O_7$ or $KMnO_4$) added is plotted (figure below). The equivalence point and mid-point of the titrations are recorded.

Results and Calculations

At Room Temperature:

Volume of Mohr's salt solution taken	Volume of $K_2Cr_2O_7$ or $KMnO_4$ added	E.M.F.
20 ml	0.0	
20 ml	0.2	
20 ml	0.4	
20 ml	0.6	

Calculations

Let S_1 be the strength of oxidant and V_1 be its volume at equivalence point. Thus

$$S_1 \text{ (N/2) } K_2Cr_2O_7 \text{ or } KMnO_4 \times V_1 = 20 \times S_2,$$

where S_2 is the strength of Mohr's salt solution.

$$S_2 = \frac{S_1 \times V_1}{20}.$$

From the graph, E.M.F. at mid-point of titration ($V_1/2$) is calculated and from equation (A) standard redox potential ($E^0 {}_{Fe^{3+}/Fe^{2+}}$) is calculated.

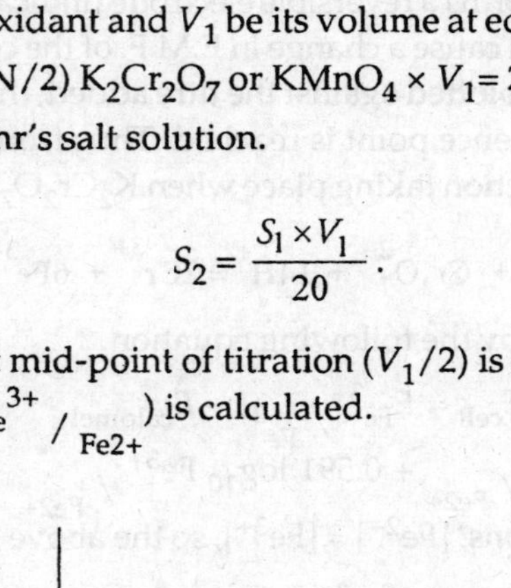

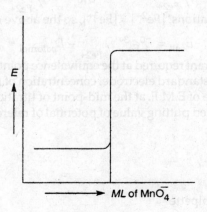

ML of MnO_4^-

Questions and Answers for Viva Voce

Chapter 2

1. What do you mean by a buffer solution?

   Ans. See Art. 1.1.

2. What is pH?

   Ans. See Art. 1.1.

3. Why each test tube of the same radius is used during the determination of pH by colour matching?

   Ans. Colour intensity depends upon the length of the solution through which light passes.

4. Can you name the instrument which can accurately measure colour intensity?

   Ans. Colorimeter.

5. The equilibrium constant of the reaction $KI + I_2 \rightleftharpoons KI_3$ decreases with temperature—what does it mean?

   Ans. The reaction is exothermic.

6. What do you mean by surface tension?

   Ans. See Art. 1.8.

7. "Surface tension changes with temperature."—Explain.

   Ans. See Art. 1.8.

8. How surface tension is related to concentration?

   Ans. See Art. 1.8 comment (1).

9. What is the Harkins and Brown equation of surface tension?

   Ans. $\gamma = \dfrac{mg}{2\pi r\,\Psi}$.

10. How viscosity of a liquid changes with temperature?

    Ans. See Art. 1.9.

11. Why is it necessary to take exactly the same volume of liquid in each case for determination of viscosity?

    Ans. For same volume of liquids the heights of the liquid will also be the same and so pressure will be the same.

12. What is fluidity? How is it related to viscosity?

    Ans. Fludity is the measure of tendency of flow of a liquid. It is reciprocal of viscosity,

    i.e., $f = \dfrac{1}{\eta}$, where f is the fluidity and h is the coefficient of viscosity.

13. What is the difference between the order and the molecularity of a reaction?

    Ans. See any book on Physical Chemistry.

14. What is the dimension of rate constant?

    Ans. $(\text{concentration})^{1-n}\ \text{time}^{-1}$ where n is the order.

15. What conditions are to be fulfilled for attaining a constant value of the ratio concentrations of a solute in two solutes?

    Ans. See Art. 1.3.

16. During the determination of rate constant for the hydrlolysis of methyl acetate why the temperature is to be kept constant?

    Ans. Rate of any reaction varies with the temperature.

17. How the rate of decomposition of H_2O_2 can be studied?

    Ans. See Art. 1.6.

18. What do you mean by the term solubility product?

    Ans. See Art. 1.7.

19. What is the relation between solubility and solubility product?

    Ans. See Art. 1.7.

20. How the solubility of a sparingly soluble salt can be determined by titrimetric method?

    Ans. See Art. 1.7.1.

21. Define solubility.

    Ans. Amount of solute dissolved in one litre of solvent so as to give a saturated solution at a particular temperature.

22. How can we study the change of solubility with the temperature?

    Ans. By constructing a solubility curve.

23. Name a substance whose solubility decreases with the increase in temperature.

    Ans. $Na_2SO_4, 10H_2O$.

24. What is distribution Law?

    Ans. Distribution law or Nernst's distribution law may be stated as when a solute is allowed to distribute between two immiscible solvents, an equilibrium is established which is expressed as

$$K = \frac{[A] \text{ in solvent } 1}{[A] \text{ in solvent } 2}, \text{ where } A \text{ is the solute.}$$

25. What is the importance of viscosity?

Ans. In factory, liquids are transported through pipe lines. Viscosity helps in determining the diameter of the pipe, time of flow, etc.

26. What is the name of apparatus by which surface tension is measured?

Ans. Stalagnometer.

27. What are surfactants?

Ans. Substance which lowers the surface tension is known as surfactant. Soap and detergents are common examples of surfactants.

28. What do you mean by chemical kinetics?

Ans. It is that branch of chemistry which studies the rate of reactions.

29. What do you mean by homogeneous and heterogeneous reactions?

Ans. Homogeneous reactions are those in which the reactants and products remain in the same physical state. Thus,

$$\text{NaOH (aq)} + \text{HCl (aq)} = \text{NaCl (aq)} + \text{H}_2\text{O},$$

while in heterogeneous reaction reactants and products remain in different physical state.

$$\text{NH}_3 \text{ (g)} + \text{HCl (g)} \longrightarrow \text{NH}_4\text{Cl (solid)}$$

30. Name two buffer solutions which are mixture of two salts.

Ans. (i) Di-sodium citrate and tri-sodium citrate (pH, 5 to 6.3)

(ii) Monosodium hydrogen phosphate and di-sodium hydrogen phosphate (pH, 5.8 to 8.0).

31. What do you mean by absorbance? What is its relation with % transmittance?

Ans. The quantity $\log I_0 / I$ is known as absorbance and it is inversely equal to logarithm of transmittance.

32. What is meant by molar absorptivity?

Ans. It is also known as molar extinction coefficient and is denoted by ε which is equal to $\frac{a}{c}$.

where a is the absorbance and c is molar concentration.

33. What is the difference between colorimetry and spectrophotometry?

Ans. Colorimetry operates in visible region while spectrometry functions in UV region.

34. What is the unit of wavelength?

Ans. It is expressed by nanometre (nm).

35. Haemoglobin, an iron containing porphyrin in blood, is reddish purple in colour. Predict the wavelength in the visible region spectrum where it should absorb?

Ans. About 490-560 nm. In practice, 555 nm is offen used.

36. Explain why spectra of solutions in UV and visible regions are broad in nature?

Ans. This is because in UV-visible region along with electronic transitions, rotational and vibrational transitions also occur.

37. What do you mean by the term conductance.

Ans. See Art. 1.10.

38. What do you mean by conductometric titrations?

Ans. The titration in which the end point of a titration is determined by measuring conductivity.

39. On what factor conductivity depends?

Ans. It depends upon ionic concentration.

40. What is molar conductivity?

Ans. The conductivity of a solution at a concentration of 1 mole/litre is the molar conductivity.

41. What are the types of titrations that can be performed by conductometric titration?

Ans. Acid-base, precipitation and complexometric titration.

42. What are the advantages of conductometric titrations?

Ans. (i) Accurate results are obtained.

(ii) In some cases, particularly in the case of coloured solution where indicator cannot work, this titration can be used to detect the end point.

43. What are the limitations of conductometric titrations?

Ans. (i) It is less accurate and less satisfactory with higher concentration.

(ii) It has limited application in redox system. This is because excess of hydronium ion required for redox reactions tends to oppose conductivity changes associated with redox reactions.

44. Is constant determination is necessary for conductometric titrations.

Ans. No.

45. In conductometric titration between weak acid and strong base, readings near end point do not lie in the straight line—why?

Ans. Salts of weak acid and strong bases are hydrolysable and effect of hydrolysis becomes the most important factor near end point and that is why conductance values are slightly higher than expected.

46. What do you mean by potentiometric titration?

Ans. See Art. 1.12.

47. What is the basis of potentiometric titrations?

Ans. Potentiometric titration is based on Nernst equation which relates the potential (E) of electrode in contact with ions in solution with the concentration of the ions.

$$E = E^0 - \frac{2.303\ RT}{nF} \log_{10} C = E^0 - \frac{0.0591}{n} \log C$$

n = no. of electrons involved, E^0 is the standard electrode potential, i.e., the potential when the concentration is unity.

48. What is salt-bridge?

Ans. Salt-bridge consists of an inverted U-tube or a suitable vessel containing a solution of an electrolyte in which mobilities of anions and cations are very close to each other. KCl, NH_4NO_3 are highly suitable electrolytes.

49. What is liquid junction potential?

Ans. It is the potential at the junction of the two electrolytes.

50. What are the advantages of potentiometric titrations.

Ans. See Art. 1.12.

51. What is the commonly used reference electrode?

Ans. Saturated calomel electrode.

52. What is the basic requiredment of potentiometric titration?

Ans. A suitable electrochemical cell is to be constructed by connecting two electrodes—

(i) indicator electrode, (ii) reference electrode.

53. How can be acid-base titration be carried out potentiometrically?

Ans. It is known that acid-base titration is always accompanied by the changes in the concentration of H^+ and $O\overline{H}$. In this titration hydrogen electrode is used as indicator electrode and calomel electrode is used as reference electrode. The potential of hydrogen electrode is given by

$$E = E^0 - 0.0591 \log C_H{}^+ \text{ at } 25\,°C$$
$$\log C_H{}^+ = pH$$
$$E = E^0 - 0.0591 \, pH.$$

54. What electrode is used in oxidation-reduction titration.

Ans. Inert indicator electrode.

Appendix

Some Common Laboratory Reagents

A. Concentrated Acids

Name	Specific gravity	Approximate normality
1. Hydrochloric acid	1.49	9N
2. Acetic acid	1.05	17N
3. Nitric acid	1.42	16N
4. H_2SO_4	1.14	36N
5. Hydroiodic acid	1.70	7N

B. Dilute Acids

1. **Acetic acid:** 285 ml of concentrated acid is diluted to one litre with water.

2. **Hydrochloric acid:** 430 ml of concentrated acid is diluted to one litre with water.

3. **Ntric acid:** 140 ml of concentrated acid is diluted to one litre with water.

4. **Sulphuric acid:** 140 ml of concentrated acid is diluted to one litre with water.

C. Salt Solution

1. **Ammonium acetate:** ($NH_4C_2H_3O_2$, M.W. 77) 230 g of the salt is dissolved in one litre of water.

2. **Ammonium carbonate [$(NH_4)_2CO_3$]:** 150 g of the salt is dissolved in 150 ml of ammonia solution and 850 ml of water.

3. **Ammonium chloride (NH_4Cl, M.W. 538):** 70 g of the salt is dissolved in one litre of water.

4. **Ammonium oxalate [$(NH_4)_2C_2O_4$, H_2O, M.W. 142)]:** In one litre water 35 g of the salt is dissolved.

333

5. **Yellow ammonium sulphide solution [(NH$_4$)$_2$S]:** 150 ml of ammonia solution is saturated with H$_2$S and to it 10 g of flowers of sulphur and 250 ml of concentrated ammonia solution are added and shaken well and is diluted to one litre by water.

6. **Barium chloride (BaCl$_2$, 2H$_2$O, M.W. 244):** In one litre of water 1 g of the salt is dissolved.

7. **Bromine water (Br$_2$, M.W. 160):** 11 ml of bromine is added to minimum quantity of water to make a saturated solution.

8. **Chlorine water (Cl$_2$, M.W. 71):** 250 ml of water is saturated with chlorine which may be generated by dropping concentrated HCl on KMnO$_4$. It is preserved in coloured bottle.

9. **Ferric chloride (FeCl$_3$, 6H$_2$O, M.W. 270):** 135 g of the salt is dissolved in one litre of water.

10. **Iodine solution (I$_2$, M.W. 254):** 12.5 g of solid iodine is dissolved in a solution of 20 g of KI in 30 ml of water and finally the mixture is diluted to one litre.

11. **Lead acetate [Pb(C$_2$H$_3$O$_2$)$_2$, 3H$_2$O, M.W. 379]:** 95 g of lead acetate is dissolved in one litre of water.

12. **Potassium chromate (K$_2$CrO$_4$, M.W. 194):** In one litre of water 49 g of the salt is dissolved.

13. **Potassium ferricyanide [K$_3$Fe(CN)$_6$, M.W. 329]:** 35 g of the salt is dissolved in one litre of water.

14. **Potassium permanganate (KMnO$_4$, M.W. 316):** 32 g of the salt is dissolved in one litre of water and is filtered through glass wool.

15. **Silver nitrate (AgNO$_3$, M.W. 170):** In one litre 17 g of the salt is dissolved.

16. **Disodium hydrogen phosphate (Na$_2$HPO$_4$, 12H$_2$O, M.W. 358):** 120 g of the salt is dissolved in one litre of water.

17. **Stannous chloride (SnCl$_2$, 2H$_2$O, M.W. 226):** In 10 ml conc. HCl, 56 g of the salt is dissolved and is diluted to one litre with water. A few pieces of tin are placed in the bottle to prevent oxidation.

18. **Potassium iodide (KI, M.W. 166):** 83 g of the salt is dissolved in one litre of water.

19. **Sodium nitroprusside:** (Na$_4$Fe(CN)$_5$NO, N.W. 307) 1 g of the salt is dissolved in 100 ml of water.

20. **Sodium cobaltinitrite (Na$_3$CONO$_3$)$_2$:** 17 g of the salt is dissolved in 250 ml of water.

21. **Ammonium molybdate [(NH$_4$)$_6$MO$_7$O$_{24}$, 4H$_2$O]:** 50 g of the salt is dissolved in 70 ml of concentrated ammonia solution and 140 ml of water. This solution is slowly added with vigorous stirring to a mixture of nitric acid and water (250 ml conc. HNO$_3$ and 500 ml of water). Finally the solution is diluted to one litre, allowed to stand for a few days and the supernatant liquid is decanted from the top.

22. **Reihardt reagent:** A solution of 250 ml of water and 130 ml of conc. H$_2$SO$_4$ is prepared. In another beaker 65 g of MnSO$_4$, 4H$_2$O is dissolved in 250 ml of water and to it very carefully previous solution of H$_2$SO$_4$ is added. Finally 135 ml of syrupy phosphoric acid is added to it and diluted to one litre with water.

23. **2, 4-Dinitrophenyl hydrazine:** 2 g of 2, 4-Dinitrophenyl hydrazine is dissolved in 15 ml conc. H$_2$SO$_4$ and to it 50 ml of 95% ethanol is diluted with 15 ml of distilled water. The mixture is thoroughly shaken and filtered.

24. **Schiff's reagent:** 1 g of rosaniline hydrochloride is dissolved in 100 ml of water, and SO$_2$ is passed to the solution till it becomes colourless.

25. **Potassium ferrocyanide [K$_4$Fe(CN)$_6$]:** 21 g of the salt is dissolved in one litre of water.

26. **β-Naphthol solution**: 10 g of β-naphthol is dissolved in one litre of sodium hydroxide (10%) solution.

27. **Benedict's reagent**

Solution A: 8.65 g of pure $CuSO_4, 5H_2O$ is dissolved in 75 ml of water.

Solution B: 86.5 g of sodium citrate and 50 g of sodium carbonate are dissolved in 400 ml of water.

Solutions A and B are mixed together and the volume is made up to 500 ml.

28. **Nessler's reagent**: 50 g of potassium iodide is dissolved in 50 ml of water (completely ammonia free). To this solution a saturated solution of mercuric chloride is added until precipitate is formed. To it 200 ml (5N) sodium hydroxide solution is added and finally diluted to 1000 ml with water.

29. **Fehling's solution**

Solution A: 34.5 g of pure $CuSO_4, 5H_2O$ is dissolved in 500 ml of water.

Solution B: 170 g of Rochelle salt (sodium potassium tartarate) is dissolved in a solution containing 71 g of NaOH in 500 ml of water.

30. **Tollen's reagent**: 6 g of $AgNO_3$ is dissolved in 100 ml of water. 2 ml of this solution is mixed with 2 ml of 10% NaOH solution, and ammonium hydroxide solution is added dropwise until the precipitate formed just dissolves.

31. **Dimethyl glyoxime**: 1 g of dimethyl glyoxime is dissolved in 100 ml of absolute alcohol to get 1% solution.

D. Indicators

1. **Phenolphthalein**: 1 g of phenolphthalein is dissolved in 100 ml of 95% ethanol.

2. **Methyl orange**: 0.05 g of methyl orange is dissolved in 100 ml of water and filtered.

3. **Methyl red**: 1 g of methyl red is dissolved in 60 ml of ethanol and 40 ml of water.

4. **Diphenylamine**: 2 g of diphenylamine is dissolved in 100 ml of conc. H_2SO_4.

5. **Starch solution**: A paste is made by mixing 1 g of starch and 50 ml of water by boiling with frequent stirring. Boiling is continued till a clear solution is obtained.

E. Preparation of Some Testing Papers

1. **Lead acetate paper**: 10 g of lead acetate is dissolved in 100 ml of water in a beaker and the filter paper is soaked in it and dried.

2. **Litmus paper**: Filter paper is soaked into the solution of litmus, dried and cut into small pieces.

3. **Starch iodide paper**: Equal volumes of KI and starch are mixed together and a filter paper is soaked into the mixture and dried.

F. Viscosity of Liquids at 20 °C in millipoise

Acetic acid	12.5	Methyl alcohol	5.93
Acetone	3.3	Ethyl alcohol	12.9
Benzene	6.5	Glycerine	0.95×10^4
Butyl alcohol	3.6	Diethyl ether	2.35
Chloroform	5.65	Toluene	6.6
Carbon tetrachloride	9.7	Ethyl acetate	4.3

G. Surface Tension of Water against Air

Temperature °C	Surface Tension dynes/cm	Temperature °C	Surface tension dynes/cm
−5	76.36	25	72.07
0	75.57	30	71.16
5	74.85	40	69.65
10	74.24	50	67.89
15	73.22	60	66.20
18	73.08	70	64.38
20	72.80	80	62.03
		100	59.20

H. Solubility Products at 20 °C

Compound	Solubility Product	Compound	Solubility Product
AgBr	7.7×10^{-10}	ZnS	1.0×10^{-23}
AgCl	1.5×10^{-10}	$PbSO_4$	2.3×10^{-9}
$BaSO_4$	9.2×10^{-11}	$PbCl_2$	2.4×10^{-4}
$CaCO_3$	4.8×10^{-9}	PbS	5.0×10^{-9}
$CaSO_4$	2.3×10^{-4}	CuS	8.5×10^{-4}
CuI	5.0×10^{-12}	HgS	4.0×10^{-4}

Bibliography

1. B.S. Furniss, A.J. Hannaford, P.W.G. Smith and A.R. Tatchell. "Vogel's Textbook of Practical Organic Chemistry", Fifth Edition, Pearson Education (Singapore) Pvt. Ltd. Indian Branch, 482, F.I.E. Patparganj, Delhi, 110092, India (2005).

2. A.I. Vogel. "Elementary Practical Organic Chemistry, Part I Preparations". CBS Publishers and Distributors, 4596/1-A, 11 Daryaganj, New Delhi 110002 (2002).

3. A.I. Vogel . "Elementary Practical Organic Chemistry, Part II — Qualitative Organic Analysis". CBS Publishers and Distributors, 4596/1-A, 11 Daryaganj, New Delhi 110002 (2002).

4. A.I. Vogel. "Elementary Practical Organic Chemistry, Part III — Quantitative Organic Analysis". CBS Publishers and Distributors, 4596/1-A, 11 Daryaganj, New Delhi 110002 (2002).

5. R.L. Shriner, R.C. Fuson and D.Y. Curtin. "The Systematic Identification of Organic Compounds", Fifth Edition, Wiley, New York (1964).

6. N.D. Cheronis and J.B. Entriken. "Identification of Organic Compounds", Second Edition, Wiley, New York (1963).

7. H.T. Clarke. "A Handbook of Organic Analysis", Fourth Edition, Edward Arnold (Publishers) Ltd., London (1960).

8. H.T. Clarke. "A Handbook of Organic Analysis", Fifth Edition, Arnold Publishers, London, (1986).

9. E. Stahl. "Thin-Layer Chromatography" George Allen and Unwin Ltd., London, Springer-Verlag, Berlin, Heidelberg, New York (1969).

10. Ray. Q, Brewster, C.A. Van der werf and W.E. Mcewen. "Unitized Experiments in Organic Chemistry", Second Edition, D. Van Nostrand Company, Incorporation Princeton, New Jersey, Affliated East-West Press Pvt. Ltd., New Delhi (1964).

11. A.I. Vogel. "Textbook of Quantitative Inorganic Analysis", ELBS (1978).

12. A.I. Vogel, "Textbook of Qualitative Chemical Analysis", edited by J. Bassett, G.H. Jeffery and J.Mendham, ELBS (1986).

13. "Findlay's Practical Physical Chemistry", revised by Levitt, Longman, London (1966).

14. R. Mukhopadhyay and P. Chatterjee, "Advanced Practical Chemistry", Books and Allied, Kolkata (2004).

15. A. Ghosal, B. Mahapatra and A.K. Nad, "An Advanced Course in Practical Chemistry", New Central Book Agency, Kolkata (2000).

16. R.K. Bansal. "Laboratory Manual of Organic Chemistry", Second Edition, Wiley Eastern Limited, New Delhi (1990).